Praise for Take My Life (but not my humour)

'Thought provoking true account of my daughter's incredible journey that will make you laugh and cry.'

Kathy Dufton (Emma's mum, bias fan!)

'Emma's inimitably raw and honest account of her fight against this disease will have you laughing, crying and truly inspired.'

Michelle Garrett

'You'll laugh, you'll cry, this book is a must buy.'

Becky Wheeler

'You will never read a book quite like this one! It had me captivated from the start. Emma did cancer on her terms. She chose humour, you can too… Lifechanging! Inspirational and motivational for anyone affected by cancer.'

Kelly Forrester – The Resilience & Growth Leader.

'This book proves my theory that a positive attitude, a strong sense of humour and a good support network can get you through the darkest times.'

Jen Parker

Emma Davies
Take My Hair

(but not my humour)

One
mum's
journey
seeing off
Breast Cancer

To
Darren, Toby & Chloe
Mum & Dad
My amazing network of friends
You are the reason I found the strength to laugh and smile.
I love you all. Xx

Introducing 'ME'
Your host for this book.

Hi, I'm Emma. Married to Darren and co-owner of two small humans, Toby (six) and Chloe (two), and Beagle Arthur (eight).

Jack of all trades, master of some, I've had many jobs over the years. Initially I gained a degree in Tourism Management (or my deckchair degree as Darren likes to refer to it) but never worked a day in the industry. I later requalified as a Chartered Legal Executive and since 2011 I've been defending nurses going through fitness to practice proceedings.

I've been with Darren for thirteen years (unlucky for some!) and married for eight, having met in a nightclub in Torquay. We started off slowly, building our way up through the ranks of pot plant, hamster, beagle, second beagle, before embarking on small humans. The hamster has been the easiest.

What do I do for shits and giggles? I love:

- Reading – criminal and psychological thrillers (anything a bit dark and stabby), legal thrillers.
- Music – anything, especially dance, trance and happy hardcore but definitely not loud shouty stuff.
- Driving, travelling, comedy, laughter, cuddles.
- Cosy nights in watching films and getting heavily involved with a tub of Ben & Jerry's.
- The occasional night out when I know I've definitely got a sleep-in babysitter (mum(s)).
- Getting outside in the fresh air.

So 2019, after enjoying fourteen months off with Chloe, I returned to work in January. That was a bit of a shock to the system, but I was ready to locate my brain and get back on it. I was quickly thrown into the daily hectic sandwich of small human drop off, attempt to be a professional and do a bit of lawyering, small human pick up.

In April I turned forty. I wasn't quite sure how that was happening to me as I remember my parents' fortieth birthdays. I think the secret is having children later in life so with two young small humans I'm in complete denial about how old I actually am. I think I stopped at twenty-five, until I look in the mirror!

I'm a bit like the Queen and like a week of celebrations, so we marked the occasion by spending the week in a Haven caravan in Cornwall. It was hard work, but it was good fun.

It was also good fun to have a joint fortieth birthday party with my long-term mate from school Mel. We hired out a bar, invited a load of people, and spent the evening drinking and dancing. Less hard work than the caravan holiday and also good fun.

I'd devised a list of forty things at forty. A bit of a bucket list if you like. They ranged from a big family holiday to Menorca, Edinburgh Tattoo to celebrate Dad's seventieth, city break with Darren to buying some matching underwear, fly a kite with the kids, go to a comedy night. And then things like learn to take a compliment, just be me, don't worry about saying 'No' more often.

It was also the year that I wanted to address my ridiculous relationship with food and exercise more. It wasn't about fitting into a certain size, but I knew I was overweight and didn't want to set a bad example to the kids with my 'sneaky fatty eating'.

Come June, two out of the three breaks had been booked and I was making good headway through the list.

I was just getting into the swing of things and enjoying being in my forties when on the 14th June 2019 I woke up and found a lump under my right breast. That's when my year unexpectedly changed dramatically and 'Operation Evict Lumpy' commenced.

Before you think *"blimey she enjoys talking about herself"* I wanted to show you a little bit of Emma pre-cancer. I'm not Emma who had cancer. I'm just Emma who was an average forty-year-old enjoying life before cancer rudely interrupted.

So what's in the book?

This is my story following my unwanted partnership with 'lumpy'. It documents the journey I've gone through to kill him off. The highs, the lows and everything in-between. Some of it was written on the same day so you get my raw emotions. Some of it was written later looking back at notes I'd made.

I've included messages from friends and family, so again you not only get my raw emotions but also those of my nearest and dearest. Some of my willing proofreaders said they loved them, others said they interrupted the flow. I'll let you be the judge of that. It was important I had somewhere to document all the love, kindness and silliness. I've trimmed them down a bit but there are lots! These bits are in italics, so if they don't resonate with you, you can just skip on by to the next diary entry.

There are also entries from a few friends and family who explain what it was like when someone drops the C-bomb on them.

I've faced every scenario in life with humour and I knew early on I didn't want this any other way. I quickly set the ground rules that I didn't want people to worry about minding their words or 'Ps & Qs' with me. You'll soon come to realise that I have a quirky sense of humour and I'm a bit sweary. If you're easily offended this might not be the book for you! I'm in no way trivialising cancer but joking and laughing was my way of getting through the situation.

I'm not medically qualified, so this book isn't intended to provide a factually documented account of breast cancer. If in doubt go see a clever medically qualified person to check it out. Indeed, I've learnt that there are multiple types of breast cancer and this book details my specific cancer. Anything mentioned of a medical nature is from information I've been given and my understanding of it. I've learnt so much about breast cancer in a short period of time and I hope my journey will equip you with tips for your own if you're going through it too.

I also know that everybody is different, and you will develop your own way of dealing with your diagnosis and journey. I wanted to surround myself with people and keep things as normal as possible. Other people I've met along the way have preferred to take themselves off quietly and then emerge when they're feeling better. We might both have/have had cancer but only YOU will know exactly how you're feeling. Do what's right for you.

Being a mum to two young children, one of my biggest concerns was how they would react and deal with the changes thrown upon us as a family. Along the way, I'll look at how I communicated 'the booby bug' and any changes to Toby. Being one, Chloe was a bit indifferent to the whole process!

Fortunately, prior to my diagnosis, I'd done a lot of work on my mindset. Ironically, I was in the best shape of my life both physically and mentally going into treatment. So, I'll also mention along the way how I've tried to retain a positive mindset and look for the positives in this scenario.

Glossary

Now I know these usually go at the end, but I've developed a few 'Emmarisms' along the way. You'll have absolutely bugger all idea what I'm banging on about, so I thought I ought to pop this here to at least give you a fighting chance.

Booby Bug – Alternative description of breast cancer.

Booby Cases – Your bra of course (how I laughed the day Toby first came out with this little nugget).

Booby Doctor – My amazing breast consultant.

Bum Doctor – Self-explanatory if you see above.

Cancer Admin – A file containing a small rainforest of appointment invites and procedural information.

Cancer Comms – The real-time exchange between friends and family.

The C Card – Curve your right thumb and index finger to form a C. Present this to someone's face to get your own way in light of the fact that you have cancer.

Chemo Cupboard – A space you need to make to house all the generous cancer-related gifts your mates buy you. Mine includes lots of hand-cream, chocolate, Werther's Originals, anti-sickness sweets, Gaviscon, fruity teabags, biscuits, lip balm, mints.

Chemo Sitters – Fricking awesome people who give up their time to spend it with you whilst you are pumped with poison. Must have a flare for creating amusement. Usually mums, they will fall over themselves to sit with you for hours on end, have cups of tea brought to them, and actually finish a conversation.

The Chop – Surgery.

Dad's Chemo Cab – A white transit van, driven by Dad, taking me in style to my chemo appointments.

Emily and Tracey's Little Jar of Cards – A jar of cards where my mates Emily and Tracey had written either funny stories of past experiences or quite lovely words about our friendship. I usually saved these for after chemo treatment to give me a little boost.

The Frying – Radiotherapy.

"Happy Chemo Tuesday" – Popular phrase messaged to me on a regular basis once everyone realised I was actually having quite a bit of fun on a Tuesday!

Lumpy – Further alternative description of breast cancer.

Melon Coffee Morning – Macmillan Coffee Morning (as misheard by a six year old)

Mummy's Magical Medicine – Chemotherapy drugs.

Nemo Chemo Bag – A bag containing useful bits for your chemo sessions. The Nemo bit is not compulsory. My comedian of a husband purchased a kid's *Finding Nemo* backpack for my supplies as it rhymes nicely with chemo. Other bags are available.

Strudwick – My maiden name was Strudwick. Any reference to Strudwick, Strudders, Strudel is me!

Wanky Week – the first week after treatment on phase two of the poisoning when I felt proper shite.

Wonderful Week – the third week after treatment on phase two when I felt fricking awesome again. Only to be poisoned again.

YESmum card – a pack of affirmation cards my 'local yocal' mum friends gifted me containing loads of positive sayings. I turned over a new one every time I had something big happening that day or I was feeling a bit shite. What I didn't realise until after treatment was that £2 from every pack went to 'Stand up to Cancer'.

I also need to introduce you to some of the group players:

Circle of Trust (long-term friends spanning decades) – Charlene, Becky, Mel, Amanda and Kelly.

Massaging Mummies (friends I made during a baby massage class with Toby. None of us massaged our babies after the class finished but we remain good friends) – Paula, Claire, Ruth, Caroline and Jo.

Shits and Giggles (two awesome lawyer mates) – Fliss and Caroline.

Strong Randy Ladies (two more awesome legal ladies I met during my days as a Legal Secretary in my twenties at Symes Robinson & Lee) – Emily and Tracey.

Local Yocals (more awesome mum friends I met when Toby was born) – Pippa, Beth, Grace, Helen and Anna.

Cake. Always Cake (new neighbours) – Becky (G), Rachel and Sarah.

ED Fan Club – a group of all my awesome work colleagues including (Boss) Becky. So many Beckys!

June 2019

Friday 28th June 2019

YOU HAVE CANCER.

Bugger – didn't see that one coming.

But I can't just jump in there, let me rewind two weeks to when I found 'lumpy'. Yes, I named the bloody thing. I declared it male and that he was getting right on my tits (literally my right tit).

Friday 14th June

Wake up. Yawn. Stretch. Happen to rub my chest and…

"What the fuck is that?"

That's pretty much how lumpy was discovered.

It didn't feel right and the look on Darren's face said it didn't look right either. Straight onto the surgery online booking system and I had a GP appointment for 10.30. Luckily, I was meeting my good friends Becky and Nicola that day so they kindly looked after Chloe whilst I went to bare my boob to my lovely GP. Just the week before I had had to bear my arse to her as I'd had enough of the ongoing 'Paul the pile' situation. Since having children though I really don't care. These things need fixing and they've seen it all before, no doubt in varying degrees of shapes and sizes.

Clearly my GP didn't like the look of it either and a referral was made to the breast clinic with advice that I would receive an appointment within two weeks.

And indeed, an appointment within two weeks materialised very quickly.

Did I worry myself silly during that two-week period? I did think about it occasionally, but I'm not medically qualified. I wasn't going to turn to Dr Google and scare myself silly diagnosing myself with all sorts of nasties. The last time I googled 'ringing in my ears' I'd self-diagnosed a brain tumour when what I had was tinnitus. Annoying, but it's not going to kill me.

In the main it was just business as usual and I was content that it couldn't have been there for long and I had taken immediate action. The wheels were in motion and there was nothing more I could do, so there was no point worrying about it.

Friday 28ᵗʰ June

So back to the day the arse end fell out of my world. Well not literally, but it felt like everything had been turned on its head. Suddenly all the plans for the six weeks of summer holiday stretching out ahead of us, painstakingly planned with military precision around annual leave allowances, was out of the window.

Today was my first appointment at the Breast Care Clinic at The Royal Devon and Exeter Hospital (RD&E).

After donning the attractive-looking cape I started out all jovial when the booby consultant came in to see me. She wasn't wearing her poker face and immediately she told me she did not like the look of what she saw.

Firstly, I went off for a mammogram. The first of many scans/ tests I would now experience. Interesting bit of kit that basically squashes your tits until you think they can't be squashed anymore.

At one point I misheard the radiographer and thought she had told me to put my other hand on my tit. So, I was standing there with my left hand on my left tit. She had said 'hip'.

Next stop was for an ultrasound. By this point I'm still quite happy. Nothing too bad has happened. I'm completely oblivious to what is growing in my right breast. I even strike up a conversation with another patient sitting beside me who was looking a little lost. Turns out she was a nurse for forty years and when I tell her I support nurses in my day job we strike up a good conversation about her career. I'm almost disappointed when I'm called away.

I whip my boobs out again for yet new faces. This time for the ultrasound of 'the lump' and a biopsy. I'm still quite happily talking away to the assistant. That is until I'm told there appears to be a second lump and they're going to need a biopsy of that as well. Suddenly everything seems to be getting quite overwhelming. Two lumps in my breast, what else could be in me?

Thank goodness Darren is with me as we traipse back downstairs to see the consultant. The mood has definitely changed now, and I'm quickly told that the first lump is cancer. Now I'm a logical, practical person but, in that moment, I started shaking like a shitting dog and firing off multiple questions to the consultant but not listening to the answers. Luckily for me, Darren sat there quietly taking it all in and it was him who would later fill in the gaps for me.

I was told that the lump I had found was cancer and the biopsy results would be needed to determine what type. The second lump was my lymph node and again the biopsy results would determine whether the cancer had spread there.

By this point it's 5pm on a Friday. All admin has shut down in the hospital. I'm told that the consultant's clinic is fully booked for next Friday, but an appointment will be made for the following Friday. How can I wait two weeks after this bombshell has been dropped on me? The consultant promises she will ask her secretary on Monday to try and book an earlier appointment. A multi-disciplinary team meeting will take place on Tuesday where a treatment plan will be discussed. Treatment. She said 'Treatment'.

This word makes me feel a tiny bit better. There is mention of chemotherapy, operations, radiotherapy, but to be honest I'm not taking any of it in.

My consultant passes me a card with the contact details of the breast care nurse team. One of her nurses is a friend I knew from when I was younger. I laugh as I tell her I'll have her as we went to Ibiza in our twenties. What goes on tour stays on tour, though, so I won't be divulging any details of our antics!

The lovely Health Care Assistant (HCA) takes us to a more comfortable room and offers us both a cup of tea. Funny how a cup of tea accompanies most situations. I was given a sugary cup of tea after the birth of both my children. I'm now being given another one at the start of a journey that will aim to get something else out of me.

She leaves and I let out the most heart-wrenching sound I think has ever come out of my body. All I can think about is that I'm going to die. I've got two young children who are going to grow up without their mummy. I'm not going to know anything about it, but they'll always have that missing from their lives. I feel numb.

The HCA returns with the teas and news that she's booked an appointment for Wednesday. I'm so grateful that instead of a two-week wait I've only got to wait five days. "Is this because it's more serious than they thought or them being efficient?" I ask. It's them being efficient.

The first person I call is my boss Becky. Becky is also a good friend and will be waiting for news but trust me to start getting practical and talk about coming into work on Monday. Maybe it's because I just want things to carry on as normal. She takes the call whilst her daughter is at her dance class. What an awful call to have taken in such a scenario and I feel guilty. She was as fantastic as ever, dispensing her calm advice and reassuring me that she would be waiting for me on Monday if I felt up to coming into work.

I next phone my good friend Nicola. Nicola is a nurse. I can't really remember the conversation, but I know we both cried a lot and she told me we would get through this together. Nicola lost her mum to cancer a couple of years ago. I feel guilty that I phoned her and maybe made her feel sad.

I didn't phone anybody else. I didn't want to go home. Mum and Gary (my stepdad) were looking after the children and I knew I needed to let her put them to bed before I told her. We went to my brother Russell's house instead where I told him, his wife Charlene and my dad. By this point it's all sunk in a bit more but it's all just such a shock.

I want to go home. I want to see my babies.

Chloe is already in bed and Toby is almost ready for his story. I want to read him his story. I avoid eye contact with my mum, just shake my head and walk straight up to Toby's room. I am his mum. I want to read him his story. He's excited to see me, gives me a big hug and I settle him down for the night.

Downstairs there's lots of crying now. I try to give the information to Mum and Gary but, in all honesty, I can't remember the details. I wasn't listening. I wasn't taking in any of the answers to my manic questioning. It's to my surprise that Darren is able to fill in the blanks. He said he could see I wasn't taking any of it in, so he sat there quietly absorbing all the information.

At some point Mum and Gary leave. To be honest, I can't remember what we did that evening. I just remember checking on my sleeping children, as I do every night, but now wondering if I was going to see them grow up, to keep achieving their firsts. I feel really sad for them and guilty at the thought of not being here for them. I'd be devastated if I lost my mum now and I'm forty. They're so small, they need their mummy.

I'm supposed to be going away on a girly night tomorrow with 'the local yocals' mummy friends. I defiantly message them with an update that it will be business as usual and I will still be coming down tomorrow.

I remember just feeling very numb and sad and very bloody scared.

At some point, Darren and I go to bed, but we don't sleep.

Saturday 29th June

I have never known a night drag on so long. It's as if time has stood still. If this is what it's going to be like until Wednesday, it's going to feel like an age coming. The morning feels like it drags on for hours and hours. We don't really know what to do with ourselves, but of course the children are oblivious.

Fortunately, Toby has a swimming lesson at 10am, so suddenly we snap into the usual Saturday morning routine. And with that, we're getting on with our day.

Toby had a sleepover arranged with Thomas, his best mate from nursery. When Louisa and Andy arrive to pick an excited Toby up at lunchtime, she asks, "How are you?" I'm not prepared to answer this greeting that's asked every time you see someone. Do I just say 'all good' when everything is very much not all good? I quietly take her to one side and tell her the news. The look of shock on her face and instant eyes welling up is heartbreaking to watch. I'm very quickly learning that this news has an immediate shocking effect on people and it's quite distressing to watch.

I visited my friend Helen this afternoon. Helen had her own journey with breast cancer thirteen years ago. Over the past couple of weeks, she has made it clear that she's happy to answer any questions I might have. She tells me that everybody's treatment will be unique to them and that things have probably changed since she had hers. In this moment I just need to speak to somebody who understands the fear I am going through and give me an inkling as to what I can expect.

We sit outside in the sun and I basically just ask her to talk. To tell me everything from when she knew something wasn't right, to being diagnosed, the treatment and how she carried on after.

Our chat is interspersed with tears. I tell her that I won't be coming down to join the girls later. Firstly, they all deserve a bloody good rest this weekend and to let their hair down. I'm not sure I'm going to be the light and soul of the party. But more importantly, I just feel this overwhelming urge to be close to my family. I don't want to be apart from my husband and children.

I must say I feel a damn sight better having had this chat with Helen. Not least because she's gone through this, come out the other side and is very healthily knocking around all these years later. I've also come away with a lot of knowledge of the various processes and perhaps what to expect. I refuse to turn to Dr Google. I'll wait to see what my diagnosis and prognosis is from my consultant.

There are people I need to update with this new information. A select few friends and family knew I was going for the scan yesterday and I need to drop the C-bomb on them. A text message doesn't seem the right way to deliver such news but then is there a right way? I also need to tell a few more people than I had wanted because a few people come as part of a group of friends. It wouldn't be kind for them to know and then not be able to talk to other friends.

Cancer Comms

"Hi. I hope you're all enjoying this beautiful weather. So, I'm just going to come straight out with this. I have breast cancer. I have a follow up appointment on Wednesday when I get told the results from yesterday's biopsy and they give me 'the plan'. I love me a good plan.

So as wank as this is, there is nothing I can do about it. I feel fine, which is the weird thing. I may sound flippant, I won't lie I'm scared, but my way of dealing with tough situations is humour, so please don't worry about carefully choosing words.

Love to you all and hopefully see you soon. **Xx**"

Circle of Trust:

"*Holy shit mate, sending you lots of love and we are all here for you, whatever you need. I'm off on Wednesday if you need me to look after Chloe for you while you have your appointment.*"

"*Love you mate, we will be your rock, for anything whether it's kids, dog and Darren or just for you to shout and we'll be with you to hold you up. Like already said… anything at any time, you're our priority.*"

"*Oh mate, not the news we wanted but now you know what you're dealing with and there will be a plan. I love a plan too and whatever that plan is we will help and support you all to get through whatever comes your way. Love you xxxx*"

"**Thank you, ladies. I really do appreciate it. I know these scenarios can be hard for knowing what to say but no airs and graces needed with me. Just knowing you're around is enough.**"

Massaging Mummies:

"*Ah Em. Shit, shit and shit. That bastard cancer. You fight it, girl, and we will be here for you with support, love and practical help. Happy to have the kids, babysit, get Alec to cook you meals, anything. I will even clean, which should make you smile! Love you so much. Never know what to say but please know we are here for you. Massive hugs for all of you. Xxx*"

"*Emma… okay… humour… You can get the boobs of your dreams. Those darn spaniel ears causing you grief. But seriously. No words. I'm here 100% for anything you need! Childcare, cooking, cleaning, shopping, maid service! You totally have this, and you will KICK its ass! Love you so much! Big hugs all round! xx*"

"Oh Em, there are no words… except for you to fight this, hun, and you will kick the Big C far away. We are all here for you whatever that is… cleaning, shopping, babysitting, cooking (but you might have better offers on that front), to offload, support or anything. Love you loads and massive hugs to you all."

"Wow, you've floored me, Em, and I'm sure you're feeling the same. All I can think of is profanities, what a load of fucking shit. I know you'll put on a brave face, but I also know you've mastered the art of asking for help, so don't forget to use those new-found skills. New blog coming? Massive hugs and good luck for Wednesday. Here for you. Xxx"

"I'm here forever. We all are. Free parking at the hospital. Every cloud and all that."

"Sorry for the delay in responding. I was busy drawing up the rotas for the above.

Seriously, thank you so much. I think it's these displays of pure kindness and selflessness which sets me off more. I am so grateful to you all and know you'll get me through this shit sandwich."

Shits and Giggles:

"Morning love. That's good you're going back on Wednesday. I'm like you, love a plan. I'm sure you know anyway, but you can talk to us as much or as little about it as you like. We can talk about anything else too. I do a great line in talking about complete nonsense. Are you doing something lovely for yourself this weekend? Sending love xxx"

"Thank you. Nonsense would be great. I'm a little scared at the moment as I don't like not having all the facts. When I do, that's when we can put the plan into action. I was supposed to be going away tonight with some friends, but actually now I just want to be at home. Weather looks lovely so some nice family time. What about you?"

"Fuck."

"Quite. That's what I thought! I must say I'm enjoying

your response the most. I can't be doing with this 'I'm so sorry…' Not like it's anyone's fault, but I appreciate responses can be hard in this scenario. Anyway, maybe my warped sense of humour, but I'm not having that change! x"

"Sorry for the lack of responses… Only had one hand free most of the day thanks to a whiney 'pick me up' toddler. A plan of action is always the best way forward. The not knowing is always so much worse. I am sorry this is happening to you, though, it is truly fackin' shite. However, we shall be here to talk utter shite and to keep things as normal as possible.

"I've got to tell you this as I know it will make you smile. I bumped into our lovely vicar neighbour Sue this morning and I told her about your diagnosis. She told me she had breast cancer in 1977, told me to send her love and thoughts from 'herself and the big guy upstairs'."

"Well I knew I had friends in high places but it doesn't get much higher than that. Well with the Big G on my side I reckon I'm sorted. I'd also like to think medicine has also moved on somewhat, so that's reassuring."

"Him upstairs and modern medicine – going to be awesome. x"

Sunday 30ᵗʰ June 2019

It's a beautiful summer's day today. The sun is shining, the children are happy playing in the paddling pool. We've decided to have a family BBQ today. Life has got to go on, that's what happens. I feel quite lost and need to fill my time. What better way to do it than to spend my time with my loved ones.

The business of talking to people, watching the kids play with their cousins, preparing the BBQ, takes my mind off things. But similarly, just watching the kids laughing brings the fear crashing back and the uncertainty of whether I'll get to see them grow up. Luckily my sunglasses hide the tears when they come and I quietly take myself off under the premise that I'm going to the toilet or have something else I need to get from the kitchen. In the lounge I sit down to sob and get myself back together. Minutes later, Chloe comes bumbling in, laughing about something and shoving her podgy little hand into mine. Children really are the best medicine as I laugh with her and wipe away this round of tears.

Just having my immediate family around me makes me smile. Makes me feel calm. Makes me feel happy knowing that they came today when I needed them the most.

Anxiety

Despite this calm I also have this physical heavy pressing feeling on my chest that I can't control. Now the old me would have convinced myself that not only was the cancer in my boob but that it had spread, and this was what was causing this suffocating feeling. My experience of struggling with anxiety after Toby was born tells me otherwise.

After Toby, I struggled terribly with anxiety. Pre-small human I had never experienced this. Sure, I'd been stressed with exams, work, planning big events, etc., but I actually thrived on that to get through the situation and it would always come to an end eventually.

The first forty-eight hours post-Toby arrival with our shiny new human was amazing, but then the bubble was promptly burst on the day three weigh in. As Toby had lost 11% of his birth weight, a relentless cycle of two-hourly feeding commenced and phrases like "failing to thrive" bounded around. What quickly ensued was a downward spiral into worry and then extreme anxiety. Maybe it was the sleep deprivation that caused the anxiety. Maybe it was the constant worry of keeping him alive and my obsession with his feeding. I didn't want to be left on my own with him, I felt lonely, but equally the thought of packing up to go out and meeting people was overwhelming. Maybe it was confidence slipping away on a daily basis. Maybe it was my identity slipping away as I seemed to be in a weird version of *Groundhog Day*.

I tried to continue to be a perfectionist wanting to meet people on time. I set unrealistic expectations of myself and would be unduly critical if I didn't live up to them. I didn't ask for help and if people offered I would often politely decline; I had this.

Now you might think I've lost the plot and these particular inner thoughts of my mind are for another book to be found in the mum and baby section. But straight away, and over time throughout this process, I recognised similar traits of those early milky sleep-deprived months.

How did I overcome my anxiety back then? Returning to work and trying to be a perfectionist both as a lawyer and as a mum did not serve me very well. When the panic attacks started, and I felt completely overwhelmed, I knew I needed to do something. So, with the support of my employee assistance program, a well-timed Christmas break, some counselling, an adult colouring book, a new gym membership and a few books on mindfulness and mindset, I learnt to realise that I needed to take time for myself. To do the hobbies I enjoyed. I also learnt to ask for help, to accept it if it was offered and I needed it and to not feel like a burden on people.

So, this post-small-human, former anxiety-ridden mum sees this pain in my chest for what it is. This is my current anxiety about my uninvited booby guest manifesting itself physically. Easier said than done but I keep reminding myself to stay calm. There is nothing I can do until I know what I'm dealing with.

As the day draws to an end, I get an email from the Lotto congratulating me on winning a lucky dip. Well would you look at that. Things are on the up. Wouldn't it be cool if my lucky dip won me the big bucks? The dark side of me thinks how bloody typical if I won the big bucks and then wasn't here to spend it!

July 2019

Monday 1st July 2019

After the longest weekend in history, Monday morning has come round. Time to drop the children to their respective places and go to work. I'm feeling pretty defiant today. Determined that it should be business as usual. Physically I feel no different to when I left my files on Thursday. I do not feel ill, no one (other than my boss Becky) will know there's anything wrong with me. I've got a job to do.

I waltz into the office like it's any other Monday morning and no one suspects a thing. One of my colleagues, who I haven't seen for a while, enthusiastically congratulates me on my weight loss. I know that she'll probably feel awful about that comment when she finds out what's going on but bugger me that weight loss has nothing to do with lumpy and everything to do with my determination to shed the timber at Slimming World over the past six months.

Becky is busy but she drops everything immediately. We decide to go for a walk to get some fresh air and some privacy whilst we talk about a subject neither of us had ever anticipated discussing. The first thing I do is apologise for landing her with the news during her daughter's dancing lesson.

Taking in the delightful beauty of an industrial estate, we walk in the sun discussing the little information I know from Friday, how I'm feeling, what I might like to do about work. Truth is I'm not really sure. I was so adamant this morning that I would keep on going as long as I could, but truth be told I'm not sure where my head is. My clients need a lawyer who has their head together and right now together it is not. I know there's going to be lots of medical appointments starting immediately and my job isn't the kind of job you can just dip in and out of. Ultimately, I decide that I'm going to need to take some time.

Luckily, I'm quite anally organised, so I have notes on all my clients with key dates and the stage of their cases. I devise a table and for the next couple of hours I transfer all this information into a fantastically impressive chronological handover. I feel rather triumphant because if I do decide to stop work at least the next lawyer will have a comprehensive handover note and my clients, who I'd only just really got to know, will have the best continuity in the situation.

Becky and I agree that I'll take the afternoon off. An email saying I'm feeling unwell and have gone home will easily deal with my absence and no need to tell anyone anything. I had arranged to go to lunch with one of my colleagues today. I decide that I won't say anything to her. As I get in the car with her, and turn the radio on, there's a story of Kylie Minogue and a concert she's doing as she missed the previous one due to breast cancer. Of course, I react to this and I have no choice but to tell my colleague. Unsurprisingly, she's shocked and upset and I also have to ask her not to tell anyone else just yet. I apologise for dropping this on her but we still have an upbeat lunch even if I have just dropped the 'C-bomb' on her.

It's a beautifully sunny day today. For the first time in a long time, I'm looking up and around. I surprise Toby by picking him up from school at kick out time and he's delighted when we can spend time in the park.

Cancer Comms

Strong Randy Ladies:

"*What the fuck. Are you actually fucking shitting me?!! Can I call you?*"

"Mate, I have a warped sense of humour, but it isn't that warped. Of course you can phone me. I don't bite. X"

"So, going with humour! It's taken you telling me you have 'C' to get a response to dates! I can do any but 31ˢᵗ. Fuck me, Em, I feel a bit sick right now, but if I haven't told you before how much I love the bones of you and Trace and how much I value you as my lifelong friends, then perhaps now is the time to do it! Who would have thought from the days of SRL that we would have been through so much together? Well this my friend is one battle that we will win together and we will be here every step of the way. Loves you lots like jelly tots and sending all my love and strength for Wednesday."

"Em, I can't believe it, sending lots of love. I can't imagine what you're feeling, and I know whatever I say won't change the situation, but as Emily says, we are here for you every step of the way. You are a strong and fabulous woman and we love you lots. xx"

"The things you have to come out with just to secure a bloody date! 29ᵗʰ is in the diary, get it in yours. Especially you, Em. Thank you so much ladies. You're right, there are no words. Although my current preference is shit sandwich, so feel free to steal that. Just knowing you are there is all I need. I am so fond of you two beautiful strong women. Even though we only meet up monthly or so I think we have a very special friendship that many people would kill for. Now you can feel sorry for me today as I melt in the sun for my first sports day. Have a good one. Xx"

Cake. Always Cake:

"I do really hope I can still come out Saturday but I'm literally having to take one day at a time right now. My emotions keep getting the better of me but on the whole I'm staying positive. xx"

"You sound brave not flippant. I will join in on your humour coping mechanism to say that I do consider this to be an acceptable reason to perhaps give Saturday night a miss. Sending you huge hugs, everything crossed and praying for the best news and outcome from your Wednesday results appointment. If there is absolutely ANYTHING you need, do not hesitate for a moment, we're here for you all. And I'll stop with the kissing emojis now. xx"

"Well, let's not write it off just yet, maybe a more low-key affair. Maybe you could sample my gin shelf? Anyhow, let's see how things go.

Thank you so much for your kindness. I've been bowled over by the love and support I'm receiving. I truly must be a top bird! Not a right tit. FYI it's in the right tit!

Keep the kissing emojis coming, loving the love. Hope you guys are well and I really do hope to see you girls Saturday if I have my shit together. xx"

"Always happy to sample one's spirit shelf. No worries, we can happily go with the flow.

Not at all, and I am seriously in awe of your outlook on this; it's truly inspiring. And to be coming out with breast puns too – you do know how much I admire a good pun, so I think you definitely get extra credit for that too in my book.

Consider it done, I'll see what GIFs I can get on the go too, love a good GIF. You don't have to have your shit together, happy to see you if you want the company and always happy to talk shit too for obvious reasons. Xx"

"Oh, fucking hell. If there was ever a need to sample that gin shelf now is the time to do it. I have some we can add, so let's gin it up. Ditto what Bec says bird, anything we can do just let us know. All my fingers and toes are crossed for Wednesday, sending lots of love to you all. xx"

Tuesday 2ⁿᵈ July 2019

Critical Illness cover

So, practicalities. Do you have critical illness cover? Life insurance? Here's a little convo that ensued this morning between me and my lawyer chum Emily.

"Now I'm only saying this as you might not have thought about it! Do you have life insurance (and I'm not saying that in the doom and gloom way of you now need it!) but if you do then make contact with the company sooner rather than later. If you have anything in place that covers your mortgage this is the sort of thing they will pay out for. I know it's not a very nice thing to think about (proper shit sandwich) but if that can be claimed and takes some pressure off you while you go through treatment then claim it! At work I also had a critical illness cover so check with yours. I know this probably isn't at the top of your list right now but knowing you and practicality it will give you something else to focus on perhaps. Typical you getting ill to get your mortgage paid off quicker! Friggen love you my beautiful friend. Although I have woken this morning thinking that was a shit dream to your text."

"Quickly responding. Already on that. We're insured right up. Show me the money."

"Every cloud."

"We have life insurance, which pays off our mortgage in the event of one of us snuffing it. Obviously that's what I'm aiming to avoid, so on balance I'll take a lump sum payout on the critical illness. It's not a life-changing amount but it's basically a year's salary if I'm eligible. I also get six months full pay and I think something else kicks in at work after that. Do you think it's the practical lawyer in us?! Really appreciate you taking the time to think about that and offer your pro bono advice. xx"

It was actually Darren who mentioned I ought to check our insurance documents. It hadn't even occurred to me. Thirteen years (actually my lucky number) we've been paying various insurance premiums, thousands of pounds, no doubt, and now we might be getting a pay out on the critical illness cover. Looking through our documentation we also have a higher level of cover, so I collect all my paperwork together to take into the consultant tomorrow. If you don't qualify for a payout with cancer then what the hell do you need to get?

Subsequently I've had conversations with people who don't have any financial provision in place. Maybe it's just something younger people don't think about. Maybe it's the lawyer in me who's relatively risk adverse and likes to cover the 'what ifs'. We only renewed our covers of insurance last December. Shame we hadn't changed the critical illness to pay off the mortgage, but hindsight is a wonderful thing! I'm so grateful we have insurance and a fantastic sick pay benefit but what if you didn't have either? I certainly didn't expect to be getting a potentially life-threatening illness this year.

But back to today.

I had today booked off anyway for Toby's Sports Day, so my absence from work won't yet be pipping any interest.

It's another beautifully sunny day as I sit with my family for hours to burn and watch Toby compete in two races and throw a bean bag a little further than his own nose! Living the dream. It's a big deal to him, though, and I yell enthusiastically from the sidelines. There are times I find myself morbidly wondering if I'll be enjoying/enduring such monotony next year. But there's so much going on my thoughts don't wander for too long.

I'm sitting amongst a group of school mum friends who are currently none the wiser. We chat away about the forthcoming summer holidays, how are we going to keep them occupied for six weeks, juggle work? Will we all come out the other side unscathed? I'm soon distracted by my friend's two-year-old languishing in tears as her sandals have rubbed and I'm scrambling into the depths of my handbag to retrieve the battered-looking plaster I know lurks in there.

Sports Day done, I head off for lunch with the family. I thought the Sunday BBQ was 'The Last Supper' before the big news but maybe this is.

This evening we go to the school's concert and picnic at Killerton, our local National Trust place of beauty. Fortunately, Toby is not singing in the choir, so he does not have to stand in the sun fighting sunstroke for an inordinate period of time. Unfortunately, Chloe (at one) does not wish to sit for any period of time exceeding thirty seconds, so it's shift work chasing her around the gardens. But I'm looking up and around. I'm surrounded by family in a beautiful setting as the sun sets.

Tomorrow I find out what 'The Plan' is. The clever medical people had better have brainstormed the shit out of my options today in their multi-disciplinary team meeting.

Cancer Comms

Local Yocals:

"Emma, you will hopefully find out your plan tomorrow, so let us know how it goes. We just want you to know that we are with you every step of the bumpy road ahead, whether it be a message, visit, having the children, cooking, etc., we are right here to help, don't ever feel that you are being a burden by asking. Be selfish, remember to listen to your body, do what you need to do. We love you loads. xx"

"Will do and thank you so much. I can't begin to describe the terrifying feeling of uncertainty. Helen, you'll already know, maybe others of you have experienced similar periods of anxiety, but what I will say is you ladies have been amazing. You and my other friends have come

forward immediately and selflessly when you all have your busy lives. I can't thank you enough as your positivity and support is lifting me right up. Thank you."

"Honestly can't even imagine, Emma, but I completely echo what Helen has said. We will do ANYTHING, anytime. Nothing is ever so important we can't help you guys out at this time in your life."

Emily:

"Hello, my beaut, hope you had an amazing sports day today. First ones are always the best. Just wanted to wish you all the luck in the world for tomorrow. I will have everything crossed that the shit sandwich results in some positive news. I just can't believe we are actually having to have this conversation. Your head must be in bits as I've thought of nothing else since last night and even dreamt about you! For God's sake, fucking shit storms. So, my positive for today for you is true friendship can never be broken and that's the way I feel about us three, so you are stuck with me for many moons yet."

"Thank you. I've had an amazing day at sports day. Toby won his race. Then we had a pub lunch in the sun. Finished off with the school choir/picnic in the beautiful grounds of Killerton. I've actually had a beautifully calm day with big periods that I actually forgot about it. So calm, the anxiety has currently buggered off. They better have brainstormed the shit out of their plan, as I've a page of questions! Watch this space…"

Wednesday 3rd July

Back to the hospital today to hear my fate!

"Summarised update to keep you abreast (courtesy of Rachel!) of the situation.

The shit sandwich situation is a **Grade 3** mixed ductal lobular. In English that's an aggressive quick growing little fucker who has mutated in my body for no apparent reason.

It hasn't spread to my lymph nodes. They've just swollen up in defence.

It's not oestrogen or progesterone fed. If the **HER 2** receptor test comes back negative they will offer me genetic testing.

Little sucker is treatable. I now await a **CT** scan and bone scan to check there's nothing else. Then an appointment with oncology. Straight in with chemo, likely by the end of the month. No lopping anything off yet.

So, there it is. I have me a plan and God do I feel a whole lot better than I did on Friday. I'm now sitting in a pub drinking gin! Thank you for all the support. My friends and family have been amazing."

It's difficult to describe how I'm feeling today. Surprisingly not as fearful as I did on Friday. Perhaps I've had time to let the news sink in. Maybe it's because I'm optimistic that the clever bods will have come up with a good old plan to knock this bugger for six.

This time I'm more prepared. I have an A4 sheet of notes divided into sections:

1. What has caused this?
2. What's my diagnosis and what's the treatment plan?
3. Practicalities.

I show my booby consultant but also tell her I'm going to listen to her information this time before I start firing off my questions. She's obviously seen this before and suggests we go through my notes.

1. What has caused this?

The million-dollar question it would seem. I've looked back at my lifestyle and wondered if I have caused this. I've been a terrible 'yo-yo' dieter. I'm not a massive drinker but in my younger years I'd have a good old sesh most weekends. I used to smoke but gave up eight years ago. I'm a sporadic gym user/walk around the blocker, with a job where I sit on my arse all day. I've had two small humans and so have been rather lacking in sleep for the past, oh I don't know, six years! I wasn't able to breastfeed for more than four weeks with either. I was on the contraceptive pill for sixteen years. I have a coil fitted. There is no family history of breast cancer.

Trust me, I've wracked my brain to come up with something that must have caused this.

The thing is, they can't categorically say what has caused this. Two of the three tests have come back as negative. If the third test comes back as negative, there is nothing 'feeding' my cancer and it's just 'one of those things'. This is difficult to comprehend. I like facts and figures. How can I stop this from happening again if I don't know what caused it in the first place? I guess this is something that I'm going to have to let go of. I've asked my questions and, instead of dwelling, I'm going to focus on the treatment.

2. The plan

My booby bug is a Grade 3 mixed ductal lobular carcinoma. A mix of two different cancers, lobular carcinoma and ductal carcinoma. I do not do things by halves apparently. The good news is that it hasn't spread to the lymph nodes.

From my limited knowledge of breast cancer, I had assumed I'd be operated on first, followed up by chemo and a chaser of radiotherapy. However, because of my type of cancer, they would rather start with chemotherapy and review with scans to see how it reacts. If it stays the same size or grows, they can adjust the chemo accordingly. If they operated first, although the lump would be gone, they would have nothing to monitor and wouldn't know if the chemo being used was effective or not. I'm told that the chemo could reduce the lump or best-case scenario it could wipe it out completely. If this were the case, the surgery would only involve the removal of a small lump. This would then be followed up with radiotherapy.

My heart is screaming 'get this bugger out of me now', but my head agrees that a better approach would be to do the chemo first and monitor how it's reacting. In the meantime, before chemo starts, isn't it possible that the cancer can spread? I'm reassured that that isn't how it works and there's no risk of it spreading further in the timescale we're talking about (weeks).

I didn't know there were various chemo drugs. I thought chemo was chemo. Every day's a school day. I agree with the proposed approach. I'm told there will now be various scans, covering my whole body, to check everything else is in order and that we are only dealing with the one area (unlikely to be anywhere else as it wasn't detected in my lymph nodes). This is very reassuring. I'll also receive an initial consultation appointment with the oncology consultant to discuss my treatment in more detail.

3. Practicalities

Down to practicalities, I show my booby consultant the insurance paperwork and ask her to point out the name of the cancer I have. Transpires I have the grimmer of the options, so a claim is looking positive.

I had a family holiday booked to Menorca (26th August) and a trip to the Edinburgh Tattoo (3rd August) as a present for my dad's seventieth. These will now both be off the cards as weekly chemotherapy will have commenced before the month is out. I'll add cancellations to the increasing 'to-do' list.

I'm told about FORCE, a purpose-built cancer support and information centre based in the grounds of the RD&E Hospital. I've driven past it all my driving life and never really once considered what goes on inside. I'm encouraged to pop in and have a chat with them to check out whether I could benefit from any of the many free services they offer.

My booby consultant passes me over to my breast care nurse and friend. I'm quick to assure her I didn't divulge any secrets from Ibiza and how lovely it is to see her after all this time, albeit not in the best of circumstances! My booby nurse dishes out a load of reading material on all aspects of my treatment. I'm going to need a file for all my 'cancer admin'. I'm also given a book called *Mummy's Lump*, which has been written and illustrated for children. I am dreading finding the words to tell Toby, so I'm sure this will come in very handy when the time comes.

I come away feeling pretty positive and empowered. I have me a plan. It sounds like a good plan and today's appointment was a lot more positive in tone than Friday's.

I telephone Becky (boss) with an update and blurt out all the info. Becky says she's going to get the team together and tell them all in one go. What a horrible thing for a manager to have to do. People are going to be upset, might have questions and she isn't going to have all the answers. I ask her if she would like me to come in and do it. I'm nearby. I have all the information and maybe if everybody sees me looking okay it won't come as such a shock to them. After discussing whether I feel able to do this, I'm on my way in.

En route, I call the critical illness insurers. Ever practical, that's me. Might as well get this show on the road and deal with the practicalities. I'm advised I can either complete a paper application or go through the questions over the phone with a claims handler. I say I'm happy to talk over the phone and an appointment is booked to go through the relevant documentation.

Sitting in a room as my colleagues file in, jovial but surprised to see me, it feels very surreal. I've made some notes on the main bits in case I lose my way a bit. I just come out with it. I explain that the reason I'm here is to show them I'm okay physically. I tell them what I have, how quickly everything has happened, and what is going to happen. I catch the immediate shock on everyone's faces, see the wet eyes brimming, hear stifled whimpers. I just keep my head down looking at my notes as I want to get all this information out.

I then quickly tell them I feel fine. That it's a shit situation but I just need to crack on with it. That I don't want anyone to walk on eggshells around me. To not feel sorry for me or worry about what they say. I've sworn a couple of times and laugh how it's quite liberating to say that in the work environment! Slowly people start smiling and we open up a discussion. Some colleagues share information of people they know who have had cancer.

All in all, we're in there for about an hour. We even had flapjacks and fruit laid on for the occasion. As my colleagues file out with a hug and words of encouragement, I think that went well, rather than a sombre affair with more questions than answers. Becky is an amazingly supportive boss anyway, but she has been brilliant in my time of need. We hug and I walk out of the office not knowing when (not if) I'll be back.

So, there we have it. Lumpy is getting right on my tits. My right one to be precise. But it's treatable and it's not spread to my lymph nodes. We just need to get this show on the road.

Cancer Comms

Circle of Trust:

"Where there's a plan there's a way forward! You seem happier now you have answers and that makes me happy! Enjoy your gin in the sunshine."

"The plan is to nuke the bastard, I like this plan! If you have any appointments on a Wednesday happy to come and keep you company if you wanted and I'm always here on any day if you need anything else. You can do this, Em, show the shit who is the boss of this situation!"

"Okay good, we have a plan of attack. Just to reiterate Becky's comments, you can do this, Em, you're a strong lady and we are all 100% in this with you in any way you want/need us. Show that fucker the door!"

Massaging Mummies:

"Wow, the little bastard won't beat our girl. We will kill the bastard. Love you, Em."

"Thank you for updating us. Enjoy that gin. You certainly deserve it. You have totally got this, the little bugger will not win. Love you. Xx"

"I'm glad you're in the pub enjoying a much-deserved large gin, I hope. You have got this, hun, and you will kill the bastard. We are here to support you every step of the way. Love you loads. Xx"

"You've got this, Em. Hit him with everything you've got. Did you have the joy of wearing one of their capes that flap open at the most inopportune moments? Massive love and cheers to those well-deserved gins. xx"

"I think I'm more in shock at Caroline calling something a bastard! I'd expect it of Scouse and look she's gone for it twice."

"As you know, I don't often use words like bastard, but at times it is the best way to describe certain things like this. X"

"Oh well I'll try and keep it clean. Who am I kidding, no I won't – be gone bastard ductal lobular! Very happy to hear it's not in your lymph. Good luck with the rest of the tests. I'm sure it's hurting your head interpreting all the info. Let us know when you're up for a coffee or gin and some offloading or distracting. xx"

"Ladies… Gin and pizza at mine Monday night?"

Shits and Giggles:

"That is one awesome plan, the oncologist sounds fantastic. I'm so pleased you've got a plan. Enjoy your gin. xx"

Strong Randy Ladies:

"Thank fuck for that! The shit sandwich is now looking to become a bit of a jam sandwich, my favourite sort. Thank God you found it when you did. So glad you now know the plan. Well, if you fancy any company at chemo I would be more than happy to oblige with more talks of shit as we routinely do. I think after today you well and truly deserve a gin (why do they not have gin glasses on emoji yet… do they not know how many gins are now available in this country?!). Enjoy the sunshine. I'll check in with you again soon."

"That's good you now have a plan for the shit sandwich, and you know what's going on. You know where we are if you need us but will speak soon and I'm also happy to oblige if you need any company."

Local Yocals:

"Sending my love and support to you today, Emma. I will be thinking of you. xx"

"Seconded, Em! Love you. xx"

"Thinking of you, Em. xx"

"As usual, you deliver the info humorously laced in your grace and charm. One of the many reasons I love you. Emma, your strength is so apparent right now and we (Beth and me, sitting in a café) send you big hugs and a ton of love. Glad there's no imminent lopping. xx"

"Your use of words is amazing! I'm sorry I haven't said much about the situation. I thought I'd take a step back and let the grownups do the talking, as knowing me I'd say completely the wrong thing and upset you even more! Gin solves all problems, so get as many down ya as possible (see, wrong thing to say, really), but get on being as brave and strong as you are! GO EMMA."

"Oh Emma. Just cried happy tears in a play café! So glad it's treatable and you have a plan of action and feeling better as you can be. We all love you loads and here every step of the way. xx"

"That is such good news of no lopping off! But hey, you have your plan and it sounds a good one, so let's kick the chemo butt. Lots of love to you. xx"

"Lopping off! Ah Emma, thank you for sharing your news with us. We're here for you every step of the way, babe!"

Cake. Always Cake:

"I think a large gin or two is exactly what you need. Good work. Plan sounds like a good 'un and it sounds like they are being very thorough and aren't hanging around with the treatment. You're amazing. Now, get that girl another double gin! Lots of love. xx"

"I'm glad they're treating you quickly and doing a complete MOT. Your perspective is amazing and ditto what Rachel said – double Gina all round! xx"

"Oh, I can't wait for a double Gina. She sounds fun. x"

"Oh, indeed she is."

"Let's invite her out Saturday."

"Yes please. And ladies, I'm still very much up for going out. Especially now. xx"

"I'll see if she's free but don't be disappointed, she has an incredibly busy diary. Hell yes, where shall we go?"

"Well, just see what you can do. Would you like to try Heart of Oak? I could book us a table. x"

"Never been, let's do it!

Thursday 4ᵗʰ July 2019

So, what do you do when you get a cancer diagnosis? Arrange to go canoeing down the River Exe with two of your mates, of course! It had always been on my list of things to do, so why not now?

However, things didn't go swimmingly (sorry, couldn't help myself) as, en route at 8.20am, I got a call from the oncology department offering me a last minute cancellation appointment at 9am. The new challenge presented was to get across Exeter in rush hour to take advantage of this appointment. Darren even manages to make it back from Torquay as I haven't found my big girl pants to do this stuff on my own just yet.

Today I meet my oncology consultant, and boy do I get a lot of information. The various scans I'll be having in the forthcoming days, the type of chemotherapy drugs I'll be having and possible side effects.

Chemotherapy

The drugs will be pumped into my veins intravenously (IV). This either means they'll insert a cannula into my hand each time or I can opt for a PICC (peripherally inserted central catheter – more about that later) line to be put into my arm which will remain in place for the duration of my treatment. Now I don't particularly like the thought of having something in me all the time, but neither do I relish the thought of being repeatedly jabbed at sixteen times. As I'll also have to have bloods taken before each treatment that would potentially mean doubling up on the jabbing. In contrast, the bloods could be taken out of the PICC line, so I decide this is the lesser of the two evils.

The chemotherapy treatment can put my body into early menopause, which may or may not be reversed at the end of treatment. I'm asked if we have children and whether we were considering having anymore. We both look at each other for one second before responding in unison 'no'. Had we not been finished on the small human front, she would have discussed harvesting my eggs. It's not until later it dawns on me that cancer can so cruelly bugger up your plans. What if I had been younger and had not yet had children? How would I react to that choice potentially being taken away from me? Even though we'd had no intention of having any more, this seems rather final and has been dictated to me.

We discuss hair loss. The possibility of using a cold cap during treatment in an attempt to protect the hair follicles from being damaged. Will I want to wear a wig or a headscarf? All things to consider and more reading material produced. The consultant recommends a great website called 'Surburban Turban'. Whilst she is out of the room, Darren checks it out. I ask how the models look and his response was, "Like they have cancer." Helpful, thank you.

The plan of attack going forward will be to have the various scans, meet with a genetics counsellor, attend clinic to discuss what I can expect on day one and have an orientation session. Sounds like the warmup to a new job, which I suppose in a way it is because I need to be quickly brought up to speed on something completely new that is going to happen to me.

I inform the consultant that I have an existing appointment with another consultant mid-July because of an issue with my bottom. I do joke with her that I appear to be all 'tits and arse' and ask whether I should still attend this appointment. I'm encouraged to do so but also inform the bum consultant (my words not the professional oncology consultant's) of my cancer treatment. I'm also encouraged to make an appointment with my dentist to check my dental health and have any treatment necessary prior to commencement of chemotherapy.

Asked if I have any questions, I decline and thank the consultant for being so comprehensive. I feel like I'm going to be getting a complete MOT on my health. I will be purchasing a notebook and pen for all my cancer admin and thoughts. Before I leave, I'm given an appointment card with various clinic attendance dates including my chemo start date of 23rd July. I'm also given a booklet with various telephone numbers of departments and/or people I should phone once this show gets on the road.

Today's visit has been a steep learning curve and created a lot of bedtime reading.

Side effects of chemotherapy

My particular combo of cancer fighting poisons are Paclitaxel and Carboplatin weekly for twelve weeks followed by four to six three-weekly sessions of Epirubicin and Cyclosphosphamide. Easy to say. The spellcheck is having a field day on these bad boys!

I was given information sheets on all the medication but essentially the information was repeated, and general side effects seemed to include: Allergic reaction (feeling hot or flushed, a skin rash, itching, shivering, feeling dizzy, a headache, feeling breathless, swelling of your face or lips, pain in your back, tummy or chest), bruising and bleeding (nosebleeds, bleeding gums (good job for proofreading as spell check didn't pick up on 'bleeding bums'. Certainly don't want that), tiny red or purple spots that look like a rash, anaemia, feeling sick, diarrhoea, hair loss, sore mouth, feeling tired, muscle or joint pain, numb or tingling hands or feet, skin changes, nail changes, low blood pressure, changes in the way the liver works, changes to your heartbeat, blood clots, affecting fertility, changes to periods, the ability to fart glitter. Not really in the case of the latter, I was just checking I still had your attention!

I'm thinking perhaps it would be easier to list what it doesn't do. Although the list may appear overwhelming, I'm pleased to report that I did not experience anywhere near the full array of delightful options listed above.

One of the things that surprised me was the information given to look after your nails. Although it is fine to wear nail varnish, I was advised not to use false nails during treatment. I've had acrylic nails since I got married in 2011. It might seem rather insignificant, silly if you like, in the grand scheme of this shit sandwich shituation, but I was actually really rather sad at the thought of having to give up my acrylic nails. I liked the way my hands looked with them and I enjoyed my fortnightly visits to the nail bar to get them done.

Another fun fact was that the treatment contained alcohol and you were advised against driving following treatment, as you could be over the legal limit. Can you imagine being pulled over and testing over the limit. "Where have you been drinking?" "Oh, just having some poison pumped in intravenously at the RD&E Hospital." I don't want to add a conviction for drink driving and referral to my regulator into the mix! After a conversation with my dad, he offered to be 'Dad's taxi' on treatment days. This became known as 'Dad's chemo cab' and involved me rocking up in style in a white Ford Transit Van.

Hair loss

This is the bit that wigged (see what I did there!) me out the most. I had long thick hair and I knew that I was going to lose it.

The option of a cold cap had been discussed with me. Not all chemotherapy drugs cause hair loss but I was told that mine would. Wearing a cold cap could (and I stress could) prevent or reduce hair loss but I was advised that it was very unlikely. It would also lengthen my treatment time as it would need to be worn before, during and after treatment. For something that would likely cause me to have 'ice cream head' for a good few hours, I decided that this wasn't for me.

To wig or not to wig? That is the question and it all comes down to personal preference. Now I could have gone to town on the wig front as they are available in all different styles and colours and are very natural looking. I've been a massive fan of fancy dress parties over the years, but I always found the wigs itchy and annoying. I was given all the information and knew that I could seek assistance from a specialist wig fitter and help with funding, but it was not something I ever entertained in this process. I'm sure a specially made wig would be a lot comfier to wear than a £10 fancy dress purchase off the internet.

For me it was all about the headgear and once you start looking into what is out there you can find loads of different options. Surburban Turban is an awesome website with a massive range of chemo hats, headscarves, evening wear, turbans and sleep hats. Equally if you just google 'chemo hats', loads of stuff pops up. So even though I always thought I looked a bit of a twat in a hat I decided that this was the option for me.

I also decided that I was going to have my long hair cut off and donate it to The Little Princess Trust. This charity makes wigs for children going through treatment that causes hair loss. I felt empowered by this decision. I was deciding that I would cut my hair so someone else could benefit from it and it would not be going to waste. Equally, with my amount of hair, I had awful visions of masses of it ending up all over the house.

The hair loss was a big deal to me and one I rather think I underestimated.

Cancer Comms

"Right, chums, I promise not to bore and provide daily updates, but I thought I'd let you know we're getting this show on the road a little quicker.

I was fortunate to be available for a last-minute oncology cancellation appointment this morning. The plan is for chemo to start 23rd July. Few more appointments, scans, tests in the meantime.

I've been told I will lose my hair so I'm going to get it all lopped off so I can donate it to The Little Princess Trust. I'll probably look like an imp with short hair! I might dig into the fancy dress box for wigs or more likely check out this cool 'Suburban Turban' website.

So, there we have it. A plan, a date. Let's get lumpy gone. Yes, I've named it 'lumpy'!"

Circle of Trust:

"Love you so much, brave girl, so proud of you. How amazing that you are controlling the hair situ, such an amazing idea. No offence, lumpy, but fuck off." Amanda also sends a pic of her four-year-old wearing a granny wig and offering to share it with me! *"Honestly, if there's anything I can do, please say, I work in town so can do any town shopping, just literally anything. xxx"*

"Ah, mate, it's good that it's getting done sooner, and well done regarding the hair situ. You've had short hair before – remember when we sent to Slinkys?! Reckon a fancy ass head scarf would look pretty cool. You really are an inspiration with your positivity. We're all with you."

"Wowsers! Let's get this show on the road. I'm off the first week of school hols, so if you need anything just shout, but obvs shout anytime. Great idea with the hair… at least it will go to a good cause… as long as I don't get you confused with Russ (my brother). You are in the right mindset with this, Em, stay strong."

"Don't think of it as being bald, it's an extreme undercut."

"lol @ confusing me with Russell. I've been checking out the Suburban Turban website but only if Sophia isn't up for sharing her wig. Darren was looking at it before me. I asked him what the hats made you look like. His response: 'Like you've got cancer.' He's referring to it as my 'twat hat'. Right, I'm off to draw up a rota for you all."

"Maybe Nicki can make you a twat hat? It would be a whole lot cheaper than that! I'll knit you one, if you want? I have some orange wool.

We could call it 'the Darren' (my husband is ginger). Looking forward to getting a rota! Phone wanted to autocorrect that to a toga, nobody needs an image of me in a toga! Rota me for every Wednesday."

"Becky in a toga would make me feel complete! Rota me in for a Friday."

"Couldn't you just borrow Ginger Boy's beanies?"

Michelle:

"Hi lovely. I'm sorry to send this as a text but I needed to update you on a bit of a shituation. I've got breast cancer. Found a lump two weeks ago. Friday confirmed cancer. Shit myself all weekend. Since Wednesday I have a cancer fighting plan and chemo starts 23rd July. I am so glad we danced like twats that night as will need to tame it down a bit next time. xx"

"Oh shit, Emma, I don't know what to say. I'm devastated for you, I can't imagine how you must be feeling. You are an incredible, strong, positive woman, I reckon you can kick cancer's arse, and I for one will be right behind you. If you fancy a visitor at any point I am there in a heartbeat. Big hugs to you, beautiful. xx"

"Thanks, my lovely. I've suddenly been given a lot of time, so would absolutely love your company at some point soon. I'm sorry to pass on the news as I can see the shock in people's faces. But I'm signed off now and enjoying the sun before they start zapping me."

"You have nothing to be sorry for. You're going through this, so don't worry about others, just focus on you. You have so many people who love you and we will all rally round you to fight this. You just let me know when you are up for a visit and I'll be there. I can do day too, or a long lunch from work, anything really. No rush, just when you're ready. Love you, chica. Xx"

Friday 5th July 2019

Chloe has a GP appointment this morning and now so do I immediately after. I'd popped in yesterday on my way home, asked if there was a free appointment and explained why. I'm quickly learning that if you drop the C-bomb you get stuff sorted. I'm of course not abusing this (well not yet), but it's worth mentioning to see if it helps.

My doctor is lovely and listens as I give her the low-down matter-of-factly. She tells me she knew what she saw but had to make the appropriate referral. I tell her that her poker face is better than the consultant's.

I also have some practical things for her. She happily signs me off for a couple of months whilst I undergo all my tests and start treatment. She says some people like to keep working as much as they are able, others like to stop work to focus on the treatment. Everyone is different, deals with this in different ways, and she will support my choice.

I also have an FP92A form for her to sign. Since 1st April 2009, cancer patients in England have been eligible for free prescriptions for five years. Once the certificate has expired, you can make a new application. Obviously not having cancer in the first place would be everyone's preference but free prescriptions are certainly a helpful benefit in this situation and for five years into the future.

Cancer Comms:

Shits and Giggles:

"Hey ladies, so glad to hear you're feeling a bit better about things now you have a plan, Em. Also, very glad to hear that nothing needs to be lopped off! How are you feeling now?"

"I'm feeling much better about it all now I have a plan. Next week is completely free of anything so I'm going to take the time to chill out and have a lovely week. Then the following week is various appointments and then boom, on your bike, lumpy."

Saturday 6th July 2019

Before any jovialities this evening, I need to get my bum checked out! Sparing you the full details, it just hasn't been right since I had Toby nearly six years ago. If I'd have been told about piles and the ongoing 'joys' they can bring, I think that would have been a dealbreaker in the having small humans department. I had already named him 'Paul the Pile'. Well, now there's something else going on in the downstairs department and short of carrying my own inflatable ring around with me it's all becoming a bit of a pain in the arse – literally.

Nothing like having a woman stick their finger up your bum on a Saturday afternoon, but it had to be done. We need to get these things sorted out and I'm way past caring about who sees what now. The thing being an Anal Hematoma (which I have named Annie in the spirit of giving my body defects human names), which I'm assured will resolve itself. Poor old Paul was nowhere to be seen as Annie was stealing the limelight. I'm invited to come back again once Annie has stopped hogging the limelight.

So, a night out with some girlies is just what I need. After devising our getaway to fall during the nightly military exercise that is the bedtime routine, so the blokes have that luxury, we all meet on the corner to get a lift to our local, The Heart of Oak. One minute later we arrive. Don't judge us for driving, it is a fuck off massive walk up a hill and I do have cancer now!

We eat, we drink and we get merry. Well, more than merry, to be honest. Yes, we talk about my unwanted guest, but we also get really quite pissed and enjoy watching Rachel ask the bar staff about five times whether we've paid for our meal!

I also devise the 'C card'. If you curve your right thumb and forefinger, this makes a lovely 'C' shape. This is the 'C card' I pull out when I need a new drink, together with bashful eyes. I think I will be making good use of the 'C card' in as many situations as I can!

Cancer Comms

Local Yocals:

"Anyone available for a Spoons brekkie?"

"Ah, I'd love to, but I've got to have some posh double-barreled name man push his finger up my bum. True Story. Bum doctor appointment today."

"Oh, you are funny."

"Enjoy, Emma."

"I just actually LOL'd in a very quiet café."

"I need a new bum! Mine's got a crack in it. I can see in the mirror a crack in the back. Appropriate, Em." (Someone's been reading Dawn McMillan's *I Need a New Bum!*)

"Ha, love this. I need a new arse and tits. Maybe there's a BOGOF deal to be done."

"It was a lady consultant wearing sparkly pumps. Smaller fingers. What a result."

"Ha! Can they sort you out?"

"Not right now. One will sort itself out with time, but Paul the Pile is gonna be a pain in the arse for a bit longer. But for now, I've got my glad rags on and going out with the girls."

Sunday 7ᵗʰ July 2019

Some days you just need your mum. A day with my mum, the kids, a play park and some sunshine. Nothing else was needed today. That was enough.

Cancer Comms

Massaging Mummies:

"Emma you still happy for us to come to you? Happy to host if not. What can we bring? Pizza, salad, snacks… who's coming, ladies?
"Yes, I'm really looking forward to it. Darren is on call, so my only option is my house tomorrow. Sounds like a plan. I'll grab a pizza tomorrow and flat bread."

Unfortunately, some of the gang are struck down by a sickness bug.

"Ed's still not great but improving. I'm just wiped out, so fingers crossed not getting it. It has been an awful bug. I would hate to pass it on to anyone just in case I'm a carrier or in the early stages, so I think I'd better leave today to play safe. Sorry. If anyone is up for a catch-up next week would love to see you and my household bugs should have definitely gone by then. Big hugs. xx"
"So, to bring a smile to Emma's face – emergency pit stop needed in Sainsbury's as the world fell out of my arse! Think I will need to steer clear of you all until this bug has done one. Free to meet up later in the week or over the weekend if anyone fancies it. Gutted to miss tonight. Love all round. Xx"
"Oh God, that is an extremely disappointing situation. Nearly happened to me in Sainsbo's a couple of months back.

Must be something horrible doing the rounds. As much as I love you, you can deffo keep clear until the world stops falling out of your arse! Although not to be the bearer of bad news but mine lasted nine days with a ½lb weight loss. I couldn't frigging believe it. Hope you feel better soon. Xx"

Local Yocals:

"How are you feeling today, Emma? xx"
"I'm fine now but God I felt rough as a badger's arse this morning. I had to enlist the help of my mum to parent today!"

Cake. Always Cake:

"I don't remember getting home last night, which for me is a sign of a cracking night. Cheers ladies. Also, did we pay?"
"I've felt better! Oh, that was so much fun. You ran off as you needed a wee. Hope you made it out of the jumpsuit in time. You deffo paid. You asked about five times!"
"Ha, I think I paid. I did make it in time. I also have a mystery toe injury. No idea what I did. Today is a day for a bacon sandwich. Oh no, wait… I'll eat an apple instead."

Monday 8ᵗʰ July 2019

Today was a practical life admin day. I like order and it was important to me that I got all the practical shit out of the way before the shit storm (if it was to be a shit storm) of treatment began.

First order of business was contacting TUI to cancel the family holiday we had booked for August. Ten of us were going on this family 'sunny holiday' as Toby called it. It was going to be Chloe's first time abroad. I'd tried to convince my mum and Darren to still go and take the children, but they weren't having any of it.

Devouring the T&Cs with a fine-tooth comb, it looked like we'd lose 50% of our money, which was a hefty chunk. Fortunately, TUI were amazing and offered a full refund to six of us. Unfortunately, my brother had booked separately, so wasn't entitled to a refund, but it was important they still had their time away as a family. They deserved it and I could live vicariously through them via the joys of Facebook. Either that or I could unfollow them for a week.

Next, I had to unpick all the travel, accommodation and ticket elements of the surprise visit to the Edinburgh Tattoo for my dad's seventieth.

Booked a hair appointment for 'The big chop'. I explained to them that I would be keeping my hair and why so as not to surprise them on the day.

A review of the summer childcare provision. Damn you, cancer, mucking up my military precision arrangements.

Devouring all the reading material the hospital has given me:- The Breast Cancer Care 'Primary Breast Cancer Information Pack', Peripherally Inserted Central Catheters (PICC lines), Having a CT Scan (Computerised Tomography) Examination, Nuclear Medicine Scans, The Provision of Wigs, The Value of Support – Force Cancer Charity, various chemo drugs.

Perhaps the best read was *Mummy's Lump*, the book I'm going to read to Toby when the time is right. When is the right time? I guess I'll know. But reading this has really helped me work out how I'm going to explain it all to him. Toby has a bit of a fascination with death at the moment anyway and knows that people usually die when they're very old or very ill. I don't want to underplay it but at the same time I don't want to scare him.

I remember an awkward conversation I had with him once on the nursery commute:

"Mummy, where's heaven?"

"Heaven?" [Shit, where did that come from?]

"Yes, heaven. Gemma had a picture of her dog on her watch and said that he was in heaven."

"Well, heaven... [shit, how do you explain the concept of heaven to a four-year-old? I'd never given it much thought and it's actually really tricky]

"Um, well heaven is above the clouds."

"Is it another planet?"

"No. It's not another planet. It's a place where people go when they die. Up above the clouds."

[Thinks about it] "So are there people walking around up there and why don't they fall down through the clouds?"

[Good question] "Not exactly. See, when people die, their bodies don't work anymore but their soul goes to heaven."

"What's a soul?"

[I just fail really miserably now as I really can't find the right words to explain this to a four-year-old. Had I had more notice of this topic I would have done some research, maybe spoken to my cousin who is a vicar.]

Fortunately, we've just arrived at nursery, so I warn them he's going to have some questions about death for them and bat the ball firmly into their court. They started this!

Without prompting, at the end of the day he delivers this very matter of factly:

"Mummy, when you die, you get buried in a box or you get burnt. You then go up to heaven on a cloud and get to run around with other dogs."

Now I'd be rather concerned at either of those two options, but he seems to have just accepted it. There were fortunately no further heaven-related questions until a year later when our dog was put to sleep. He was then happy that Benji was up in heaven running around with Bruce (another family dog).

Back to today.

It was quite a full-on day of logistics but it got done and I feel good having ticked a load of stuff off my 'to do' list.

The Local Yocals came round for tea tonight. It might have been at my house, but I was not the hostess with the mostess. They swept in like a professional team of caterers, bringing their three courses, meaning I didn't have to lift a finger. These girls are the best and I was very grateful for another evening of laughs and giggles.

If people ask you 'how can we help?' and you can't think of anything, an evening in with your friends could be just the tonic.

Tuesday 9th July 2019

Practicalities of the dentist all done and dusted with. Teeth will hopefully see themselves through this forthcoming period now.

I did ask if I was entitled to free dental treatment as I was exempt throughout both pregnancies and the following year. One of my free crowns is courtesy of such benefit! Sadly, the booby bug does not qualify you for free treatment, but it was worth an ask.

So, I was having a good day until:

1. I came home to find Arthur had eaten a massive chocolate bar someone had posted to me.
2. Reading the following in my consultant's follow up letter: "She is a lawyer involved in fitness to practice proceedings. I note that she is quite small-breasted…"

How do we go from lawyer to shit tits?! On a positive note, I've just purchased a new carpet with the holiday refund.

Cancer Comms

Linda:

"Oh, thank you so much for my choccy. That was very

sweet of you. I do have to report that the bloody dog got involved with it before I got home! Bastard beagle, he's done this before. He did save me some. I wonder if this is where the expression 'as sick as a dog' comes from? That'll teach him."

"OH NO! Hope I've not inadvertently poisoned your dog now!?"

Circle of Trust:

"Small-breasted, lol. Ask for an upgrade."

"OMG I've actually pissed myself! I really shouldn't laugh at dog poisoning and small-breasted birds with booby bug, but it made my horrific day funny."

"I was laughing with my boss about it. It's just the context: She is a lawyer involved in fitness to practice proceedings. I note she is small-breasted... They're advertising my job for six months. She said whoever is employed will have big shoes to fill. I said 'or a small bra'. How do we go from lawyer to shit tits?!"

"That's great news that they're getting you cover at work, eases the pressure. You can concentrate on sorting your bangers out."

"Small-breasted? I'd like to hear her describe mine!"

"Mate, if yours are small, what are mine?!! Non-existent! Arthur certainly does have a sweet tooth, doesn't he? I'm glad the carpet cheered you up. Such a forty-year-old thing to get excited about, isn't it?"

"£150 to save the dog! Most expensive chocs I've ever received."

Massaging Mummies:

"Oh wow. That is hilarious. Oops – hope Arthur isn't sick! I'd hate to imagine how she'd describe my boobs if yours are small!"

"Did it go on to say... I note that she is quite small-breasted with

51

amazing ambition and personality and wonder and amazement…
They'd probably refer to my G-units as a third person."

"Oh Em… That's disappointing… New carpet?"

"Ha no, new carpet was unrelated to choc incident. The things you get excited about at forty!"

"Little things please us. Hope Arthur is better, and you have recovered from your vet bill. Consultants always know how to word things and make you feel good… Or not!"

Local Yocals:

"OMG did they actually write that?! Fucking hell!"

"It's bloody Slimming World! First thing to go is the boobs!"

"I know, I call them my 'itty bitty shitty titties' but that's my prerogative! Arthur's off to the vets for some sickness tablets."

Cake. Always Cake:

"Oh dear. I'll get the PALS number for you to make a complaint! They would say that mine are non-existent!"

"Wow what a super flattering comment! Clearly a charmer. I think I'd be more pissed with the chocolate, though. Ooooo nice, where for? Is this because of the chocolate consumption?"

"To be fair I refer to them as itty bitty shitty titties, so her term is less derogatory! I must have good scaffolding in place as I thought they were at least of average size 36C."

Wednesday 10th July 2019

I'm being taken out today by my lovely work colleagues Ruth and Julie. It's a gloriously sunny day and we're off to Exmouth for some crazy golf and lunch. We, of course, have the obligatory fact-dispensing conversation, but once that's done and dusted, we enjoy a few hours of fun in the sun. It's amazing to have someone else taxi me around for once. As I sit back and raise my face to the sun after lunch, I feel lucky to have such good friends and actually quite fortunate to now have this gift of time to spend with them.

Tonight it's Toby's parent's evening. I love looking at his books and seeing how well he's developing. All good to report on that front. His teacher asks if there is anything the school can do to support us as a family through the following months. I let her know we haven't told him yet, we will do soon, but if she could just keep an eye on him, we would be very grateful.

Similarly, nursery have been amazing and asked if there is anything they can do when I told them. They have kindly re-sent the email to all parents reminding them of when they should keep their children off nursery and the exclusion periods. I know small humans are little snot boxes and bring all sorts home, but it's worth asking your nursery to send out a reminder. One of the members of staff lives near us and offered to pick Chloe up and take her home, if there was ever a time when I couldn't manage it.

Multiple hospital appointments + small humans = need for watertight logistics

We already run a tight ship of school buses, after school clubs and nursery to tie in with the 9 – 5. (Well, the 8.30 – 4.15, but you get the picture.)

We decided to keep Chloe in nursery four days a week because:

1. most importantly we did not want to change her routine
2. I would need her there on treatment days and the days I was feeling rough and couldn't parent and

3.   I am so lucky to get full sick pay for six months, so it didn't have a financial impact.

We did end up swapping her Monday to Thursday to Tuesday to Friday to coincide with Friday being the day I would likely feel the worst.

Toby was, of course, in school, so all his arrangements were kept the same.

But all this was kicking off during the six-week school summer holidays! I was off now, so that took the pressure off, but we turned to family and friends for Toby to cover appointments and treatment days. So many people offered and so we took them up on it.

Now was not the time to try and solider on alone when I had an army of people waiting to help. I used to feel guilty about asking people for help as I didn't want to impose. Even if people offered, I would still check if they were sure. Since my anxiety attack a few years back, I no longer have these worries. People wouldn't offer if they didn't mean it. It can help them cope and feel useful. There's nothing worse than feeling like there's nothing you can do to help a loved one. So if their offer would really help you out, snap it up. Equally, if you need help, don't be afraid to reach out. The worst they'll do is say no if they can't or don't want to help.

Cancer Comms

Michelle:

"You're wrong. The card does make things better. It makes me feel loved and lucky to have such awesome thoughtful friends. xx"

"Oh, Em, my heart breaks for you. I wish I could take it all away for you. But yes, you do have my love, love you to bits. xx"

"Feeling the love. It's just a testing chapter in my life but it will make me stronger. It's also making me slow down and appreciate the beauty around me and spend time with people, which is amazing. Once the treatment kicks off, and I get into a routine of knowing my good days, we'll sort a catch up out. xx"

"You will kick it's arse, I know you will. Like I said before, when you're ready I will be there in a heartbeat. You just let me know what works. xx"

Thursday 11ᵗʰ July 2019

Today I have the pleasure of Jo keeping me company. Jo, who I bumped into in Aldi car park last week all smiles, asking "How are you?" and then me having to piss all over her positivity with my cancer diagnosis. I'm really starting to hate telling people. Seeing the shock on their faces and the immediate teary eyes quickly followed with an apology for crying.

"Just a little message to say sorry for crying on you. Your positive attitude and strength will fight this fucker off, I have no doubt… My lovely friend is a nurse and sometimes deals with chemo day cases. She is super lovely, they all are, you will be in amazing hands. And I mean it: any help at all you need please don't hesitate to ask… Big hugs, Strudders. Xx"

"Thank you, lovely. I'm so sorry I told you there, but I'm realising there's really no good place and it's a shocker. I don't like pretending everything is okay, but also I hate knowing I will upset people. Now I have a plan and am over the terrifying uncertainty I'm okay. I feel very well and I'm in such a good head space at the moment, I've got this. Thank you so much for your kindness. I'm blown away by everyone. xx"

As always with Jo, we have a hilarious catch up and again, for a few hours, I forget about Lumpy.

Telling people and the inevitable 'I know someone who had cancer' stories

I found there was no easy way to tell people. It's a shocker. It's a horrible thing to have happen to you and it's a horrible thing to have to tell people. Ten out of ten people will be saddened that this is happening to you. Unless they're heartless arseholes. Then I'd question whether you need them in your life.

I knew too many people to phone them all individually, which was why I had to send out texts to groups of friends. I didn't want to tell everyone in my contacts list, but there were certain groups that needed to know. I wanted to keep it upbeat and clear that it was business as usual.

But then there would be individuals I'd bump into out and about. As we're all typically British and polite, one of the most used openers is, 'Hello, how are you?' What do you say in that scenario? 'Oh, you know, fine,' and try and move the conversation along. I couldn't lie to people when I was anything but fine. I found I was just telling them but then quickly following it up with, 'But I have a plan and treatment starts…'

What I found fascinating was that everybody knows someone who's either had cancer or knows someone whose long-distant aunt has a long-lost cousin who's had cancer. It's more common than you think, but I guess these stories only come out when you yourself get a diagnosis. It can sometimes be a bit too much, hearing all the stories, but I found that they were always given with good intentions. Similarly, the advice that was given was with good intentions. Some of it was actually really useful, but the most useful advice came from my friends who had actually had cancer themselves. I found it very comforting to speak to them because they 'got it' completely. They'd walked my walk and it was so reassuring to know they'd come through it.

It's all a matter of choice, though. Until there are outward visible signs that something medical is going on in your life, it might be your choice that you don't say anything. I don't think there's any right or wrong way of dealing with this. At the end of the day, it's you going through this and you've got to do what's right for you.

Friday 12ᵗʰ July 2019

Back to the hospital today for a radioactive marker to be inserted into the tumour. This is to mark the location of lumpy so that during future surgery if, sorry I mean when, the bastard has shrunk away to nothing, the consultant will know where to go poking around.

The procedure is carried out under a local anesthetic and is done and dusted in a matter of minutes. I have to chuckle with the assistant at the 'well done' given to me by the consultant. I feel like a six-year-old!

Next, I meet my sister-in-law Charlene. Charlene is a nurse and is at the hospital doing some training. She's offered to come with me to FORCE. Charlene was there at the birth of both my children. Seems like she's getting up close and personal with me on another one of life's great moments.

The FORCE premises are beautiful. So bright and airy. Comfy chairs where you can rest with a cuppa and help yourself to magazines and fruit. You're greeted by a smiley face from one of the volunteers and offered a cuppa.

I don't really know how to start the conversation. I just say I've got cancer and they were recommended to me. Could I talk to someone? I'm offered a seat, a cuppa and then a lovely lady takes me off to a private room for a chat about all things FORCE.

She is so calm and unrushed. I keep myself pretty well together until she asks me if there is anything immediately concerning me. This is when I tell her I'm so scared for the children. I don't really know how to tell Toby and, every time I think about them, I get upset. That's enough to set me and Charlene off. Whilst I remain practical and action-focused I can keep the tears at bay. She reassures me it's perfectly normal to feel this way. That there is counselling available should I feel I would benefit from that and services that can involve the children.

I would highly recommend you check out whether there are any cancer support charities local to you. I simply had no idea as to the extent of services FORCE provides: Information and advice, welfare benefits advice, support and counselling, complementary therapies, acupuncture, managing fatigue, keeping active through walking groups and exercise programs, various managing stress and anxiety sessions, mindfulness sessions, wig fitting service, pampering sessions. It's endless. You can even use the site as a base to sit and relax, and have a cuppa in-between appointments. A lot of these services extend to your friends and family if affected by your cancer. All this is FREE – bloody amazing.

It's been a bit of an eventful morning, so it's off to the pub for lunch with Charlene and later Amanda joins us. As we discuss the complementary therapies, there's a consensus that they're both affected by this and will need the massages!

Useful support information

If you're local to Exeter, you can contact FORCE cancer charity on 01392 406151

Macmillan Cancer Support: www.macmillan.org.uk

Breast Cancer Now. The research and care charity: www. breastcancernow.org 0808 800 6000

Cancer Comms

Local Yocals:

"Hi Emma, how are you doing? Any dates for chemo?"

"All good here. Everything went well today. Charlene came with me to FORCE to check out what they do. Actual marker implant was fine. Done in fifteen mins. Afternoon spent in pub. Chemo starts 23rd July. Everyone else okay?"

"Well done, Emma, big hugs."

"What's a marker implant? An afternoon spent well, I think!"

"For when the chemo shrinks lumpy away and they need to do a little bit of surgery to remove the surrounding area they know where it was."

"Aha, I see! Thanks for the explanation."

"Bloody clever."

"I've read so much of the info they've given me I've qualified myself as a medical practitioner and have started using their jargon! In reality, I'm probably getting it hysterically wrong and shouldn't attempt it in front of anyone who actually studied for five years!"

"Ah, glad it went well. Sounds like a good plan. Glad you had the afternoon in the pub too. xx"

"Love that your humour is still going strong, Emma. Can't wait to catch up with you all Monday."

Saturday 13th July 2019

It's the weekend. No appointments. No prodding or poking. Fun and normality are on the cards. So, as I can sneak out later for bingo with the school mums, it's off to Planet Play with Toby and

Chloe first. Out of all local soft play hells, this is the least hellish and the kids love it.

Sunday 14th July 2019

The kids are well creamed up about going to the zoo. Chloe particularly enjoys the Ma-ming-oos (flamingos).

We're happily mosying around the various animal encounters when I get a text from my colleague Zach after lunch:

"Last minute I know, but do you fancy going to see Tom Jones tonight in Taunton? My uncle is on the tour and has two free tickets."

And with that, we quickly arrange babysitters (thanks Mum and Gary) and a few hours later find ourselves (Darren and I, not Zach!) sitting on a picnic blanket in Taunton, having a little party in the park scenario, chilling out, laughing and then listening to the legend that is Tom Jones. He puts on one hell of a show and it's an awesome way to end our weekend, just the two of us. I do have a moment during one of his beautiful songs about loved ones, but then I've just got to roll with the feels.

Monday 15th July 2019

Today I have my initial telephone conversation with Suzanne at Reframe (www.reframe.co.uk). (Boss) Becky gave me the details from Human Resources (HR). At first, I wasn't sure if I was going to phone them. I've got an excellent team at the hospital and I thought it might just be one more thing of many I had to do, but I'm so glad I did.

Reframe specialise in offering assistance to people going through times of critical illness. I'm assigned a case manager,

Jodie, who is my point of contact and my nurse, Suzanne. I can phone them whenever I want for advice and/or information. Should I need it, Jodie can help me out with practicalities such as finding local childcare, transport, finances, etc. Suzanne worked for many years on an oncology ward and I quickly realise is a font of knowledge.

I've signed consent forms that allow them to access information from my treating practitioners. If I wanted to, I can access a second opinion from nationwide practitioners. I'm not sure I'll need half the stuff they're offering but just knowing it's there is really reassuring.

We talk all about my diagnosis and my treatment plan. Suzanne can post information on my online portal. It's a long and reassuring chat and I come away feeling like I've got another weapon in my arsenal.

Tonight, I'm off to a Tropic Skincare party with the Local Yocals. A good old pampering session with the ladies is just what I need before everything goes a bit nuts.

Cancer Comms

Michelle:

"Hello my love. I just wanted to say thank you. I went for a run this morning, first proper one since my 10k race, and I started to struggle, legs hurt, out of breath and mentally I started to give up. Then I remembered the beautiful photo Darren posted last night on Facebook of the two of you, and how gorgeous and happy you looked. I thought if you could put a smile on your face, a genuine one, with the shit you're going through, I could bloody well run 5k. So thank you, your beautiful mug got me through and I did it for you. Mwah xx"

"Yes, you are also a strong woman. Glad my aging mug helped! We had such an amazing night last night. We really

bonded and for a few hours we forgot all about this new challenge and were just us."

"No aging about your mug – it's just lush. So glad you had a great night, I can imagine it was exactly what you needed, and deserve. xx"

Tuesday 16ᵗʰ July 2019

First call of business today is a visit to my surgery for my bloods to be taken to make sure I'm fit and healthy to start chemo next week. Today it's done with a needle but going forward I'll have my PICC line, so it'll be painless.

Today is also the day I'm having my hair all lopped off. I'm going in all confident that this is my decision to do this. I have retained the power and it will be going to The Little Princess Trust, a great cause.

I show the hairdresser the picture of the pixie-looking haircut I would like and she sets to work chopping off my lovely long locks. She presents me with my long ponytail that I'm sure will do wonders in creating a wig for a child. This makes me smile.

I don't really like my new haircut, though. It's not that she's done a bad job, she hasn't. It's not quite like the picture, but as I leave I actually feel quite sad and, for perhaps the first time, I feel bloody angry. I thought I had this under control but actually I'm angry that I've had to have my hair cut off. It isn't a vanity thing, maybe a confidence thing. I suddenly feel like everyone is looking at me. Of course, they're not.

As I walk to the school bus stop, I feel so self-conscious. Some of the school mums know about the booby bug. I'm met with a mix of *"Wow, your hair looks lovely"* and *"It really suits you"*. From some *"Did you fancy a change?"*

I'm also so nervous about Toby's reaction and what he's going to say. This is going to be the start of the changes that are coming.

He jumps off the bus as usual and then, "Mum, what have you done to your hair, you look like a boy!"

I have to try hard to fight back the tears. He's not being unkind, he's just making an observation in the way that kids do. He laughs, "Boy hair, boy hair!" Then one of his friends joins in with him as he gives me a quick hug and skips off down the path.

We get in the car to go and pick Chloe up and I decide that this is now when I have 'the conversation' with him. It goes something like this:

"Toby, Mummy has to tell you something. You see, Mummy has a nasty bug."

"You're poorly? You don't look poorly."

"Well, at the moment I feel absolutely fine, and I look absolutely fine, don't I? But, you see, Mummy has a nasty bug. And do you know where it is? It's in my booby."

This elicits laughter. I'm trying to keep it lighthearted so as not to scare him, but at the same time letting him know about the changes that are coming.

"Mummy has a nasty bug inside her. It's called breast cancer. I need some really strong medicine to get rid of it and it's the strong medicine that might make Mummy feel a bit poorly."

"Can you see it? Can you show me?"

"When we get home, yes, I can show you the bump."

"Can I touch it?"

"Yes, you can touch it."

"Does it hurt?"

"No, it doesn't hurt. But when Mummy starts taking the medicine, it might make me feel poorly or be a bit grumpy."

"But you're grumpy sometimes anyway."

"Yes, I can be! And I'll have to take the medicine for a little while, so I'm going to need you to help Daddy, is that okay?"

"Yes, I can help Daddy."

"And do you know the cool bit? They're going to put the medicine in my arm."

"How are they going to do that?"

"It's called a PICC line and it goes into Mummy's vein and gets pumped around my body."

"Cool, like magical medicine?"

"Yes, and Mummy might lose her hair, which is why I've cut it short. We don't want lots of my hair all over the house, do we?"

"No, that would be disgusting. You do look a bit like a boy, though."

"I think you can still tell I'm a girl, though, can't you? And I've sent my hair away to a charity so they can make a wig for other people with cancer."

I didn't want to tell him it was wigs for children with cancer. I didn't want to downplay how serious cancer was, but at the same time I didn't want to tell him it could make me very ill.

By this point, we've arrived at nursery.

"Do you have any questions?"

"Can I put the number into the gate?"

And with that, he's out of the car and the conversation is over.

That night I tell him I've got a new book for us to read called *Mummy's Lump*. After I've read it, I ask him if he's got any questions. He doesn't, which in itself is a small miracle, as he's normally got questions about questions!

So that's my main concern done. I've told him. I've told him enough about what he needs to know, and I've told him that he can ask me anything, any time.

As for the conversation I had with Chloe about this? Remember, she is eighteen months old. I went into the tiny detail of everything and how I was feeling as she sat bouncing around my lap. Her response?

"Milk please."

Cancer Comms:

"**Well, here it is. It's not really at all like the picture I showed her and is even shorter. I thought I'd feel in control, but I don't really like it and it's made me feel a bit sad and angry about all this. But I've had my cry and now got myself back together to have some fun in the sun with the kids this evening. Things are now back into perspective. It's just hair, it will grow back. xx**"

Massaging Mummies:

"*It looks LOVELY! I know you are super used to your long locks, so it must feel really weird (wait until you come to wash it!), but it really does look gorgeous. Not what you'd have chosen, I know, but you're rocking it.*"

"*You look gorgeous, hun, I love it, and like you say, your hair will grow back, maybe even in a different colour! You have taken the control of having your hair cut, you are amazing. x*"

"*Ah Em, I like it. You remind me of someone famous (but I'm useless at names so I don't know who). Girl, I wish I had your balls. You are kicking the Big C's ass already. Your mind and attitude will surpass anything. Love you. Xx*"

"*I think you look amazing. I'd do anything for your thick hair. Who knows, after chemo you might be a ginge too! And remember that your hair is going to help someone feel so much better about themselves too. You are one amazing woman and don't you forget that. Love you so much. Xx*"

"*Wow, I so would. Not everyone suits short hair, but you truly do. Cancer can have your hair, let the bastard take it coz that's all it's taking! Love you millions. Lumpy should be shitting itself.*"

"*I think maybe Emma Thompson in this photo!*"

"**Oh, I'll take Emma Thompson. I love her in** *Love Actually.*

Thank you so much for your lovely comments. I'm
a little cross with myself for letting a haircut set me off.
I think it's more the lack of choice in all this which has
made me cross. So, I'm back focusing on all the positives.
I'm going to save so much time from all that bloody hair
straightening."

"Em, you have been unbelievably positive over this. I don't know if I
would have the same strength of character you have shown when stuck
in the middle of a poo sandwich. You are allowed a wobble or two or
three or... Good luck tomorrow. Will keep fingers and toes crossed for
you. Massive hugs, you beauty. Xx"

"You have this, hun. Oh my God, you are an inspiration on how strong
you are and I look up to you. You are allowed as many wobbles that you
need. We are all here to support you along the way. Good luck tomorrow,
thinking of you. Love you and hugs. Xx"

"Good luck tomorrow, Emma. Take that knitting with you and finish
that scarf! Hope they don't make you wait about between it all too long.
Will be thinking of you, you incredible human."

Shits and Giggles:

"OMG I love it! It makes you look younger and your eyes ping!"
"Blimey, that's gorgeous!! It so suits you. You look very foxy. xx"

Local Yocals:

"Emma, you look amazing!"
"Seconded! I love it!"
"Oh, Emma, I don't blame you for having all the feels, massive hugs,
but you look awesome, I really love it. Loads of love."
"You did a really brave thing by just making such a big decision, and
then ensuring it's going to someone else in need is just bloody awesome
and selfless! I too really love it – you'll have everyone fooled looking so
sophisticated. xx"

"It looks absolutely AMAZING and you look stunning. xx"

"Will be thinking of you tomorrow. xx"

"Hope it all goes smoothly. Let us know what happens. Loads of love. Don't be annoyed at yourself, you're allowed wobbles, whenever you want. xx"

"Emma, you look absolutely stunning! Sorry it's been a tough day emotionally. Let all the feelings come and go and if you can just accept that they are part of this journey. We love you to bits. Thinking of you tomorrow. xx"

Cake. Always Cake:

"Don't be sad, I like it! Have a play with some funky hair gel (not that I'm any good at styling) but YouTube is. And also, someone somewhere is going to benefit from your lovely locks, be proud of that."

"I really like it! And like Beck said, think of the little girl who will have your amazing gift of new hair. Bloomin' hairdressers, they never listen. I asked mine to dye my hair like Emma Stone, dark ginger, and it was bright orange and hideous. It was for Merryn's first birthday and it will forever be captured in the photos."

Wednesday 17th July 2019

Today will mostly be spent in hospital having various bits and bobs done.

9.30am oncology, 10.30am CT scan, 11.30am full body scan.

I'm again issued with the latest NHS fashion trend of easy access gown. At least these days they have an extra panel so there's less risk of you inadvertently flashing your underwear to unsuspecting passers-by.

First off, it's a CT scan.

CT (Computerised Tomography) scan

A CT scanner uses X-rays that produce a series of cross-sectional images obtained throughout the body. A computer then reconstructs the images and helps my consultant see what nasties are going on inside me and helps plan my treatment.

This machine is like a giant polo. I'm positioned comfortably onto a bed and told I will be fed to the polo. Well, of course, that's not the terminology they use, but in essence I will pass through the polo. I'm warned that I might feel a warm sensation 'down below' and not to worry that I've wet myself. I'm glad they did warn me because it does indeed feel like you've whazzed yourself and that would have been very embarrassing at my age.

Nothing scary about this and it's soon over within a couple of minutes.

Nuclear medicine scans

Next up I'm having a full-body bone scan.

Before the scan takes place, I'm injected with a small amount of radioactivity into my hand. I have to go to the 'Nuclear Medicine' department. It sounds exciting. The reality is somewhat disappointing! When the radioactive dose is injected into my hand it feels a bit like when you get stung by a stinging nettle but to be honest it soon passes and isn't horrendous.

I then have to wait for a bit before I can have the scan.

Again, I'm laid comfortably on a bed. It is explained to me that the machine will pass over me. It will come down close to me but it has sensors on it so it will not touch me. I'm not so keen on this one but actually it's fine. Another excuse to lie still for a bit and relax.

After a morning of scanning it's off for lunch with Darren.

There were no nasty surprises at the hospital but there was a surprise for me at the end of the day. I was not expecting the doorbell to go at 7pm and for my bezzie mates to be standing on my doorstep bearing gifts. My surprise was obviously apparent as I greeted them in my borderline indecently short unicorn PJ shorts!

Becky, Charlene, Amanda and Mel had turned up bearing a whole load of gifts, a bright orange knitted beanie hat, which was quickly nicknamed 'The Darren' and nipple cupcakes. Such is their attention to detail, Becky even put hundreds and thousands on one nipple cake to replicate random stray hairs I always joke about having to pluck out. If that isn't true friendship, I don't know what is.

I now have a headscarf and lots of other bits I'm sure will prove useful as this show gets underway.

It's an evening of fun and laughter and cringing when I bring the stack of photos from girly holidays past down. Thank God there was no social media in those days! If Carlsberg made bezzie mates they'd make these girls. What an awesome end to the day.

Cancer Comms

"Operation evict lumpy update:
Even more admiration for the **NHS** after a day of appointments running early and with lovely people.

Nothing horrifying occurring today. Have sampled more machinery. Interesting warm feeling downstairs during the **CT** scan, which would indeed make you think you'd whazzed yourself if I hadn't have been warned beforehand.

Being injected with radioactive stuff in the Nuclear Medicine department was rather underwhelming. I have not developed the ability to fly or run through walls.

Received my invitation to **FORCE's** pamper session

on the 13ᵗʰ August with make-up experts. That'll be a challenge for them with me, but I'll give it a go!

At peace with the hair situation now. Toby was worried people might think I'm a boy, but I pointed out I still look like a girl and have boobies. Hope the latter stay now I've said that.

Couple of things Friday then we're off to Woolacoombe Bay for the weekend.

Thank you as always for the continued laughs and messages. You are awesome. Xx"

Circle of Trust:

"You're winning at this evict lumpy game. My mum said she thought she'd pissed herself with a CT scan."

"You're defo still gunna look like a girl, boobs, dresses and you can get false eyelashes, slap on the eyeshadow and lippy and you'll be fine! Does this also mean no more leg shaving? Pits? Minge? If so, bonus. You're the awesome one, not us."

"Em, you really are inspiring me with all this. It was fun catching up with you and the ladies tonight. Those photos have made me want to go on a girly holiday... How about when all this is over... Kavos 2020? Maybe a weekend in Butlins? Oh, and I think your hair looks lovely."

Massaging Mummies:

"Absolute soldier facing it all head on. Taking no prisoners. I love the way children's innocence occurs. Even if the latter does have to happen (I'm really confident it won't) they will give you new top bollocks. Making memories, bird, that's what it's all about. Here whenever you need us. Love you. xx"

"Well done, Em. Sounds like a full-on day. Disappointing you can't fly now but you're still superwoman! Have a brilliant time in Woolacombe."

"Well done, hun, you are amazing. Hope you get on okay today and

then have a fab time all together. Xx"

"Emma, my lovely. Caroline pipped me to the post. But hope it all goes well today – underwhelming given the shit sandwich is possibly a good thing. Have an amazing weekend away and let us know if you fancy an Alec BBQ at some point as from today, we are both on holiday."

"Smash today like me on a packet of crisps. Have a wonderful family weekend, babe. xx"

Shits and Giggles:

"Ahh, you don't need any extra special powers. You're already a superhero. Dan thinks your hair looks fab. He said it makes you look younger and really suits you. That's like a more expressive man saying it's the best hairdo ever. X"

Local Yocals:

"I'm glad you had a good experience today – did you get the results straight away or do you have to wait? xx"

"I think they take about two weeks to report but I'm told it's unlikely they'll yield anything so I've put that out of my mind. x"

"That's a comfort then. Love you."

"Wait until you have your chemo, Emma, fuzzy/itchy in the down-belows too. Glad all went well, have a fab wkd away. xx"

"Oh gawd, really? Bit like when you wash with that minty fresh shower gel? My bits have never felt so fresh. Chewing gum for your fanny. xx"

Cake. Always Cake:

"Oh, I've had the whazzing dye effect scan before, it's really weird! Sad times that you're not able to fly. Hope you have an awesome weekend away, quality break with the familam – can't beat it. xx"

Jo:

"I think the hair looks fab, shows how skinny your face is now. You could always whack some 'hair gel' in, something along the lines of Something about Mary."

"Oh yes, that's a strong look."

Thursday 18th July 2019

Cancer Comms

Circle of Trust:

"Thank you so much for last night, ladies. That was very much unexpected. Clearly because of the unicorn hot pants. Your gifts were thoughtful and so generous. I had a great evening and for a couple of hours it just felt like a group of girls catching up and I forgot all this other stuff. You are all amazing."

Friday 19th July 2019

Early doors at 8.30am for my initial patient assessment on Cherrybrook, the ward that I'll be frequenting to have my magical medicine pumped into me.

It's not as scary a place as I had envisaged. To be honest, I'm not sure what I envisaged. I'm right into *New Amsterdam* on Amazon Prime at the moment and wonder if I'll be sitting around with a group of cancer chums laughing and playing cards whilst the poison drips into us.

Today is just a one-to-one chat, though, with my Cherrybrook nurse. She goes through my medical history and does her checks just to see that I'm well enough to start the treatment. Other than cancer, I tell her I'm feeling perfectly fine. She explains what I can expect when I come in and how the medication is administered. She also informs me I'll need weekly PICC line care from either a community nurse or practice nurse. There's a hub at Whipton Hospital where I can go, or I can visit my own GP surgery. She recommends the hub as visiting my surgery would mean I'd be sitting in a waiting room with poorly people when my immune system won't be at its best. I'm given a pack of PICC line care 'stuff' in the event I have a community nurse visit me at home. The decision is mine.

I'm also given a very fetching plastic sleeve that I can use to cover my PICC line site when showering to keep it dry.

The appointment doesn't take too long, and I don't have many questions for her.

Next, I'm off to get my acrylic nails removed. It feels like another little part of me that I'm being forced to give up, but I remind myself that it's temporary. Besides, my nail beds will probably be grateful for the rest.

2pm and back to hospital for an ECG to check in on my heart. It doesn't start off too well when the room I'm taken into is flooded from the air-conditioning! I'm then taken to a really weird room that basically looks like a disused locker room with a machine in it. I can see people working in the offices opposite and I hope they can't see me lying down, my splaying norks out. I doubt they can because it's dark in my room. Anyway, everything looks fine in the old ticker department.

And now the best part of the day. We've booked a last-minute weekend away in a caravan at Woolacoombe Bay. Not quite the holiday in the sun we've had to cancel but a much-wanted break as a family at short notice. When we pick Toby up from school we're off. He's a bit surprised to see us all, including the dog, and a load of bags. We only get up the road to drop the dog off when we have to tell him what's going on, else he's going to do our nuts in constantly asking. He's so excited I'm not sure what would have been worse: him constantly asking where we are going or his over-excitement of, "Are we nearly there yet?" He's very excited to be staying in another 'holiday hotel bungalow' (caravan). Chloe, as always – slightly indifferent.

Holiday weekend July 2019

It's always hard work on holiday with two small humans, so I'm not going to pretend it was laid back or restful. But the holiday park was amazing. We went bowling, to the arcade, soft play, swimming, played in the parks, enjoyed the dodgy entertainment. The kids were in their element. They got to wear their new best clothes I'd stowed away for Menorca. They stayed up way past bedtime. We were on the go so much I can honestly say I didn't think about what was starting next week.

Cancer Comms

Michelle:

"*Hello my lovely. Just checking in to see how you're doing and say I'm thinking of you. Is it Tuesday you start your treatment? Big hugs. Xx*"

"Hi my beaut. Thank you. D-Day is indeed Tuesday. Time to get this show on the road. xx"

"*Can't imagine how you must be feeling but the sooner you start the sooner it can do one. I have a little something for you, I was going to nip out at lunch tomorrow and drop it off. Xx*"

"Weirdly, I'm feeling okay about everything! I'm in no pain, I have no symptoms, all the scans and tests haven't been too horrific. I've had three weeks off work so far and I feel prepared, like I just need to get something done.

74

Weirdest position to be in. Oh, I've also received shit loads of cards and gifts, so it's like another birthday! I'll be home tomorrow, so feel free to ring if you've got time to stop. xx"

"That's great but you are such a bloody trooper and such a sunny shiny person. Okay, well if you're happy to see my mush then I'll pop in for a bit, would love to see you and give you a big squish. xx"

Nicola:

"Right, hope you have your superhero cape dusted off and your eye mask on point. Time to let lumpy know it's no longer welcome in this family. They are all lovely there. They were amazing with my mum. xx"

Monday 22nd July 2019

'Chemo Eve'.

You know that sicky feeling you get in your tummy when you've got something going on that's a big deal like a job interview, presentation, wedding or commencement of cancer treatment? Well, that's the feeling I woke up to today. Although I've been really trying to enjoy each day of feeling well ever since the word 'cancer' came rudely into my life, I've been eager to get this show on the road.

I've had a number of messages today of "How are you feeling?"

So, I'm going to take a minute to really consider 'How am I feeling?'

Physically in myself, I feel fine. No pain, no symptoms. Ironically, I think I'm possibly in the best shape I've been in for a long time. Makes me an ideal candidate for chemo, apparently.

Mentally I feel prepared, positive, optimistic that the end goal is to eradicate any sign of lumpy and any fledglings. To get to that end goal, I've got mini goals to achieve. Bite size goals that are much more manageable.

I've just got to keep talking my way through this. Feel the feels. Don't be stoically British and accept help if offered. Ask for it if needed.

Today is the day I decided that I will write a book about this. I've never written a book, although many people have told me I should. I don't really even know where to start but I know that to get somewhere I just need to start. And that's what I feel about 'operation evict lumpy'. I don't know what the final outcome will be, or how the journey will be along the way, but I just need to start.

Today is also the day I had a new lounge carpet fitted with the refund from our cancelled holiday. Twiddling my toes in the sand would only have lasted seven days. I hope twiddling my toes on this thick pile will last a lot longer!

It's also been a day that saw a period of complete manicness when I unexpectedly hosted a number of visitors simultaneously bringing gifts. I caught up with my neighbour Gilly, good friend Michelle and good friend Pippa.

Michelle arrived with beautiful flowers and a little bag of goodies. I will especially enjoy the "Fuck You Cancer" adult colouring book. Beautiful doodles to colour with such an array of words: *Clusterfuck, Cockwomble, Twatwaffle,* being a few of my favourites. Perhaps I could colour and frame these for Christmas presents!

Pippa did not arrive empty-handed either. She had batch-cooked a good few dinners for our freezer. So generous was her offering that I had to palm a frozen lasagna off to Gilly to store!

She also arrived with a basket containing many thoughtful gifts put together by my lovely 'Local Yocals' group. Not for the first time this week I've cried happy tears at the generosity of my friends. Sweets, biscuits, colouring, little toys for the children, hand cream, lip balm, positive affirmation cards (YESmum cards), photos of trips we've been on together. Digging into the YESmum cards, I pulled out "You are not alone." This couldn't have been more fitting because I truly am not alone.

I've had to clear out a cupboard in the kitchen for all the generous gifts, which I have now dubbed 'the chemo cupboard'.

Cancer Comms

"Chemo Eve.

The Notice to Quit has been served on lumpy and judgment obtained to evict. So tomorrow I'm sending in the heavies in the form of Paclitaxel on a weekly basis for twelve weeks. That's just for starters.

Popular question for today 'How are you feeling?'

Ready. I feel ready to get this show on the road. I've been so lucky to have these past few weeks to prepare, get all the necessary admin sorted and most importantly spend time with the people who matter the most to me whilst I'm feeling fit as a fiddle.

The kindness and generosity of everyone has been more than I had ever imagined and for that I am truly grateful. Xx"

Circle of Trust:

"You've got this, lumpy's days are numbered. I've said this before but you are stronger than you know and on the days you don't feel as strong, remember you have all of us to be the extra strength you need to get through. You are not alone in this battle, this is a war and we are fighting by your side. We are here for you. You can and will do it. Love you. x"

"You most certainly have got this. Remember on the shit rough days you take it hour by hour. It's gonna be a strange one as like you said you feel as fit as a fiddle but the treatment that's going to cure you makes you ill. It's a headfuck. Lumpy won't know what's hit it tomorrow and this time tomorrow night day one will have been done and dusted. We aren't

the prettiest of cheerleaders and may be a bit old for the outfits, but we are all here cheering you on. Love you mate. X"

"Thank you. Oh now see you've painted a lovely image of you all in cheerleader outfits and I'd quite like to experience that in real life!"

"Bring it on is what I say! I'm so pleased you're feeling ready cos that's the attitude that's going to get you through it. And like the other ladies have said, when you don't feel quite so ready or strong, we're here for you. Love you lots. Xxx"

Massaging Mummies:

"Good luck tomorrow my lovely. If you need any help with the kids over the next few weeks you only have to ask, we are around. Stock up on ginger biscuits and mouth ulcer gel. Love you loads and hope it goes well tomorrow. Massive hugs – go get lumpy. xx"

"Let's get this lumpy bastard shipped off and out of here pronto. Lumpy doesn't know what's hit it, especially appearing in your boob, Mrs Davies. Tomorrow is just another step closer to getting rid of the bastard. I'm here 24/7 no matter what you need or when. Please use us all. Massive hugs, bird. Rinstead mouthwash is good, my mum said. I can pick some up if you need it."

"Good luck, Em, will be thinking of you! Here any time for anything. You totally have this, lovely lady. Lumpy doesn't stand a chance. xx"

"Good luck tomorrow, take it day by day and think each day you're getting closer to lumpy going for good. You go girl, will be thinking of you. If you need anything 24/7 please just ask. Big hugs. Xx"

"Adios, lumpy! Put your armour on, Em, you've got this. Good luck and hugs. I'm sure the nurses will look after you. I'm here if you need anything and of course can help if you start to feel poo and need some food ideas or your personal chef isn't sure what to cook for you. One step closer."

Strong Randy Ladies:

"I was just thinking about you! Shall I text a "good luck", is it a "good luck" situation?! Is it a hell let's get the show on the road and get the little fuckers out and on their way? God knows! All I know is that you've got this with all your friends and family behind you. I know you're going to smash the "C" out of the breast and on its merry way. Twelve weeks will be gone before you know it. Keeping everything crossed that tomorrow goes well for you and that you don't get too many side effects – none at all would be lovely, of course!"

"Been thinking about you tonight too. As Emily says, your friends and family are behind you and we're here for you if/when you need us. Sending lots of love for tomorrow and fingers crossed for minimal/no side effects."

"Thank you, ladies. I think good luck works in most scenarios, so let's go with that."

Local Yocals:

"Blown away, ladies. I'll send something more reflective of my appreciation later when I do my 'cancer admin' but I just wanted to let you know your thoughtfulness has moved me to tears. xx

So, in addition to the generic update, you guys get a personal one.

I wanted to say a huge thank you for your very personalised and thoughtful gifts. I am actually rather lost for words (yes I know, surprising) at the thought that has gone into them. But not just for me, for the kids and Darren. Pippa will confirm that I did shed a few tears. I don't cry with sadness about the cancer, but I cry with happiness at all the outpouring of love and laughter I've experienced these past few weeks.

This is the card I've been dealt, and I know I will get

through this whilst surrounded by so much love. **My favourite saying has always been 'what doesn't kill you makes you stronger' and seems rather apt now!**

I can't wait to give you all a personal thank you hug the next time I see you.

But enough about #attentionseekerme! What's everyone else been up to? xx"

Cake. Always Cake:

"Will be thinking of you tomorrow, bird. You got this. See ya, lumpy. xx"

"Got everything crossed for you. Go kick some cancerous ass! x"

Jo:

"Good luck with chemo week one. Hope it's not too unpleasant and boring. Thinking of you… Here if you need anything.

Cancer chose the wrong bird to fuck with, Strudders, I know that… Chemo schmemo, you'll nail it. Will be thinking of you tomorrow. I'll check in to see how it went but don't worry about replying if you're shagged afterwards. Big love E to the D. xx"

Michelle:

"Thank you so much for today. That was so fun and random. I love the colouring and can't wait to get started on that. I do apologise if my dark humour caught you by surprise. I've got rather accustomed to this scenario and must remember that it can be shocking/upsetting to others. Go get yourself signed off so we can hang out. xx"

"Aah, you're so welcome my lovely. It was lots of fun and very random and one of the best lunchbreaks I've had in ages. Do not apologise for your humour, not at all. I was more worried about saying the wrong thing, not

that there's a right or wrong thing to say in these situations, but you did bloody scare me there for a bit! But nothing to be sorry for – you do and say what you need to, to get you through this. Thinking of you tomorrow and sending you muchas love and hugs, you're a trooper Em, love you. xx"

Tuesday 23rd July 2019 – Chemo Round One

The day has arrived – Chemo Day!!!

Big breath – delve into my 'YESmum' cards.

"I am not alone today."

Glad I left that one on the top and didn't shuffle it back into the pack.

PICC line (Peripherally Inserted Central Catheters)

I have chosen to have my chemo administered and weekly bloods taken via a PICC line. The major benefit of this is once it's inserted it can stay in place for the duration of my treatment. I really cannot be doing with being jabbed repeatedly to have a cannula inserted each treatment time and my bloods taken. Other options include a Hickman Line (tunneled central catheter) or a TIVAD (Totally Implanted Vascular Access Device or port).

The PICC line is a long, thin, flexible worm, sorry tube, that's inserted into a large vein in my left arm and fed in until it's positioned above my heart. Sounds gross but in fact it was intriguing to watch the vascular nurse locate a nice juicy vein using an ultrasound machine and then feed it in after administering a local anaesthetic. It wasn't particularly painful and once in I couldn't feel anything. It's then secured in place on my arm, popped under a dressing and then a bandage. Once an X-ray confirmed it was located in the correct position, I was good to go with my first session of chemo.

Down on Cherrybrook and I'm ready for the poisoning to begin. It's a bit slow going though and before you get onto the good stuff the pre-chemo meds are pumped in and various saline infusions.

I'm having two lots of IV chemo: Paclitaxel first and then Carboplatin. The nurses do their checks and then we're off with the Paclitaxel. And then after a matter of seconds we're literally switched off because I have an immediate reaction to the stuff. I can feel my chest restrict and I go the colour of a tomato. Darren calls for the nurse who immediately switches it off and gives me some oxygen. Apparently, it's not uncommon for this to happen but I've literally had a couple of drops. What a lightweight!

My immediate concern then is what if my body cannot tolerate the medication. I'm told there's various things they can do to get the drugs in. They'll give me a saline flush and then try running it over two hours instead of one. I'm pleased to say it goes in without a hitch second time round followed by a chaser of Carboplatin.

I'm sent home with some strong anti-sickness tablets, which I'll now take for five doses, and my appointment card to return next week.

It was a long old day!

Darren has ordered me a backpack to put hospital essentials in: snacks, chargers, phone, kindle, etc. He's kindly ordered me a child's *Finding Nemo* backpack, which he is calling my Nemo Chemo bag!

Chemo bag essentials (Nemo theme optional)

- Snacks
- Own choice of lunch
- Water bottle

- Things to keep you occupied – book, magazine, drawing, crafting (whatever floats your boat)
- Headphones to plug into your own tunes
- Phone and charger (or charge extension pack)
- Cushion (If you fancy having a nap. I had one of those neck thingymabobs)
- Friends (unlikely to fit in your bag but awesome at passing the time)

Toby was very excited to inspect the plumbing (PICC line) that has now taken up residence in my left arm. Chloe also seemed excited at the change but then quickly lost interest. My only fear was that she might yank on it and pull it all out, but it's stuck down pretty well.

Phoned Dad to book my reoccurring 'Dad chemo cab' for my Tuesday sessions.

The day finished off with an amazing thunderstorm, which I watched from the Velux window in our attic room overlooking the development. I love thunderstorms (when I'm inside in the dry). It almost felt that the weeks since diagnosis were the calm before the storm and today was the start of the new journey. Quite apt then to finish the day with an actual storm.

It also reminded me of one of the most amazing experiences of my life when I was sailing around the Whitsunday Islands. We'd had to drop anchor as the storm approached and everything went eerily calm. Then the heavens opened. Afterwards I remember being sat on deck in my bikini and raincoat, with the boat gently rocking, a bell ringing with the movement and Moby playing. It was a beautiful moment and one I always try to recall when the storm part of life is kicking in.

One of my picture frames also has the quote "Life isn't about waiting for the storm to pass, it's about learning to dance in the rain". I've been approaching life like this for a good few years and I'm not about to stop now.

Managing communications with friends and family

My phone has been lighting up like a Christmas tree over the past few weeks. As lovely as this is, in addition to my ever-growing 'cancer admin' file, I'm finding it quite overwhelming trying to respond to everyone. Essentially everyone is asking similar things and I'm copying and pasting a standard response. I already have various WhatsApp groups set up for friends, so I add a work one into the mix " ED fan club". Not that I'm bigheaded or anything!

Other groups of friends are conveniently bundled into groups: 'Circle of Trust, Local Yocals (mummy ones), Massaging Mummies (mummy twos), Cake Always Cake, Shits and Giggles, school mums'. I love the messages. Makes me feel normal and brings a lot of positivity to the day. But my God the rate I was going I was going to need to hire a PA just to keep up with my 'cancer admin'. So now I have my groups and I make sure I limit my time to phone watching in the evening. I'm also intending to give a little update each week so hopefully that will make managing my 'comms' easier.

Having spoken to various people I have met through this process, everybody deals with communicating their news/updates in different ways. I have favoured the company. Letting people know what's going on. It's just kept things 'normal' for me, plus their well wishes and funny tales of everyday life has really kept me going. There are others who do not want any communication. No phone calls, no texts whilst they retreat into a time of quiet and stillness.

My advice would be 'you' establish the ground rules and let people know. This is not a time for you to be worrying about other people. It is a time for you to focus on yourself and do what is right for you.

Cancer Comms

"Chemo take one.

Having watched *Grey's Anatomy* for years I consider myself an expert in a range of medical matters! Seems they speed things up for your viewing pleasure as today was a loooooooong day.

As a now frequent flyer with the **NHS** I sampled their long-haul service today. I did ask if there was a loyalty card. Sadly not, but you do get free sandwiches, biscuits, ice pops and tea. Perfect. A cup of tea sorts everything.

PICC line went in, all okay. No drama.

Same couldn't be said for the lumpy zapping drugs. Pre-meds all loaded in fine but they had to immediately stop the drugs as I turned the colour of a tomato, eyes popped out like Hulk and I couldn't breathe properly. Turns out I'm a bit of a lightweight in the chemo drugs department and my body thought 'fuck this shit'. Saline was run over thirty mins and they tried again over two hours. All good second time round. Then a second drug, which went well. I think it's going to take about four hours each week.

So, a full days' worth of work today, nine to five. It might have taken a long time but it was an all right day. I read loads, laughed with Darren and chatted with the staff. So plenty of positives to outweigh how long it took.

Now I'm starting a (free) sweepstake on when I lose my hair and start looking like Andy from Little Britain. I'm going 4th August. Winner gets first rub and I'll shout them lunch. In the event of multiple winners, I'll get you a scratch card! Game on.

As always, thank you for your support. Xx"

Circle of Trust:

"*Oh wow, sounds like quite a day you've had and yet still chirpy! Stronger lady than me, that's for sure. I'm glad you had an all right day. Hmmmm okay, so I'm going to say 7th August. No idea what that's based on. What if you win? I guess we take you out for dinner. xxx*"

"*Glad you got there in the end with the chemo! I can always pop down throughout the day. I'm going Monday 5th August, but when it does go I've got a cracking eighties mullet wig ready for you and if you're right I'll wear it out to dinner.*"

"*I'll put my money on Thursday 15th August, as it's A-level results day so I'll be pulling my own hair out that day! Love Mel's idea if you win. Sorry to hear today was so tough, hopefully now they have the idea of how you'll react it will be smoother next week. Do you glow in the dark now? I hope Kels wins for that photo opportunity.*"

"*Oh God mate, the first bit sounded horrific, your poor body. You've started now and you're doing great. I'll go 6th August. Xxx*"

"I also had a visit from one of my 'insiders'. Lovely to see you, Kel, thanks for popping down.

Noted. Thanks player 1.

Noted. Thanks player 2.

Noted. Thanks player 3.

Noted. Thanks player 4.

I sadly ditched my matted crap wigs as could have had some public fun with them. I've still got a few though!

"*I misread that as pubic fun and thought you were getting a merkin!*"

"*With a bit of glue and cut up pair of tights I can make you a wig the next time I strip Murph (dog). Me and the kids can have a 'make 'n' do' day. Glad it all went okay, although a long day. Hope you feel okay over the next few days. Remember Amanda is on call 24/7. I'll go for the 14th for the shiny head day. xxx*"

Charlene sends me a picture of her dog sitting beside a ball of hair after she's stripped him. It looks like Donald Trump's hair.

"*Knew I should have saved it.*"

"Could have had a bit of a Trump hair do!"

"Chloe does 'The Boris' well, so we could go to a fancy dress party as the two most dysfunctional political figures."

"So, the sweepstake game has proven to be quite popular. I was considering a spreadsheet, but I can't be arsed, so keep a note of your entries and I'll update when I get a nice shiny head."

Massaging Mummies:

"Emma, you are incredible. You should so write a book (even just for yourself). Oh no for the first reaction but glad it settled from then. If you are drawing a rota for sit ins over the next twelve weeks pop me on it (I'd love to waste four hours with you). As for the locks, put me down for the 9th August. You have a fine thick mop up there, it'll take some knocking. Love you. xx"

"You don't do things by halves, do you! Well done on surviving day one and glad the chemo concentrated itself on killing lumpy and not your sense of humour. Am also happy to kill four hours with you any time, so pencil me in too. As for the sweepstake, I'll go for Monday 7th – do we need a specific time or just a date? Love you so much and so bloody proud of you. Anything I can do? Am on holiday so free to do shopping or baking… massive hugs. xx"

"Oh, good lord, I'm not sure the RD&E tea could sort anything – I'd have to take my own teabags in! As for the drugs, hopefully they will sort everything out. That reaction sounds nasty, glad attempt two was better. I'll join the rota. My bet for the hair is 13th August – I love to rub a bald head, so soft! Well done lovely, you'll know what you're in for from now on so onwards and upwards."

"That's one down, bird, even if it was a bastard to start with… I'd happily waste four hours with you too. Will only feel like one when I'm yapping away. My mum said to feel free to text her any time day or night if you've got any questions or symptoms. Can I bring you anything or do anything? How's Darren doing? In the hair stake please put me down for

the 8th August. I'm so up for a bald rub. Amazed by your strength already. xx"

"You do like to keep the nurses busy! Glad they sorted out the medication in the end for you. I might see you around at Whipton Hospital for your PICC line care and bloods. Also put me down on rota, just need a bit of notice to sort work but much rather be with you for four hours than at work. Put me down for 10th August for the bet on hair. You are amazing and an inspiration. xx"

"I would offer to bake or cook but you're gonna feel (well hopefully not) like shit as it is. I can order you a takeaway."

"Fuck me, please don't, I can't risk having the shits. Mummy ones have beaten you to that anyway and arrived with frozen edible goods!"

"On a serious note is there anything you fancy eating? I have a bored chef at home so would be good to put him to work. Or I am keen to bake cookies. xx"

"And also, I'd love some company. Do you think they'd let you all in in one sitting or we're going to have to operate a one in one out policy!"

"Start charging, Em. Offer a free alcopop and you're onto a winner."

"My mum said she was looking forward to being skinny and getting sympathy for looking ill… She put on three stone and looked rosy most of the time. Joking aside (just this once), eat, sleep, go out, drink plenty of fluid, one day at a time. Hour at a time if need be. Why don't we all get together in the hospital restaurant and then do sittings in with Em on one chemo session?"

"Considering changing group name to chemo chums rather than massaging mums. Let's be honest, none of us ever massaged our children and already you've all been more active in this new adventure."

"Think we'd get kicked out if we all went on mass. Jo, you might just get kicked out anyway.

Shits and Giggles:

"Oh Christ, I can just picture you turning into the red Hulk! Bloody Nora, what a day! Thank goodness it's over for now. When is round two? How is Darren btw?"

"Same time, same place, next week. It's my new Tuesday fun things to do at forty! Darren is okay. He goes quiet, so that's when I know he's having an internal man moment that he can't vocalise! Otherwise all good, keeping busy, just getting on. X"

"Crikey, what a day! I hope you're chilling now with a gin, or at least a cuppa! Glad he's okay. Men are never very chatty about things, are they? xx"

"Love you long time, lady xxx Wish I lived nearer. I would bake you some buns and take the piss out of you looking like Andy."

"Love to you both. I'd make some lovely lemon drizzle, if any would fancy it. xx"

"Post the baked goods."

Strong Randy Ladies:

"Nothing is ever easy, is it?! Still, at least it's going in and doing its job! Never liked Tuesdays anyway. Shit day. You got some good books? I'll bring my cheesy shit next week to keep you going or send you to sleep. One or tuther!"

"What a nightmare for you! Hope it all went in okay after that, lovely lady. xx"

"On the basis that I am massively competitive I have just googled on average how long hair takes to fall out and was given the two to four week mark, so therefore covering both bases I'm going for three weeks, which is 13th August, and I will look forward to my stroke at that point. If, however, it is a long time, I want and bagsy 22nd August. I don't think it will take that long but no one else is allowed that date as that's my date forever and I will not share that one. Glad you've had a positive day and *fingers crossed that there are no more Hulk-like experiences. xx"*

"What are you like? I think I've gone too early but hey, I don't want to win. Where's the fun in that? I shall absolutely let you have the 22nd. I'm so looking forward to seeing you guys on Monday. Remember it's all about me this time #attentionseeker. Only joking. Therapy for all. xx"

"To be fair you're entitled to the 'all about you' time! Think you have defo earned this one, my love. Hope you feel well enough. Can't wait to see you more so than normal actually. xx"

"Never would have thought you were competitive, Emily. Bet you're one of those mums shouting at the boys on sports day. I'm going for the 7th August! It's all about you, Em, on Monday. I owe you a few sessions from the past few years, so I'm all yours .xx"

Local Yocals:

"Been thinking of you lots today, Emma, hope it went to plan. xx"

"Hope it's gone smoothly today. You are so deserving of everything, we just hope it carries you through in some small way. Thank you for the update. We love you loads. Xx"

"I don't know how you make it possible that I have read a message all about chemo and I'm laughing?!? Oh, Emma, you do have a way about you. Sounds like an eventful day! Goodness, glad they sorted out the reaction to the drugs. one down, eleven to go. YOU'VE GOT THIS."

"I'm the same as Pip, I chuckled! Is the sweepstake for real cos I love a gamble! If so, I'm going for Monday 29th. What a day you've had! Was it an instant reaction to the drugs? Must have been alarming! So glad that you had Darren with you. Are you allowed to take in books, tablets, etc. to read and watch stuff? xx"

"Tuesday 30th."

"I'm glad to see the NHS is exceeding all its expectations, and the free food and drink is on point! Pleased to hear you survived the first one and you now have some breathing space for a few days. I bloody love a sweepstake too – Thursday 1st for me!"

"Ahh Emma, love the update, so glad it went okay in the end. Fab NHS. Did it make you feel sick at all or were you okay? Sweepstake, I will go with Wednesday 31st!

Cake. Always Cake:

"Been thinking about you lots today."
"Thank goodness. You did it!"
"I was always more of an ER viewer. Dr Carter was and still is a dream boat. Scary side effect but I'm glad you were okay on take two. I'm going Saturday 5th August, a tactical guess if I do say so myself. Hope you don't feel too crappy over the next few days. If you guys need owt just shout. xx"

ED Fan Club:

"Well, good evening lovely colleagues and welcome to this exclusive group.

Everybody has been so supportive I wanted to keep you updated and thought this would be the best way to manage my fan mail!

If at any time you want out, please feel free to go. I know what it's like when your phone keeps lighting up like a Christmas tree. I'll try to avoid it anyway and only post significant updates in here.

Please always feel free to message me personally if you'd like to. You know me, I enjoy a dash of inappropriate humour.

So, without further ado, here's today's ramblings. xx"

"Amazing to see you have not lost your sense of humour in amongst all this, Emma. Day one down... keep the updates rolling. xxx"

"I hear the new haircut is looking good. Appreciate a picture."

"You're my hero, ED! Well done, and thank God for free tea! I will make sure there is the odd inappropriate joke sent across now and again. xx"

"It sounds like you are sending in the heavies straight away. xx"

Picture sent

"Was there a McDreamy or McSteamy to feast your eyes upon?! Glad take two went better than take one and hopefully next time will be a bit of a smoother ride. X"

Pictures of McDreamy and McSteamy then followed. They were very welcome.

"Ha, I actually thought of that. Sadly, there was just methodical and reliable Vince. But slow and steady wins the day and doesn't see you before the NMC, so we'll keep him."

"I can check his record if you like."

"Your hair looks great, but when you start off as GORGEOUS as you, you can carry off anything. Aw… come on, if you're going to feel nauseous it may as well be from sickly compliments. xx"

"Glad take two went better and hope you're feeling okay now. Loving the new hair. It looks fab and you totally pull off the boy hair. Pleased to hear you were at least provided with a free luncheon. You've got this lovely. xx"

Jo:

"No matter how shit you feel, no matter how boring today was, you nailed your first chemo session. Been thinking of you, poppet. Shout if you need anything."

"Oh, Emma you pleb, I nearly wet myself reading that… Pelvic floor fucked after having kids… Okay, sweepstake dates I'll go August 12ᵗʰ… Sounds scary with the reaction to the chemo but you were in the best possible place… Will you be going every Tuesday? If you need company shout, cos I'll be there… Amazing attitude as always, birds. Well done for getting through it."

"Why muchas Gracias. I'm going to start a list. Turns out I'm quite popular!"

"Course you are, total ledge you are. xx"

Nicola:

"Right today is the first day of get lumpy gone. Go and kick some butt beautiful. Thinking of you. TTFN."

"Hi super lady. Love you, amazing beautiful lady. Randomly I've just got back from visiting my bra lady. Did not give any names but talked about your lumpy (hope that was okay). She said re underwear and bras if you need something that won't rub, etc. on lumpy then she will be happy to help. She's lovely. My boobs are in a nice new house tonight. Been thinking of you. Hope you're not too tired."

Wednesday 24ᵗʰ July 2019

The day after the day before.

Feeling fine and ready to get on with the doing.

Today just feels like any other normal day (except, of course, I'm not at work). Mum came round for 7.30am to help with getting the kids off just in case I was feeling a bit ropey. They love that, she loves it, we all love it.

My daily goals now are not to overdo it, drink plenty of water, walk the dog daily and eat healthily. Anything else is a bonus.

Cancer Comms

Michelle:

"Thank you for the update, lovely. Thought about you a lot yesterday. Thinking about you today too. Thank you for your usual sunny funny outlook on things. Hope you're okay. Love ya. xx"

"Oh, I'm delighted you're thinking about me. Now I'm thinking about you too. Was also thinking about you the other night as I coloured in 'fucknugget'!"

"Glad you've already made a start!"

"It's my Christmas presents for everyone, so need to crack on in between writing my bestseller!"

"You're such a brilliant writer, I've no doubt it will be a bestseller! Remember I got first dibs on Cuntweasel."

"Oh, there will be a nod to your adult colouring book, don't you worry!"

Nicola:

"Hi my beaut. I wondered if you might be free next Tuesday to come sit with me from 10.30 to natter and knit? Asking you first but don't worry if you've got plans. I'm in this for the long haul. xx"

"I will totally be sitting with you, beautiful. Lots of nattering, laughter and knitting to happen. Forgot to say I'm reading a book called Why Mummy Swears, *I think you would like it. x"*

"I have it!"

Thursday 25th July 2019

I receive my certificate from The Little Princess Trust today thanking me for my hair donation. This is a great pick me up and makes me smile knowing my locks will help make a wig for a child going through this journey.

Suzanne, my nurse from Reframe, checks in with me again. I really look forward to talking to her. I feel so lucky to have this additional support via work where I can speak to someone qualified yet totally independent. It just feels good to talk to be honest.

And today is Toby's last day of term for the summer. He's finished reception and a whole year of school. He's excited for the summer holidays. I'm a bit sad that I don't get to take him on his 'aeroplane holiday'. On the plus side, I now get to spend the whole summer with him. As chemo has only just kicked off, and I'm told there's a cumulative effect as the drugs build up, I'm hopeful that we can enjoy some fun times over the coming weeks.

Friday 26th July 2019

'YESmum' card (to be rolled out on chemo days and any other days when I'd like the world to open up and swallow me whole):

"All of my feelings are okay."

And so, it begins. I'm not a morning person by any stretch of the imagination but I could have quite happily pulled the duvet over my head this morning and told the 6.30am alarm to sod off. I felt rough as a badger's arse. A quick look in the mirror confirmed I also looked as though I'd had a heavy night. The yellow 'sleepy dust' also a reminder that my body was trying to push something out of it that was not welcome.

I was flying solo today with both children, which perhaps with the benefit of hindsight was not the best of ideas. It's all a learning curve right now until we work out what our new normal is.

Luckily, I have an awesome neighbour, and Gilly came in to watch the children whilst I attended my first appointment at the Whipton Hospital hub to have my PICC line flushed and bloods taken. This is another regular appointment every Friday for the foreseeable whilst I have this little plastic worm in my arm. The nurses flush the PICC line with saline, draw blood to check it isn't blocked, clean the site and re-dress it for me. They also take bloods so the results will be ready prior to each chemo session to check I'm well enough for more poisoning.

I mention to them about a fluttering feeling in my chest when I lie down on my left side. They recommend I telephone the ward. I phone Cherrybrook and they suggest that perhaps the line is in slightly too far and could be pulled back a bit next time I'm in.

The day was plodding along quite uneventfully until I received an unexpected appointment letter in the post to attend for an ultrasound on my abdomen. Bearing in mind I had not received the results of my recent CT and bone scan, and an abdomen scan was never on the agenda, this put the fear of God in me. Why the hell had I been referred for a scan of my abdomen? What had they found? What's in that area? Only a load of your major organs.

To say I was again petrified was an understatement. I wasn't even too sure who to phone, so I started with Suzanne at Reframe. She calmed me down, told me she would check protocols and try contacting the hospital.

I phoned the breast care team and left a message for a return call. They could tell me that the results had been reported, that there was mention of my liver, but that she wasn't permitted to inform me over the phone.

In the meantime, a colleague from work had come round at 2pm to visit. Typically, the children who had been happily painting (against my better judgment) turned into performing circus monkeys and Chloe decided to throw herself fully clothed into the paddling pool! Helen had successfully had her own battle with cancer four years ago and had come round to find out how I was getting on with my journey and depart her wise words of wisdom. This was successfully done in-between random shouts of "Don't push your sister down the slide" and "Toby this is your final warning, 1, 2, 3…"

Not feeling too well physically, and emotionally I was extremely anxious, I did get some clarity from the hospital. My results had come back clear but had picked up something that they just wanted to double check. I was reassured that this was very normal and was only a precaution because of my condition. I even received a call from my oncology consultant who apologised that the appointment letter was received out of context, prior to me receiving her explanatory letter, and her surprise at how fast the appointment was actioned.

Bless him, when Darren walked through the door, he was bombarded with two hyper children who had utilised all their resources, strewn throughout the house, and an emotional wife. I had to take myself off for a warm hot soak in the bath and then – so rock and roll – I went to bed at 8pm. I was done with today.

Cancer Comms

Strong Randy Ladies:

"Hey lovely, how have you been feeling since the chemo? xx"

"Great minds, Trace."

"Ha, I'm going to do a copy and paste job: Bit difficult getting going today as quite achy but I'm breathing, so I class that as winning. And how are you guys? It's not all about me. xx"

"It's totally all about you. xx"

"I'm fine, though. Day three of sinner holidays and I haven't killed any not so small humans yet, so I class that as a win too. I'm trying to work less and enjoy them more (not so easy when they work against you), but I'm classing this as my last summer with Rocky before he doesn't want to or absolutely refuses to spend time with me as he starts senior school. Onto the next chapter. Where have the years gone? xx"

"Sinner holidays!"

"Oh, sinner holidays. Sounds interesting! But I agree. Try and live in the moment. xx"

"It's the only way. None of us know what's around the corner, do we, and this has proved that. Getting old is a bit sucky, isn't it, but the sun is shining and it's another beautiful day, so on a more positive note let's see what we can do to smile today. xx"

"Absolutely. I've got more visitors today so that will be nice and will also help with kids. Have a lovely day, ladies, and looking forward to seeing you both Monday. xx"

"*Love it, sinner holidays. Take it easy, Em. Looking forward to catching up on Monday. xx*"

Michelle:

"*How're you doing lovely? As you're joking about it, I'll throw in 9th August. Really want a rub.*"

"Bit achy today but still breathing, so consider that winning! Don't tell the other competitors but I'll let you rub my egg until your heart's content. xx"

"*Breathing is most important. Sorry to hear you're achy, hopefully that will ease as treatment goes on? That'll stay between you and me my love, egg rubbing conjures up all sorts in the imagination. x*"

"I just think of the lucky egg in *Cool Runnings*. What are you thinking of? x"

"*Oh… the same egg. Totally the same egg. x*"

Saturday 27th July 2019

Amazing what twelve hours of sleep can do for you. Twelve whole hours of sleep. I can't remember the last time I slept for so long.

I'm still quite achy but God do I feel a damn sight better than I did yesterday.

Toby is having a sleepover at his best mate's house today, so he was packed off by 11.30am. Just me and the girl today and we're going to chill out with Nanny.

Darren needs a lad's night out to blow off some steam, so he's off to a beer festival with the boys. With Chloe in bed, me and Mum settled down to a girly night of ice cream and a cheesy chick flick. Just what I needed. I'm loving all this extra time I'm spending with my mum. Never too old to need your own mummy.

Cancer Comms

Circle of Trust:

"Do you ever just look at your friends and think, we are going to be some weird fucking old people one day?"

Sunday 28ᵗʰ July 2019

We're supposed to be going to a BBQ at our neighbour's house today. I feel a bit rough to be honest, but once I'm up and about I figure I'll give it a go. Worst case I come home. Best case I sit in the sun and let people bring me food and drink. The latter won out and it was awesome to see my friends whilst the kids played in the sun.

Toby is obsessed with showing people my PICC line and telling them that's where my magical medicine goes in to get rid of my booby bug. Both my friends work at the hospital but make suitably impressed noises when I show them!

A good day but unfortunately not a good night tonight. Ever since the PICC line has been put in I get this weird fluttering feeling in my heart when I lie on my left side. It's really been wigging me out. I'm not feeling great tonight, physically and emotionally. Lying in bed I get the fluttering feeling again. I'm feeling hot so pop downstairs to take my temperature. Normal. I don't feel very normal, though. I feel like I'm on the verge of a panic attack. This is all too much. It's too big for me. Everyone says I'm brave but I'm not feeling very brave tonight.

I can't have this PICC line in me. Although I can't physically feel it, the thought of something in me feels really intrusive. I'll have to think about them taking it out and just being jabbed at more often.

I go to Darren and ask him to cuddle me in bed. I just lose my shit sobbing whilst he holds me. I sob that I'm terrified of dying. It's not my time and I don't won't to die. I feel so desperately sad for the children. He lies there holding me until I fall asleep.

Monday 29th July 2019

It's a new day and I feel much better after letting out all of my emotions last night. Maybe I just needed to let it all out. I'd been working up to the start of treatment, keeping my shit together, and now it's started, and I actually feel a bit pants, the reality of everything is hitting me. What I can do, and must continue to do, is keep sharing how I'm feeling with Darren and him with me. I could see it in his eyes that I'd scared the shit out of him last night and I know this must be difficult for him. Even more so in some ways as he'll feel so helpless.

I have both children at home with me today, so I need some back up. My lovely friend Claire invited us all round to her house. Her and Alec couldn't have been kinder making us lunch and running around after my children. To my surprise, all the rest of the 'Massaging Mummies' arrived and it turned into one big massive play date. Chloe even got over excited and threw herself into the paddling pool fully clothed twice. I think the clever little bugger has already figured out I'm a bit slower off the mark at the moment and is taking full advantage of the situation.

The evening is finished off nicely with my lovely friends Emily and Tracey aka 'Strong Randy Ladies' coming round for tea. They also come bearing many gifts and beautiful flowers. One of their amazing gifts includes a glass jar containing lots of little envelopes with little snippets of memories we've shared. I'm going to open one each time I have treatment or each day I'm feeling a bit low.

Sitting round the table with Darren we of course have to break the ice and talk about the Big C.

Emily – "You don't look as poorly as I was expecting."
Darren – "What did you expect her to look like? A dug-up corpse?"

And with that the ice is well and truly broken. The tone has been set and they quickly realise that it's business as usual and anything goes.

Oh, and I ought to say I received confirmation today that I have a valid claim on the critical illness insurance. I should bloody think so too. I mean, what the hell would you need to get otherwise for a successful payout? In all seriousness, this is great news, as it means we can pay off some debts, change the car as it was starting to misbehave and squirrel some money away for a rainy day.

Cancer Comms

Massaging Mummies:

"Thank you so much for today lovely ladies and your gorgeous families. Keeping things normal and catching up is the best medicine ever. And on a Monday, you get me at my best, no dribbling mess today. Missed you, Scouse. Thank you so much Claire and Alec for looking after us so well today. xx"

Strong Randy Ladies:

"Just leaving now. xx"
"Thumbs up. Although the chef isn't home yet. Starting to panic!"
"You're not cooking, are you?"
"Am I fuck. I've got cancer."
"I nearly spat my bloody pasta out!"
"Are you eating? He's cooking lasagne. Winner, winner, second dinner?"

"Fuck me, I best stop eating then. I'll ditch my ready meal! Leaving now too. xx"

Local Yocals:

"Evening ladies. Hope you're all well. So, I understand that I need to post all my fav meals as 'meals on wheels' is the real deal. You girls are so special and are going far beyond generous. It's very touching and very much appreciated. Darren is working overtime this week, so I'll be sampling Pippa's delights.

To be honest, I like most things and actually I'd like to sample your favs. I will develop a score card system for you all based on taste, presentation and texture and present the winner with a return meal at the end."

Tuesday 30th July 2019 – Chemo Round Two

"I appreciate each day and each moment."
(YESmum card)

I met a lovely lady today, being my chemo neighbour, called Dawn. She was there with Trevor who I found out was her brother and not her partner as I had insinuated!

I'm a rooky to this chemo malarkey. Dawn is a fair few treatments ahead of me, so it was really helpful to speak to someone who had been in the trenches longer than me.

I thought I would come out of this a bit skinnier. Well, turns out it's likely that I'll pack on some timber from the medication and maybe inactivity.

I really enjoy my chat with her and hope to see her again in a few weeks.

Emily and Tracey' Little Jar of Cards

"Yes, I do remember our Exmouth night out where Paul had to pick Emily up as she was shitfaced. I agree it was not your finest hour!"

"Paul remembers it too! We carried on clubbing and left Paul to it."

"Poor boy. What a nightmare! See, after kids I didn't get out much and I felt free! I now know my limits. Sort of. x"

"Yeah why did you two leave me, you fuckers, and carry on clubbing. I may retract my statement about true friends!"

"A true friend will fuck off quietly if she disgraces herself and let the others carry on with their partying. Therefore, you are a true friend."

"I can't actually remember whether that happened or not as I was, as you pointed out, 'shitfaced'."

Cancer Comms

"Chemo take two.

With my phone lighting up like a Christmas tree, here's your update on today's drug fest.

POP QUIZ – how much do you think one bag of my chemo cocktail costs? Keep reading…

Equipped with my flashy Nemo Chemo bag (photo available upon request) courtesy of my hilarious husband, it was loaded with charging gadgets, snacks and the essential guest item (knitting) to accommodate today's chemo sitter Nicola. Nicola is also going to make me some snazzy bandages to cover my PICC line. I reckon we could be onto something with my captive audience.

Pleased to report that today was very uneventful with no red Hulk incidents. Spent the day drinking cups of tea,

knitting and making friends with people either side for four and a half hours. All very upbeat until Celine Dion came on with her uplifting song from *Titanic* but I was grateful that the band wasn't out playing their last song for me. The Lebanese man to my left even commented that I had an easy cancer, how reassuring!

I won't lie, it hasn't all been plain sailing and humorous. Friday was a very achy, tiring and difficult day with an unexpected scan date letter received out of context. But a few phone calls and that was sorted. I think I probably scared Darren on Sunday with my emotional outburst at my fear of dying! We must also remember that our dark humour, which is getting worse, might not be appreciated by all, but apart from that that's week one in the bag, and the happy times spent catching up with friends and family far outweigh the downtimes.

The presents keep rolling in and I reckon I can drag this out for at least another month yet!

Quick sweepstake update, the hair shows no sign of parting company just yet and we might need to revisit the sweepstake dates. I might also need to revisit some threading or waxing to remove the hairy caterpillars taking up residence over my eyes and upper lip. I had hoped for some savings there!

I've also stirred up some healthy competition in one of my friend groups who are delivering frozen edible offerings. I've informed them I shall be scoring their offerings and the winner gets a return meal. What an amazing investment. One meal in return for twenty! Winner, winner, chicken dinner (quite literally).

So, I hope the update is welcomed. Please tell me to bore off when you've had enough.

As always, you are awesome, keep the lols coming. You are not imposing on me, bothering me, annoying me. I love keeping in touch. And please keep telling me what's going on in your world. Xx

ANSWER: 5k per bag. But like the L'Oreal advert, 'I'm worth it'."

Circle of Trust:

"Hope session number two goes okay, Em. xx"

"Thank you. Just when I was feeling back to normal it's poison day! I'm thinking Prodigy's Poison."

"I'll pop down, let me know when you're settled in and hooked up."

"She's having a right old laugh down there hey, Em. Lady next to her even knows about my grey pube!"

"Round two done, Em. Love the twat hat."

"Loving the updates my lovely and after seeing the Nemo chemo bag I think you should share it on here, it's so cute. So, working for the NHS I know I'm biased, but fank fuck for the NHS. 5k a bag, jeez! I wonder how much it does cost to make and how much is marked up by the greedy pharmaceutical companies? P.S. what cancer does the Lebanese man have? Bit cheeky, no cancer is easy."

"Haha, well God help him when I'm lumpy sitting. If Darren's packing your bag up for suitable sitter, for that I expect mine to be cans of gin."

"I've always been a big fan of the NHS and I can't fault the service they've been providing me. Everyone has been fantastic, and the staff are lovely. Lebanese guy has had all sorts of nasty cancers and I think he meant it in a helpful way."

"Such a cool bag, you're looking great too. Always welcome the updates and I'll book a Tuesday off so I can have a chemo day with you. Keep doing what you're doing, good day or bad day, you have so many people in your corner. xx"

"Love the Nemo Chemo bag! When it's my turn to accompany you to your poison party you'll need a bigger bag for the games I'll bring, however if Kel gets gin then I'll take a tequila."

"Awww, bless him, makes me a bit sad if he was the one who came and sat there when I was there. Did he have anyone come and keep him company? Though I expect after an afternoon sitting next to you he went home with a smile. And definitely a good sign – if he can get those nasties under control then you can get lumpy gone."

"Well done, Em, you're doing good. I think it's a lovely chemo bag of goodies to help the day go by!"

Massaging Mummies:

"Emma, you are bloody amazing. I adore your updates and am very pleased to hear your day was uneventful in a good way. I can sort your caterpillars out this week for you if you like, I still have my kit. When is good for you? You are absolutely worth every penny. xx"

"5k? I don't think you're bloody worth it! Thank God for the NHS. Well, bird, I'm not surprised by how amazingly you're handling this. I wouldn't expect anything less, you're a super woman. Your updates are needed. As always, I'm only a phone call away. Is there anything you need or would like? Love ya, bird. Xx"

"I will get the chef to enter the food competition! Any requests? He was thinking of doing you and Darren a boeuf bourgignon, but will take requests. He's keen, so just let us know. Am so pleased today went smoothly. Cannot get over how well you are handling all of this – you are one strong and brave woman. If dark humour works for you then sod those who can't cope with it! We are always here for you but also here for Darren and the kids too. Love you so much. Shout if you need any help with childcare. xx"

"Good job, Em. Two down! Well done to Darren, who is obviously being amazing too. I'd quite like to see this Nemo bag. I'm glad it went as well as expected yesterday and you're making your neighbours jealous with your type of cancer – the poor Lebanese man didn't stand a chance really, did he – poor boob-less human. Hey, no need to change the sweepstake, I might be in with a chance. Thank you for the update. It is good to know you're okay. Thank God you've been paying your taxes *for so many years – you're really getting the return. I will happily take requests for dinners or childcare. I'm not competing against Alec, though. Have a good day. x"*

"Oh, game on. I seem to have created a mummy one vs mummy two cook off! Claire, I friggen love Beef Boyrgignon (ah spelling!), so big thumbs up to that. Ruth – take on the chef. You can do it! Jo – I'll have a crispy shredded beef and special fried rice please. Paula – if you can decamp the caterpillars that would be absolutely amazing. I wonder if we could find a night for you girls to come to tea at mine soon? x"

Shits and Giggles:

"Brilliant update. Thanks for keeping us updated my love.

Hope you've fitted in some good beach time over the past week too. I'm sorry it's been a bit of a shit one. It's never a bad thing to keep husbands on their toes, though – if you're not worrying or surprising them once a month, they can get complacent!"

"Is it wrong that my brain fixated wayyyy too long on the cost of the bag and why on earth did chargers, snacks and knitting cost £5k... I had to re-read it but now I understand. Anyway, brilliantly funny and oh so Emma-like update. Loved it, pal! I don't however love that you even have to write all of this... Much love."

Strong Randy Ladies:

"This will make you laugh... Got home last night, husband's keys in front door just sitting there waiting for some random person to walk in the house! Luckily, we have gates, so they would have to mount the gate first. Anyway, ho hum, go inside to find all three children still awake! Baby screaming the place down as he had got woken by two feral children who are still not settled at 10.30 at night as husband has riled them up playing football instead of my half hour down time before bed, which I

clearly do for the benefit of my own health! So, when I arrived home nice and relaxed as got all the angst off my chest, I then realised I wanted to stab him in the other eye as well as the first. Unfortunately, he's now blind, but it's okay as he can still work with the use of his hands and feet... for now. xx"

"Laughing at your message, Em. Double stabbing does not bode well. I would maybe suggest some written instructions? Fuck knows to be honest. Hope today is proving slightly calmer."

"And... the fucker has just had the cheek to ask me for hanky panky! With the side note of how many times it's been in the last six months! Glad you have enough time to count, chap, as I certainly don't. WTF! On a side note, your boy is a good 'un (yes mine is too but I can't see the wood for the trees right now!), he clearly adores you and the worry is etched on his face. Give him a big hug tonight, he is doing a good job, bless him. £5k, WTF... that's £60k you're sucking up in twelve weeks. Poor NHS, no wonder they are stretched. But have to agree you are more than worth it. I'm sticking with 22nd then. After the shit storm maybe it will prove a good omen. xx"

"Cheers to round two done! Maybe if I drink the rest of the bottle I will be obliging. xx"

"Glad to hear things went more smoothly today or as smoothly as they can! 5k a round, at least you'll get your national insurance back! I agree with Emily, your hubby is a good one. He is obviously worried. Sending a hug for you both – you are amazingly strong."

Local Yocals:

"Thinking of you today."

"Yep, hope today goes well and you're in and out without any tomato face."

"If you are feeling particularly adventurous, we could leave the meals unnamed and you could play freezer roulette."

"Just a warning, ladies, but Pippa has made a strong

start with her casserole. Couldn't shovel it into my face quick enough. Major yummers. xx"

(Beth – Pippa's sister) *"I'm hoping having the same gene pool will give me some leverage on the others. Hopefully cooking skills is a genes thing."*

"The competition is on. Might even cook with meat to win this fucker."

"That's what I like to see. A healthy bit of competition where contestants completely depart from their morals!"

"I can't tell you how much I delight in your updates! Thank you for taking the time to keep us all so well informed. Absolutely love you to bits. x"

"I'm laughing and crying in equal measures. (I'm blaming the hormones!) I admire your honesty and I love your ability to mix this with some hilarious anecdotes on your journey so far! Thank you for the updates and just keep putting one foot in front of the other. x"

"Love you, Em, thanks for sharing with us. (PS you are totally worth it!)"

"That was hilarious, keep up with that spirit and yes you're totally worth it. x"

"I seem to have created a mummy one vs mummy two cook off! I'm going to need a bigger freezer. Perhaps that could be your next gift?! I wondered if we might be able to arrange a play date catch up? I have both kids on a Monday so I'm going for safety in numbers! x"

"You're hilarious, Em. Get yourself on freecycle. I'm in for a play date and a low-key parenting day."

"We are free too and banking on safety in numbers too. x"

"Oh, Emma, I absolutely loved your update, you are doing so amazing. Shocked at 5k a bag! But, of course, you're worth it. Ha ha, that's awesome, I'm just glad you will have a well-stocked freezer!

Cake. Always Cake:

"Loved that update. You have a cracking way with words. 5k. Oh my Christ. Totally worth it. I didn't give you my date, but from your update if

your hair is still luscious and thick then I am going to say 20th August.

ED Fan Club:

"Wow, just wow… £5k… but, as you say, you are most definitely worth it! Glad sesh two went okay and keep the updates coming, I say! We miss your humour in the office. xx"

"Loving the updates, your unique take on it all is just brilliant! Glad week two went okay. But £5k, blimey… obviously it's money well spent! x

"Matraves is going to be a rap start" (Kate M sends me a video of her singing Jessie J 'It ain't about the money'. Genius.)

"Love it. Kate the queen of lyrics."

"This is absolute gold, Matraves! I feel you've missed your vocation."

Jo:

"How was today's drug fest? Hope it was less traumatic than last week."

"Wow… £5k, that's an expensive night out. What a brilliant message, though, your sense of 'dark' humour will keep you sane and follow your emotions. If you need to cry do it. If you need to make inappropriate jokes do it (but share them with me, obvs). If you're up to a visitor at all shout and let me know, but I suspect you're inundated with requests to see you, so please don't worry if you're booked right up taking things day by day. If you're free Thursday or Friday and think hmmmm wouldn't mind seeing Jolar today, holler me up… Big love as always, Strudders."

Michelle:

"Hey you. How was round two? Meant to message you earlier, sorry. Doesn't mean I wasn't thinking of you. xx"

"Photo please! Still reading… Will never have enough of hearing *from you my lovely, but will be even better when you've kicked this thing into touch. So, I'll never tell you to bore off. I'm still off work so have lots of daytime playtime ahead when you fancy company. xx"*

"Oh, do you want to be my next chemo babysitter next Tuesday? We could play Cards Against Humanity! Or maybe not! No worries if you don't fancy spending your time surrounded by people on drips, though! I have both kids on Monday if you'd like to help me co-adult? Or equally sack the cancer and kids off and we'll fix another sophisticated dinner date. Don't go back until you're ready. I'm realising more than ever it's just so important to look out for number one. Lots of love to you my beautiful chum. xx"

"Hell yes, I would love to next Tuesday. That sounds really fucking weird but I'm honoured you would ask me, in a weird kind of way. I'll be there in a heartbeat. I am yours for the day. We can still do childcare another Monday and sack the kids off for another dinner date. We can do all of the above. But yes, put me down for next Tuesday. xx"

"Perfect. I reckon the colouring book and some small card games then for our outing. Do you want to park at mine for say 10.30? I have my 'Dad chemo cab' booked for 11am and we can travel in style in his transit van! It starts at 11.30 and takes about four and a half hours."

"I'm in. Sounds like I'm excited. I am, to spend time with you and support you through this shit. If I could make it go away even better, but just to be able to be there for you somehow means the world to me. I'll be there for 10.30."

"Excited is the wrong word. Happy. Nope. Fuck's sake. Want to be there for you, so whatever I can do. xx"

Nicola:

"Would not be anywhere else. You are one amazing beautiful lady. You did make me giggle today. Will run a PICC line cover tomorrow, when

I get home. I'll try and find some superhero fabrics just for Toby. Stay amazing lovely.

Nicola's Words

When I was nearing the end of this book, I asked a few people if they might like to write something. I thought it might be interesting to get another perspective on what goes through your mind when someone you care about is diagnosed with cancer.

Here's the first of those entries from my friend Nicola, who I've known since I was three!

Emma's approach to cancer as in my eyes:

Yes, she has it.
No, it doesn't have her.
It can do one and leave!

I remember the day Emma told me she had found a lump. She went to the doctors the same day to get it checked. Emma was fairly confident that it was nothing to worry about, but that it should be checked anyway. On returning from the appointment, Emma told me that she was now on a two-week waiting list for further checks; this was done in a very matter of fact way. We spoke about everything and anything but not what had just happened.

Emma was in my thoughts every day over the next two weeks; our friendship has gone in different directions over the years but is still as healthy and strong as ever.

On the day of Emma's check-up, I messaged her first thing in the morning, then 17:30 just to let her know I love her and am thinking of her. Then Emma called and confirmed our worst fears. It was cancer.

I listened as Emma cried and told me what was going on.

There was nothing I could say to help or make her feel any better, so I said nothing at all and just listened to her and told her that I loved her.

The one piece of advice I did give was that if directions and decisions go down a different route than was planned or expected, then that's okay. Follow your heart, do what is right for you and your beautiful family. Don't hold regrets, say the things that need to be said. However she travelled this journey, it would be HER journey to travel. There would be no rights or wrongs. Just keep moving forward. Emma has encouraged me to say why the piece of advice which I had given was so hard to do, and why I found the next activity so hard. I had recently lost my mummy to cancer, after nursing her for eighteen months. We had been on our own life-changing journey of love, laughter and tears.

The next activity I was asked to do was sit with her as her first chemo sitter. I would totally do anything she asked, but oh my word I had sleepless nights. The last time I was there I was with my mum as an emergency admission, of which Emma didn't know.

As I sat with Emma, I felt so humble and proud. Watching her having chemotherapy, making the best of a very hard situation, when others around her were sad and low, she brought smiles to their faces only the way Emma can. That chemotherapy sitting, we laughed, I made lots of cups of tea, and we talked about everything and anything, and not just about the cancer.

So, her unique cancer journey began…

Wednesday 31ˢᵗ July 2019

A good day for a scarecrow hunt I'd say, with Mum, the kids and the Strudwick clan (my brother's wife and kids). Sadly, the heavens opened. Not so sadly, I guess, as we find ourselves in the pub instead.

My amazing friend Nicola is very talented on the old sewing machine. She's quickly knocked me up an arm sleeve to cover my PICC line rather than just a bandage. It's grey with clouds on one side and jellyfish on the other. Much better. Subsequently, I've googled, and there's a whole host of different sleeves you can order. Even some to match your sports gear should you be so minded. I'll be sticking with my jellyfish and clouds.

Tonight is Chloe's parents' evening at nursery. I always find these evenings amusing. What really can you say about a one-year-old? She eats, sleeps, shits and plays on repeat. Living her best life, I'd say.

Fear

I want to talk about fear.

Fear – An emotion induced by perceived danger or threat, which causes physiological changes and ultimately behavioural changes, such as fleeing, hiding, or freezing from perceived traumatic events.

As I'm writing this at the end of my treatment journey I was trying to decide where might be the best place in a book to talk about this. I've decided here would be the best place to talk about it because 'spoiler alert' the fear does quieten. There were even times I actually forgot I had cancer and many, many days I just functioned like a normal person getting on with their everyday life. If you're setting out on your own treatment journey, I thought you might like to hear that sooner rather than later.

Now, of course, I can't pretend to know how you're feeling just because I had cancer. Everybody is different and everybody deals with things in different ways. I can only try to explain to you how I felt.

When I was told I had cancer, I have never experienced fear quite like it. Usually a pretty articulate person, the fear immediately came swooping in, rendering me speechless. I couldn't formulate my thoughts and I certainly wasn't listening to the answers. I am so glad that Darren was with me and sat quietly absorbing all the information so he could reiterate it to me later.

The waiting in-between – being told you have cancer but awaiting the results/plan – seems like an endless void. Physically I felt fine, no aches or pains, but mentally I was a bit all over the shop. I can't really put a title on it. I wasn't angry or cross. Maybe overwhelmed. Scared. Desperately sad and worried for the children. Numb.

I think it was the not knowing exactly what was in my body and whether it was treatable was what caused the greatest fear. That dramatically decreased when they told me the 'kick ass plan'. They delivered it with such confidence that I was certain with a bit of hard work I could kick this setback into touch.

After diagnosis, I was thrown into various consultations, appointments and scans. Although I was 'apprehensive', this was nowhere near as bad as the initial fear I felt. This felt like I was doing something and getting on with it.

There were a couple of unexpected times when the fear came rushing back. An unexpected scan invitation, a feeling of claustrophobia with the PICC line, a couple of times when the drugs made me feel very poorly and I couldn't catch my breath/felt faint. Stumbling across something on social media that caused me to read something that was probably better not seen. When chemo finished and, all of a sudden, I didn't have the safety net of visiting my lovely chemo nurses and my community team.

Each time I really felt the fear I spoke to someone about it. This someone was usually my lovely booby nurse, my nurse through work Suzanne, Darren or my friends. I did speak to family as well, but I could also see the fear in their eyes and didn't want to cause unnecessary upset. I told them the important stuff.

When the treatment started, there really wasn't too much fear, especially when results started showing it was working. I was so busy being busy that I didn't have much time to think about it.

The episodes of feeling fear were few and far between when treatment got underway. The last one I recall was just before my surgery when I had this fear that I wouldn't wake up or that they would find unknown nasties inside. I did wake up and they didn't find anything.

There's a saying: "Feel the fear and do it anyway." To be honest, I didn't have much choice, I had to do it. But I could be the author of a solution rather than my own misfortune. I decided early on that I was not going to be stoically British and try to attempt this on my own. I knew that it was only my body that could fight this, but my army of supporters would help my mind and that was what was going to get me through this.

Mindset and mindfulness

Ironically, when cancer came knocking, I was in the best possible health both physically and mentally.

The good physical health is self-explanatory, but having good mental health and maintaining it can be more difficult to explain. It's all a bit of a journey and something you need to practice.

At the beginning of the year, I'd spent January doing a 'Mindset Reset' challenge set by Mel Robins, author of *The 5 Second Rule*. In her book she basically talks about counting down from five when you're faced with a difficult task and when you get to zero just do it. By doing this, you don't give your brain a chance to talk you out of doing it. I was already practicing this both at home and work, or even when I didn't feel motivated, and was already benefiting greatly from it. Less procrastination, less time to worry, just getting on and getting shit done.

Her challenge basically asked us to look back at the previous year, what had gone well, not so well, things that had stopped us and what we were going to do differently this year. I practised talking to myself in more favourable terms, using positive words and stopped being so harsh on myself. I steered away from negativity and worked on quietening down the little voices (not actual voices) inside that were holding me back.

I stopped overcommitting. Blimey that was liberating. If I didn't want to do something, I would politely decline and wouldn't feel guilted into doing something.

I was very aware that going back to work in a demanding role with the logistics of two children was going to be hard work, but that it was important that I found time for me. Time for me and Darren. Time for my hobbies.

I would also make sure I got outside in the fresh air on a daily basis. This might mean a walk around a not-so-glamourous industrial estate in my lunch break, but at least I was getting outside and unplugging from technology.

I changed my diet and started eating better.

Every morning when I woke up, I would allow myself a couple of minutes to think about the day ahead and what needed to get done. If I was dragged out of slumber by a shrieking child before the alarm, I would do this exercise in the shower instead.

At the end of each day, I would think back and make a note of three things that went well. I know this might sound a bit tree hugging but it's easy to dwell on the bad stuff and think the whole day was shit when in reality there is always something good to be found.

If I started to feel overwhelmed or panicked, I'd really concentrate on my breathing. Not worrying about what had been, what might be coming, but concentrating on what was happening right now. And, of course, right then, in that moment, I was fine. I would take some deep breaths in through my nose, hold it and then slowly breathe out through my mouth.

Sometimes I would press my thumb and forefinger together and think of my happy memory. Remember Whitsunday sailing, thunderstorm, bikini, Moby? No? Check out 23rd July again! In that moment, I have never felt so calm and still, without a care in the world, and it's a place I take my mind back to when it's racing away from me.

I bought myself a good old-fashioned alarm clock and left my mobile downstairs overnight. Straight away my sleep improved, and I was going to sleep thirty minutes earlier now I wasn't mindlessly scrolling. With it not being on the bedside, I didn't reach for it in the morning. I'd wake up and only knew what was going on within my own four walls and not let the rest of the world in until my first glance much later.

Come June, although I was a bit tired, I had found a happy medium. So, when cancer came knocking for me, although it was one hell of a shock, I was already in a good place mentally, I just needed to stay there. Throughout my treatment I took the rough with the smooth, knowing there would be days when I would feel utter shite, but even on those days searching for slices of positivity. And if a day was truly shite, I knew it would end eventually, that tomorrow was a new day, and one day nearer the end of my treatment journey.

Once I got going with my treatment, I didn't entertain the idea that it would not work.

During the course of my treatment, I got to meet up with loads of people. I remember conversations with some medical professionals who asked about my well-being with not being able to do what I usually did. To the contrary, I was very much enjoying meeting up with friends and family. My problem was that I needed to perhaps slow up a bit more and acknowledge my new limitations. That was a work in progress!

Looking Back – July

So, I've decided that at the end of each month I'm going to look back to see just how far I've come. I'm all for living in 'the now' but especially at the moment. Putting one foot in front of the other and just dealing with each thing as it arises but I also hope that by looking back monthly I'll see just how far I've come and it will spur me on for the next month.

And look just how far I have come. I've gone from being in complete fear at the beginning of the month, totally overwhelmed and never feeling so scared in my life, to undergoing scans, getting a plan, putting in place loads of practical measures, accommodating a PICC and having my first round of chemo. Oh, and I decided to write a book about it, which I'm finding very cathartic. If it ends up being for my eyes only, a place where I can hold my thoughts and memories, that's good enough. If it ends up being shared and helps other people, well that will be something special. So yes, actually I'm very proud of myself as I've achieved a shit load with the help, support and encouragement of my friends and family.

August 2019

Thursday 1st Aug 2019

Toby was booked into a holiday club for the day today so off he still goes. After Chloe's safely deposited at nursery, I've got the day to myself. I meet my work friend Ruth for lunch to catch her up with everything that's been going on.

This evening the massaging mummies swoop in to cook for me in my own house. Paula brings her waxing kit with her to remove the caterpillar that is growing on my upper lip and my re-appearing monobrow. The irony is not lost on us that I'm having hair removed whilst undergoing chemo, when you're supposed to lose it. I'm actually looking forward to not having hair forceably removed from my face when it all decides to bugger off!

I love my evening with the girls. Giggles and natter, it really is the best medicine. They're very mindful of how I'm feeling and keep asking me to tell them if I'm tired and need to go to bed.

Cancer Comms

Circle of Trust:

"Do you think we could take a karaoke machine to chemo, Em? We could play some crowd pleasers and get everyone to join in!"
"Yeah I think we could probably do that when no one is looking. xx"

Local Yocals:

Send them a picture of my stacked freezer.

"Anyone fancy coming for tea? Seriously, you guys are going above and beyond. You are very special women."

"Well done, guys. So glad you have a good stash, Emma. xx"

"I'm pitting the two siblings against each other. Sampled Pippa's spag bol last night. Yummers."

"That is some stash! You know us, we're a bunch of feeders."

"Might as well fuck my Slimming World membership off now then!"

Friday 2nd August 2019

So, this was the day I started to feel proper pants last week. I feel fine today. Nothing. I'm just going to run with this. I don't know how long it will last, I don't care, I'm running with it. Today is a good day.

Cancer Comms

Massaging Mummies:

"Morning ladies. I just wanted to say a massive thank you for last night. I have woken up feeling fine (I do have the easy cancer!) and I reckon it was because I had such a lovely time last night. Just your company would have been enough but all your generosity with food, treats and waxing goes above and beyond. I'm so grateful I've got you ladies in my life. Have an awesome day and see you soon. xx"

"Aw, I absolutely loved it. My food next time. Love you all."

"It was a lovely evening yesterday. Feel like I have a hangover for some reason."

"Such a lovely evening. Thanks for the wonderful and entertaining company. Looking forward to Jo's feast next time! Glad you're feeling good this morning, Em. Take it easy. xx"

Sunday 4ᵗʰ August 2019

Aren't children bloody amazing?

My beautiful ten-year-old niece Skye has chopped loads of her hair off into a sophisticated bob in support of what I'm going through and also donated her locks to The Little Princess Trust. She's also set up a Just Giving page and raised over £200. We pose together for a picture before tucking into a roasty.

Monday 5ᵗʰ August 2019

I've been reading some stuff off the Macmillan website where people refer to 'Scanxiety' – the anxiety you get around the time of scans and waiting for the results. The anxiety is certainly back again today, as it's the extra ultrasound that's been ordered. Although the ultrasound will need to be reported on, the radiographer tells me that she isn't concerned by what she sees on my liver and likens it to a birth mark. Thank feck for that. All these years and I didn't know there was a birth mark on my liver.

The relief floods from me. We're off to Sidmouth Folk Festival for a family day out and I can now enjoy myself. I catch up with friends I haven't seen in a while, and they compliment me on my new short hair do. On this occasion I thank them. Everyone's in good spirits, I don't want to dampen the mood.

Cancer Comms

Local Yocals:

"How're you doing, Emma? Can't believe tomorrow is your third lot. Where are the weeks going?"

"All good, thank you. Just off to Sidmouth Folk Festival. Absolutely no ill effects this week. xx"

"Fantastic. Enjoy your day, my love. xx"

"Oh, that's great news. That sounds brilliant, have fun. Hope tomorrow is okay. xx"

"Wow, that's incredible, Emma. So pleased for you, lovely. xx"

Tuesday 6ᵗʰ August 2019 – Chemo Round Three

"I believe in myself and my capabilities as a human being."
(YESmum card)

Emily and Tracey's Little Jar of Cards

"I know we only see each other once a month-ish but I class you as one of my bestest friends. You are kind, strong and beautiful, inside and out. I love you lots like jelly tots. xx"

Cancer Comms

"A quarter of the way through phase one. Yes, I'm still talking about 'Operation Evict Lumpy' and not the Redrow development opposite us.

Today's chemo sitter was the lovely Michelle. For future

chemo sitters, she is going to be a tough act to follow. To pass the four hours, she packed the Nemo Chemo bag with knitting, Play-Doh, painting, Disney Top Trumps, Cards Against Humanity, The F*#K game, ginger biscuits and pear drops. The fun was endless, and we had a lot of interest from the nurses.

JOB OPPORTUNITIES: Now taking expressions of interest for future chemo sitters. You must be available for four hours on either the 13th or 20th August, be able to make a good cuppa, come with the LOLs and potentially withstand a hot climate. I also want to know what you would put in the Nemo Chemo bag. Transport provided courtesy of 'Dad's chemo cabs' in his trusty Transit van. As I turned up to my wedding in an A-Team transit, I'm noticing a pattern developing for all important life events.

I found out important info today. The nurses love pens. I negotiated an earlier time slot for next week on the promise of pens, so I'm hoping my colleagues will come good for me.

The ultrasound of the abdomen yesterday was fine. Just focusing on my liver, nothing untoward going on. So, I've had a full MOT now and no other nasties. The relief is fantastic, and I now feel on an even keel. Just have to blast the booby bug away.

My amazing niece cut her long hair off this week in support of me. She's donated it to The Little Princess Trust and is fundraising for them. What a beautiful thing for a ten-year-old to do. I've shared her page on FB if you'd like to support her reaching her target.

I feel I've got off lightly with no side effects from last week's drug fest, which was unexpected and amazing.

Hair sweepstake: we're mostly premature. Still stubbornly holding on and haven't woken up to find a chihuahua sitting on my pillow.

Chemo cupboard: fully stocked with all manner of creams, lip balm, mints. If you're feeling a bit chapped and dry when the cold sets in, pay me a visit.

Edible freezer tapas: generously restocked by the lovely Beth. I could happily feed the street for a day should we get snowed in tomorrow.

Me and Michelle love a good quote. I've had a lot of comments this week about people admiring the way I'm dealing with this, being brave, etc. I don't think I'm particularly brave, but I like this one:

'If you don't like it, change it.

If you can't change it, change the way you feel about it.'

I can't change the situation, but I can control how I feel about it. The positives this week greatly outweigh the negatives. More time spent with family and friends. More time spent with friends on chemo days catching up. More appreciation for the amazing family around me.

An impromptu visit from a group of friends for tea. Paula is a beautician and brought her waxing kit. The irony was not lost that I'm going through chemo yet having hair actively removed from my face!

Have a great week and let me know if you fancy spending a day drinking tea on the NHS with me. Also let me know what's going on in your world. Xx"

Circle of Trust:

"Em, I hope you're keeping these updates, as will be good for you to look back on! I actually went back to one of my colleagues and said I'm going to have to have a good think about what I need to pack in the Nemo chemo bag as your friend had painting and all sorts! Although glad of the biscuits. Nice little afternoon treat for me."

"Well done, mate, so proud. Also proud of Skye, amazing kid."

"I'm glad all is going okay. I'm happy to chemo-sit once kids have gone back to school. I'll request some Tuesdays off and get my witty thinking cap on. Very proud of Skye. All for a good cause, thank you folks who have donated already. Being part of the NHS with the ridiculous amount of paperwork, we all love a pen. I await to be signed off for RSI! First day back at work after a week off and guess what… yes… it was lovely and busy with a hint of stress. Being a Nurse Rocks!"

"Yes, Kel, get your thinking cap on. Although I'm equally happy just to natter for hours on end. Thanks, Mand. Charlene I'll sort you out with some pens."

Massaging Mummies:

"Good work, Michelle! Lol – possibly able to withstand a hot climate. I do not miss that about working in hospital! PS did you see this lady? Beauty vlogger Dawn Lee on why she's sharing her cancer journey. She basically says what you quoted. xx"

"I'm tempted to get back on the blogging."

"Ed says he can source pens from work for you! He has lots from reps! You should start blogging again. You're amazing. xx"

"Excellent, I'm going to have these nurses wrapped round my little finger! Would you like a pen, Caroline?"

"Yes, I love pens… never have too many but must be black. Sounds like you already have them wrapped around your finger… keep going. Definitely get back to your blogging, you're amazing. xx"

"I love that quote and I love you. I'm here in bed laughing my head off about the pens. So, I can come on the 13th August and I wouldn't even need to bring Nemo as just having me with you will bring all the joy and distraction you'll need. You are truly amazing how you're facing this and the attitude you've chosen. Lumpy is basically fucked. xx"

"Put me down for 10th September if you haven't already filled that spot!"

"Next opening is 24th September, any good?"

"Book me in."

Strong Randy Ladies:

"Glad so far so good. Long may it continue. Skye, bless her heart, so sweet of her and dutifully donated as that's the least I can do for such a sterling effort by such a thoughtful little girl. In terms of job opportunities, I would love to make an application but at full capacity during holidays. But will happily put myself forward when sprogs are back at school and normality has resumed. Getting a sitter for one is possible but for three that really only comes for emergency situations. God knows how people get time off with four! Well that's stupidity anyway, isn't it? Looking forward to our catch up, although I'm cooking Beef Fucking Wellington. How the hell did that happen? Good job you have cancer, or I'd tell you to fuck off these days!"

"Tell me to fuck off anyway. I don't expect anyone to bow to my 'C' card, I'm just pissing about. I also don't expect anyone to come for four hours, or at all for that matter. Everyone is mega busy and I'm just so appreciative of the support in all the forms it's taking. xx"

"Nah, you deserve beef wellington, it's the least I can do, so I will try my best (and I will get brownie points for cooking something decent for a change). I would love to come keep you company too. You can count me in for September."

"Also, I should say any chemo sitting doesn't have to be for the full four hours! Any company is welcome. xx"

"I'll do the duration in September. I'm sure we can entertain each other for four hours! I'll have a think about chemo bag goodies. xx"

"Hey lovely, glad the chemo is going well. I would like to apply for August 20ᵗʰ, but if that slot is filled no probs. Chemo bag items so far after rooting through nephew's toys/games box: plop trumps (top trumps using facts on animal poos), forgot we had that, difficult riddles for kids (I'd say more for adults), bug bingo. Other items TBC. Bless Skye, what an amazing niece. Such a lovely thing to do."

"Cool. Well, the next available vacancy is currently 1ˢᵗ October! Turns out it's a popular role! I could also add you

to the cancellation list. **Plop trumps – amazing. Maybe you guys could double up on the 1st October and we could have a picnic?"**

"I'd be worried if you had no offers, so that's amazing that you have lots of willing friends and family. I'm up for the 1st October."

"I'm definitely in for the threesome."

Local Yocals:

"Absolutely bloody brilliant, Em!"

"This weekly nugget of literary gold never fails to make me smile. As always, thank you for so openly and honestly sharing your journey with us, and here's to another session crossed off the calendar."

"Sounds like you're nailing this, Em."

"I'm glad you're enjoying. It feels very cathartic to do and gives me such a positive purpose. I'm thinking about blogging again. xx"

"Oh, Em! I'm glad it's gone so well again, and that Michelle was so great. And OMG what a relief about the rest of body scan: absolutely brilliant news. Wow, this is so sweet of your neice too. Amazing that the hair is still clinging on. Glad you're still well stocked, think it's my turn week after next, so get ready for some mediocre lasagne. Love the quote too. I'm sure it's so hard with the feelings like a rollercoaster but you're handling it all brilliantly. How are the YESmum cards? Love the way you put everything and yes blogging would be great."

"Well done, Emma, sounds like you are really kicking this chemo's ass. Lots of love. I would love to come along on a Tuesday at some point."

"I AM NOT ALONE TODAY. And yes, I love the cards. This one was top of the pack. It's very evident that I'm very much not alone."

"So true. You have an army of people with you. xx"

"Never alone, Emma, we are here every step."

ED Fan Club:

"I would love to come to a chemo session, let me have a look. I'll try my damndest to distract you with humour."

"Great update, Emma. Michelle and your niece sound ace!"

"You are such a wonderful human, ED, and are being such an inspiration. I would love to come and make you giggle and fill your Nemo chemo bag with all sorts of stuff (sounds pretty filthy, but I assure you it wouldn't be…) xx"

Jo S

"I'd like to apply for the position on August 20ᵗʰ please. I appreciate my application may be late. I apologise for this, as my three-year-old daughter is being a fucking moron this evening. If I'm too late I will reapply for another position at a later date. Pleased it seems to be going well and fabulous news on the scans being clear. All energy on getting lumpy to fuck off and leave your bangers alone. Well done to Skye. What an amazing thing to do. Will take a look at her page shortly. Fuck's sake, don't say you wasted a haircut if the stuff ain't gonna fall out. Can you ask for a refund from the hairdresser?"

"Dear Mrs S. Thank you for your recent application. I agree the timing is less than ideal and in an ideal world it could have chosen a different host but here we are. Your generosity to give up your valuable hours is greatly appreciated, and I hereby formally accept your proposal to accompany me on the 20ᵗʰ Aug. Full details will be forwarded nearer the time but in the meantime thank you for your interest. Yours sincerely, Mrs D. xx"

Michelle's words

As today's chemo sitter, and a dear friend who took the time to read the first draft of this book, here are her words:

My dearest Strudel,

When I first got your message telling me you had cancer, I literally burst into tears. I couldn't believe this could happen to my beautiful, sunny, funny friend. You know people are diagnosed every single day, but when it's someone you know and love, it's entirely different. It seems surreal, especially at our age, as I still class us as young! I also felt angry – why does this always happen to the good ones? Why you, who's always upbeat? Who's just celebrated her fortieth birthday? Who has a beautiful young family?

But immediately hearing your positive attitude and fighting plan, I knew you would beat it. And boy have you! In your own inimitable style. I know you've had dark days, and hell who wouldn't, but I truly see you as an inspiration. When I've had difficult days with some of the things I've had going on over the past few months, I've thought of you, what you must be going through, feeling, etc., and you have motivated me to get through. It was also the kick I needed to make a lot of the changes I was previously hesitant (scared) of making.

To know you're cancer free is just the best news – thank you for sharing your 'journey' with us, for your openness, honesty and humour. As I've always said to you, don't you ever change, you are awesome exactly as you are!

Wednesday 7ᵗʰ August 2019

Pick a park day today. A game invented by Toby where we see how many parks we can visit in one day. I'm calling in reinforcements again and doubling up with a school mum friend. The idea was they would keep each other entertained so we could sit down and chat. Never really works out that way, does it? I draw the line at monkey bars, though. I just don't have it in me today. Nor any day for that matter.

Friday 9th August

First off, an appointment with my oncology consultant to see how I'm getting on. I meet with her colleague and tell her I think it's working as I can't see the lump anymore and I can't really feel much. She seems rather impressed as well, so my unqualified opinion that the poison is working was right.

Then a cuppa in Waitrose to kill some time before my next appointment.

Genetics and BRCA misprints

Today I have an appointment with the Peninsula Clinical Genetics Service. This is offered to me as my results are Triple Receptor Negative, there is no history of breast cancer in my family and I'm 'young' to have cancer.

Prior to this appointment, I've had to complete a family tree spanning both my mum's and dad's sides of the family. My mum is one of four and my dad is one of nine (seriously, was there no TV in those days?!). I need full names, dates of birth and addresses, so this is a major piece of work. Of course, my mum produces a neatly written list at my request. I don't even bother asking my dad but instead opt for my Auntie Julie on that side of the family. Seeing it on paper it brings home that cancer is more common than you think, as there's been leukaemia, lung cancer and bowel cancer in my family.

If I choose to opt in for testing, they will be looking at my BRCA 1 and BRCA 2 genes.

My simplified understanding of genes is this: Genes come in pairs and we have loads of them in our body. They carry information that is passed onto us from our parents, one copy from our dad, the other copy from our mum. We then pass these onto children. If our parents have a dodgy gene there is a 50% chance they will pass it on.

These genes are stored in our body like books on a bookcase. These books tell our body if a bad cell comes along and to attack and kill them. Now if there's a spelling mistake in the book, or a 'misprint' in this case, the body might miss picking up on a bad cell and that's when someone is at greater risk of developing cancers. A misprint in your BRCA 1 gene causes an 80% risk of breast cancer and 20 – 60% risk of ovarian cancer in a woman's lifetime. A misprint in your BRCA 2 gene is also associated with breast and ovarian cancer but the latter risk is lower at 10-20%. There is also the risk of other cancers. If there is a misprint in BRCA 1 or BRCA 2 there tends to be several family members with cancer. That is not the case in my family. If a misprint was detected in my genes the testing is then extended to my mum and dad to see if they carry the faulty gene.

If there is a misprint in my genes, that puts me at greater risk of developing breast cancer again and/or ovarian cancer.

Do I want this testing?

There are three possible outcomes:

1. Normal result – no misprint found. With one in six of the general population developing breast cancer I am the unlucky statistic.
2. Misprint found – high risk of cancer.
3. Uncertain result – a 'variant of uncertain significance', which is classed as a normal result.

To be honest, I think forewarned is forearmed, so I'd rather know what I'm dealing with.

If the results come back having found a misprint, there are various options to monitor my health:

1. Regular screening in the form of a mammogram and MRI in

respect of breast cancer. Unfortunately, there isn't currently any screening available for ovarian cancer.

2. Surgery. In terms of breast cancer, this is a risk-reducing mastectomy, which can be performed with or without breast reconstruction. In terms of ovarian cancer, it's the removal of the ovaries and the fallopian tubes.

That's a lot of information to consider. I feel the best thing to do is to get the testing and then await the results before I even start contemplating whether I need bits and pieces removed. I see little point in worrying about that until it's confirmed I've got something to worry about. For the time being, I need to focus my energy on the chemo that is actually happening right now.

The testing is quite simple, I just need to relinquish some of my blood and then I'll have the results in eight to twelve weeks. As I'm off to see the community nurses next for my PICC line care, I take some extra phials.

What a morning of medical stuff!

Cancer Comms

"I'm pleased to report that the cocktail of drugs is already shrinking my uninvited boob raider. xx"

Circle of Trust:

"Holy shit that is awesome! Way to go you, you have totally got this!"

"Excellent mate, this is the news we've been waiting to hear. xxx"

"I've got to copy Becks and say holy shit, this is bloody awesome! And with only three chemo sessions. Adios lumpy."

"Fantastic news, Em! Fuck you, lumpy. How are you feeling after your Tuesday cocktail sesh?"

"Ah man, that's great news, Em. Well done. xx"

"I can't quite believe it really. Just feeling tired today, standard school holiday madness! No aches or pains. x"

"Absolute legend you are. Little bit disappointed I haven't seen you in the twat hat but obviously that's very minor in comparison! You'll just have to wear it for me in a private setting."

"I'm surprised you haven't got any aches and pains with the shapes you were throwing yesterday."

Massaging Mummies:

A collection of whoop whoops and woohoos!

Shits and Giggles:

"Hey lovely ladies. Em, what a fantastic update. You are unfailing, positive and fabulous. Michelle also sounds a beaut."

"Em, you make your treatment sound like it's a laugh a minute. I'm sure it's not! How many sessions have you got left? I wish I lived nearer, as I would totally book myself in as a sitter!

"Well to be honest once I got myself into the right head space it's been fine. I've had three of twelve weekly sessions so far in round one. Then I change to a harder drug once every three weeks for four to six sessions. But it's already shrinking."

"That's bloody great news."

Local Yocals:

"How are you, Emma? Xx"

"All good my end, thank you. The lump is shrinking to the extent the consultant struggled to find it today!"

A collection of 'What the fucks' and 'fuck yeahs'.

ED Fan Club:

"*I've started stealing pens on your behalf, Emma. We'll arrange a clandestine drop off. I can leave them in a brown paper bag on a street corner for Darren to pick up when he takes the dogs for a walk.*"

"**Excellent work. Oh, and in other news I'm pleased to report that the cocktail of drugs is already shrinking my uninvited boob raider. xx**"

"*I always thought Darren was a bit too tall for you! Joking aside, that's awesome news.*"

"*Bloody chuffing amazing news. xx*"

"*I'm really pleased to hear your news. See... cocktails are good for you! xx*"

"*Surely the upshot of this is that we should all regularly have cocktails anyway.*"

"**Yes, I was rather pleased. I celebrated by purchasing a fake pot plant. It will have better chances of survival in my house. Have a fab weekend all. xx**"

Saturday 10ᵗʰ August 2019

The 'massaging mummies' are amazing. Today Paula and Ed are hosting a BBQ and we're all going with our kids. The garden is massive so they can all run around and once again I get to sit down and relax and get 'stuff' brought to me. Feeling a bit tired this time round but nothing too horrendous.

They're all surprised I've still got a full head of hair. I'm surprised. That night my head starts itching a bit. Is this the start?

Cancer Comms

"**Kids asleep within seconds. We broke them! Thank**

you so much for a wonderful afternoon, girls and boys. Amazing way to spend a Saturday. Xx"

"Oh, bless them, Em. It was an amazing afternoon – thank you P&E for hosting/loaning garden and to the rest of you for grub and giggles. Love you all. xx"

"Absolutely loved it. Thank you so much. Love you all loads. xx"

Sunday 11ᵗʰ August 2019

It would appear that it is indeed now the start of the hair loss. I scratch my head and a few strands come away. Even though I knew this was coming, it's still a bit of a shock. I had dared to hope that I might get away with it. We're not talking falling out in clumps, just the odd few hairs at a time.

Tuesday 13ᵗʰ August 2019 – Chemo Round Four

"I am resilient and strong."
(YESmum card)

Emily and Tracey's Little Jar of Cards

"I wonder how many dinners we have all had. Maybe we should have a sweepstake on that. Hmmmm… Lots. Have you cooked any?"

Cancer Comms

"Coming live from the trenches today, number four (almost) successfully in the (old) bag.

Today's chemo sitter, Anna, played a strong hand.

Chocolate doughnuts and fingers straight off the bat followed by card games, Pictionary (abandoned Yatzy – game for 6+ but beyond us) and Go Fish for entertainment, interspersed with laughter and putting the world to rights.

So, another week ticked off. People are surprised at how well I'm looking. What are you expecting? Something from Zombie Apocalypse? So lucky to have had another week of no notable nasties, just feeling a bit tired. But let's be honest, anyone looking after small humans during the summer holidays are feeling the burn.

My skin is starting to protest at the drug cocktail. Not enthralled to return to my teenage spot face but it's better than the alternative and I'll sort that out once it's Lumpy Game Over.

After four sessions, my hair is slowly departing. A slow, finding it in various places around the house type situation, rather than a wake up with an egg head situation. So, if your sweepstake date was later in August, it's still all to play for.

I received a text to trial a 'Dyson Supersonic Hair Dryer' this week. I thought about having it and sending a full head/egg head photo with the caption 'Blimey, it really is supersonic.'

The best news is that lumpy is already downsizing and making plans to do one. I look forward to my next scan to confirm this.

I also had an appointment with Genetics where I'll eventually find out if there's a fault in my genes which puts me at a higher risk or whether it was just randomly my turn to take one for the team.

People are wishing me 'Happy Chemo Tuesday'. Right now, I'm quite enjoying my Tuesdays. I get to sit down for four hours and chill out with a friend without having to shout out, "Take your willy out of your sister's ear!" and, "Don't stick that up Arthur's bum!"

There also seems to be a general shift in your messages adopting my stupid and optimistic approach to this scenario. Glad to have you onboard and thank you for sticking with me.

Lastly, I apologise if I miss any messages. It is not intentional, and I think I might hire a **PA** to deal with my life/cancer admin. All chemo sitting positions are filled for this first batch of twelve sessions.

Until next time, you fantastic supporters... xx"

Circle of Trust:

"Amazing update... as for the hair, I have my very own hair story. One of the partners at work told me today: 'You have the same hair style as Professor Snape, you should dye it black.' Comment came out of nowhere! Bit paranoid now!"

"Oh yeah, it's just uncanny!"

"Better to look like Snape's hair than Hagrid's, I guess."

"Glad you've had another good week my love. Good to hear. You should definitely play that prank on Dyson. I wonder what they would do?"

"I had Thursday in the sweepstake, sounds like I'm in with a chance of the prize! Is the prize the Dyson you're gunna trial?"

Massaging Mummies:

"You just shouldn't be so popular and nice. Absolutely smashing this, bird. I do think you should still shout those things in the chemo ward. "Don't stick that up Arthur's bum!" lol. Keep being brilliant. Oh, and I had the 8th on the hairstake, can I change it to the 28th? Fuck's sake. xx"

"I think if you read the twenty-eight pages of small print you are stuck with your first offering!"

"Bulllshit!"

Shits and Giggles:

"Your childcare sounds much more exciting/weird than mine. Glad it's gone well today. I think of you every Tuesday, wondering what games you are playing and awaiting your update. Chocolate today – tough to beat. When's your next scan? I do hope you'll be having a farewell lumpy party, wish it Auf Wiedersehn properly."

Strong Randy Ladies:

"How you manage it every time I don't know, but I am in stitches. It's like you spend a whole week planning the next update but I rather think you are just terribly quick witted! Well, if you are going to lose your locks and become a spotty teenager again, then I guess you will require your humour. Who would have thought that a byproduct of cancer would be reliving your teenage years – fuck that! I just about survived the first round with hellish drink sessions and jumping off cliffs into water! No wonder we got spots the amount of shit we shoveled down our necks. We must have taken after those big pelican birds that just arch their necks back to feed and swallow (I'm talking alcohol still now, no naughty thoughts you!). Well, I am, of course, over the moon to hear that lumpy is heading in the right direction, although will be even happier when he fucks right off! You will be pleased to hear that I currently have the shits in Turkey as a result of no doubt stuffing my face with all humanly possible when I secretly tell myself 'I've been quite good'. So, a day on the toilet it has been for me today.

But on the bright side, the small human is in nursery as the intelligent side of me booked that from the UK. The unintelligent side of me missed the two other arseholes off and thought they would be 'old enough to not kill each other on a daily basis and give me a break'... hell no. Why did I think that! They have just returned from the pool 'bored', where one has supposedly 'strangled' and drowned the other! Which I know is a lie as they are still fucking arguing. I am now threatening kids club for naughty children and relishing the prospect of an hour's fucking peace.

On a lighter note, glad chemo four has gone well and hair is still there in the main for now. See you soon for beef wellington, which I'm not thinking about while on holiday in forty-one degrees here, hence why I'm inside. xx"

"I'm rather enjoying the comprehensive response and although you're on holiday I sense you're rather envious of my four-hour quiet kid-free day! Sorry to hear you've got the shits, though. Maybe a bit of weight loss? I reckon get them in club, double bookings, for the remainder of the hols. God, there is no way I could relive my teens/twenties. I'm surprised I'm still alive. xx"

"That's great news that lumpy is starting to realise he's not meant to be there and is being evicted! Although it's not nice circumstances, I am enjoying your updates/humour and Emily your replies! I would quite like to go back to my twenties for a weekend, although absinthe does not appeal to me these days. How the hell I drank that, I do not know! Emily, I think you need to book yourself into a retreat somewhere before you have a meltdown. I feel history repeating itself when we turn up for our beef wellington and the host is pissed!"

Local Yocals:

"Glad it's all going well for you, Emma. Shame about the hair departure, though. You might have escaped that one. You will look beautiful whatever happens."

"Fish for entertainment. That was 'Go Fish'. It was an absolute pleasure, Emma!"

Cake. Always Cake:

"Always glad to see your progress on eviction of lumpy."

"Cracking update as always, bird. Glad you're still feeling good and that lumpy is being sufficiently zapped. Marvellous. xx"

ED Fan Club:

"*Fab update. Super pleased to hear chocolate has been involved today. Otherwise what is the point?!*"

"*Wonderful update – it just made me go out and buy chocolate – I have shoved it in my fat gob so fast – I forgot to take a photo. I'll just have to buy more and share! xx*"

"*Another bloody good read, Emma! Keep them coming. x*"

Nicola:

"*Hi sweetie. Right, hope your Nemo chemo bag is packed. Water topped up and lots of laughter and natter about to commence. Thinking of you, beautiful lady. Loves you. Xx*"

Jo S:

"*Happy chemo day. Hope it's going okay and you're still feeling well? Look forward to my update later.*"

"*As always a brilliant update Strudders. Looking forward to my chemo sitting next week. Hoping there will be multiple bald patches by then. You truly are absolutely incredible and I'm super proud I get to call you my friend. Big love, Strudders.xx*"

"**I look forward to it too. Awesome way to pass the time catching up with my friends. You're an awesome friend as well. xx**"

Friday 16ᵗʰ August 2019

"I can use all difficult feelings to inspire positive change."
(YESmum card)

Another week survived. I'm not being dramatic, I'm referring to the school summer holidays! We've had holiday club for one day, soft play hell – although sadly that fell on chemo day, so my lovely neighbour Gilly took Toby off for the day – I-bounce and a couple of catch ups for play dates round friends' houses. I've tried to organise as much as I can to be with other people, safety in numbers. To be honest, this is always my parenting tactic, but it feels even more important now.

The hair is coming out thick and fast now. The most shocking experience was one night this week when I was washing it and I watched huge clumps fall at my feet. There were also some tears that fell at my feet as the reality of what was happening hit me again. It seems to be how it works, for me anyway. I'm busy being very busy in my weekly cycle of poisoning and parenting that I don't really have time to fart, let alone dwell on what's happening to me. It's in these quiet moments, though, that it sometimes catches me unawares.

I remind myself that it's okay to feel sad about this but actually it's only hair. It will grow back.

Cancer Comms

ED Fan Club:

"So, for one time only, Jono (former colleague)/Emma request your company at the prestigious Freshas Thursday 22nd Aug. We will be there 12-2 to accommodate all lunch breaks for this reunion show. Signed photos available upon request.

Enough of the messing around. We'd both love to see whoever would like to come and see us, so please feel free to pass on to anyone not in this group. I'm really looking forward to catching up with you. xx"

"I would very much like a signed photo, and will the calendar be out in time for Christmas?"

"And in other news, I've just had a community nurse singing your praises, JT. You helped her a couple of years ago and she couldn't have been more grateful. xx"

"All in a day's work. x"

Nicola:

"Oh sweetie, it's okay to feel sad. You have always had a strong mane. The mane's ability is still there. Get lumpy gone. New amazing hair awaits. I know it's so easy for me to say this as it's not me, and you have heard it hundreds of times…"

"I know. It'll be okay in a bit. Think it was just a shock when I washed it this morning and big clumps were coming out. Hair everywhere! Just another little thing to get used to. I'm just so happy the lump is shrinking after only three weeks. xx"

"You're amazing, beautiful. Remember it's okay to be upset and shocked. Let the emotions flow so they're not stuck inside. Address them as they pop up. Cuddles are good. Shrinking after three weeks. You go girlfriend. xx"

Saturday 17th August 2019

Exciting day today. Another day of soft play. Well, that is what I'm doing with Mum and the kids. Exciting for them but the exciting bit for me is that Darren has flown up to Manchester to pick up our new midlife crisis car. We needed a new car, being forty I'm now midlife (assuming I make it to eighty!) and there is certainly a crisis going on. I insist that this is my car. I'm the one who's had to do the hard work for the insurance pay out, after all. Now I can't tell you exactly what it is other than it's a shiny blue Audi and goes like shit off a shovel!

Monday 19th August 2019

Cancer Comms

Circle of Trust:

"First outing for the twat hat!"

"You look lovely. How are you feeling?"

"Looks good, my lovely! You can carry a hat off well, I just look like a special person/village idiot when I don a hat. xx"

"I had Thursday in the sweepstake… Did I win? (Not that I'm at all competitive!)"

"I love your hats, you look proper country bumpkin in your flat cap. xx"

Tuesday 20th August 2019 – Chemo Round Five

"Each day I do the best that I can and that is enough."
(YESmum card)

So great to see Dawn and her sidekick Trev again during treatment for a good old natter and laugh. There are plenty of 'cancer support' groups I could access, whether in person or via online forums, but to be honest it's not something I've really entertained. My way of dealing with this has been to focus on the weekly treatment and then leaving the cancer chat at the hospital door. There are so many appointments in my already crammed calendar that I don't particularly relish the thought of adding another one into the mix to specifically talk about cancer. Also, I worry that other people's anxieties might rub off on me.

Emily and Tracey's Little Jar of Cards:

"Shit happens but sometimes it actually does when you're at a friend's for dinner and everyone can hear from the living room!"

Cancer Comms:

"Chemo number five, I'm still alive. No cause for alarm, staying alive is very much still the plan, just a good word to rhyme with five. Last week on the ward we had Elton John "I'm still standing." Had to chuckle at that.

Today's chemo sitter was the lovely Jo. Weighing in with an impressive friendship bracelet making kit, strawberries, Haribo and a trashy *Take a Break* mag, the entertainment bar has been maintained. We also perfected Gin Rummy, so card games are becoming a staple regular.

Found a couple of 'I love nurses' badges (autocorrected to badgers!) to give out today. They went down a storm, the badges not the badgers. Free gifts continue to prove useful.

Been a week of changes. Out with the BMW, in with the Audi thanks to this recent turn of events and insurance. Silver lining and all that. I shall enjoy zooming (read sticking to the laws of the road) around in that listening to my happy hardcore at a moderate level so as not to impair the kids' hearing. Or looking like a twat because I'm just a bit too old!

If you had a date in the hair sweepstake this week you might be quids in. Well, head rubs in. We are quickly reaching the birth of a female Matt Lucas, I'm moulting quicker than a cheap rug. It's been a bit sad to see it coming out in handfuls, and I had a few wobbly moments, but I've felt the feels and I'm readjusting. I think it's more because up until now you couldn't tell anything was wrong with me and this is obviously a very outward sign that all is indeed not okay. I looked at my Little Princess Trust certificate and that cheered me up knowing that 75% of my former thick locks would carry on on a little child's head, in comparison to the remaining 25% that is succumbing to the toilet, shower, soles of people's feet who enter the house!

I've opted for a hat or scarf situation. The idea of a wig wigged me right out. Boom boom.

To shave or not to shave (my head) was mooted but I've decided that I'll let it keep doing its thing and also I couldn't be arsed with any fallout from competitive sweepstake players in it to win it! If you're still in, remind me of your dates.

Another week of no major side effects. Just felt a bit generally shit on Friday but a play date with good friends sorted that out.

So, there we are. Nearly halfway through round one and this player is going strong. Follow up scan on Friday, so I'll know by next week exactly what's occurring with the little bugger.

Hope everyone has had a fab week and as always let me know what's going on in your worlds."

Circle of Trust:

"Bring on next week... My turn to chemo sit. I'm hoping my strippers don't disrupt the ward too much."

"I'm sure that will make a lot of people's days. Bring your A game, though, if you want chemo sitter employee of the month!"

"Ah mate, I'm so proud, you're really trooping along amazingly. I hate that you're going through this, but bloody hell, you're doing it and in the summer holidays too, which is incredible. Of course, it's going to be hard seeing your hair fall out, but hair grows back and, like you said last week, you'll have all your grey pubes and head of grey hair come back but lumpy will be gone and you can have your body back. Love you mate."

"It's true what Amanda said. I'm in awe of how you're dealing with all this. But remember, you're allowed those wobbles, as it's all part of it. Cancer is a fucking bastard and I hate that you are having to go through this."

"Ah get away, I couldn't do it without my amazing tribe of supporters, so I'm not taking all the credit."

"Nice one mate, number five done and dusted! I look forward to a spin in the new car. Minus kids, then we can whack the happy hardcore up loud and pretend we're eighteen again. I too am very impressed with how you're dealing with this. An inspiration to us all."

"Here I am just catching up. Wobble away, Em, it's only natural. As for the head shave... my date has passed, so if you need to do it for your sanity I have the clippers! All joking aside, a lot of the people I've met found it easier to get it done, so it saves more heartbreak. Don't be a warrior. Please don't look like the doll from Toy Story! You're doing amazing. I await my chemo sitting duties. I think we should get a trip in the new car, girls only! I'm happy for the hardcore but steady on the volume though for poor hetti (hearing aid)."

"I'm here. Sorry to be the last one to join the party. Emma, you are amazing, you have totally got this. Kicking ass like a chemo ninja. Don't worry about the hair, you're just making yourself more aerodynamic!"

Massaging Mummies:

"Keep on smashing this, you absolute beauty, you. You're allowed to be sad, upset, pissed off, woeful, mad, any emotion... it's good to express them all. Our hair is a huge part of us (sadly) and any change is very hard to adjust to and that's when we want to change, not when we don't have a choice. I love Matt Lucas. I'd give him a go. I had the 8th August, so I'm well out of the sweepstake. I did ask to change my dates, but you got all lawyery with me lol. So pleased the side effects are minimal. Remember, I'm here whenever you need me. Whatever I can do. Maybe one night next week we can have the Chinese? Massive huge hugs, you awesome human being, you. xx"

Shits and Giggles:

"I bet you look gorgeous – I am 100% certain I've got a cone head under my hair, but I bet you look flipping marvellous. And I can't wait to see what your hair comes back like."

Strong Randy Ladies:

"Well, I'm still looking good for 22nd then. Some fucking good has got to come of that day. So glad that round five has passed well and that you're still feeling okay. Lack of hair, pahh! Scarfs are the new hair these days! If I was brave enough, I'd shave mine with you. Save me a shit load of time, but unfortunately my features are not as favourable as yours and I fear the big nose would stand out even more – if that's possible – and that wouldn't be a good look. Well, looking forward to our catch up tomorrow and I will try my best to remain un-shitfaced for your arrival! God, red wine is my friend this week!

"Ah, my friend, you are fucking amazing. I have not forgotten your special day and maybe if I have a dodgy mohawk I will shave it off in both your honours to mark this particular anniversary. Unique to you girls!"

"Oh, ladies, what a pile of shit! Emma – glad chemo is still going well. Hair loss = shit sandwich and you're more than entitled to have your moments, my lovely, but Emily is right. Head scarfs are in. I'll treat you to a designer head piece, my friend, seeing as I can't do much else."

Local Yocals:

"Hurrah for another good day today, Em! The hat yesterday was fab – meant to tell you."

"Ahh, that's great news, Emma, glad you had a nice time with Jo and are still in good spirits and strength. Completely understand how you must feel about the hair. Yes, the hat is a fab idea, looked great. Let us know the results next week and always feel like you can let us know when you're feeling shit. Love and hugs."

Cake. Always Cake:

"I've got the Bee Gees stuck in my head now. Glad to hear your update as always. Phoebe showed me her poorly finger today but I'm going to send this to you as a message to lumpy. xx" (sends picture of Phoebe flipping the bird!)

"Best. Photo. Ever. You need it on a mug or something. Cracking update, as always. I love what your chemo buddies do. Apart from the circumstances that you're there together, it must be lovely spending that time with them. Looking forward to our posh ladies who luncheon. I may even wear a frock. xx"

"I shall opt for expandable-waist trousers. xx"

"Oh yeah, love a stretchy waist."

"It's my standard now."

Jo S:

"Come on, Strudders… Awaiting my Tuesday night chuckle. Hope you're feeling okay. Thanks again for letting me come along today, my love. xx"
"Thank you so much for spending your whole day with me. I loved it and you are awesome. xx"

Wednesday 21st August 2019

I was supposed to be joining my colleagues today on our annual 'Away Day' but alas that will not be happening this year. They haven't forgotten me, though, as throughout the day I get lots of pictures of smiley faces forwarded to me. Out of sight, but definitely not out of mind.

Cancer Comms

ED Fan Club:

"Hope you're all having an amazing away day. Sorry I couldn't join you, but I have both children today and that would have been one hell of an H&S Risk Assessment for poor old Tony!
Pics please.
Look forward to hearing all about it tomorrow."

Pictures follow of my smiley-faced colleagues, cake, exercising and colouring.

Thursday 22nd August 2019

The day the female Matt Lucas was born into our house!

I declare the winners of the hair sweepstake as Emily and Charlotte!

What an amazing day. Weird to say, considering it's the day I go bald.

First off, it was amazing to have lunch with my work colleagues. Dining *al fresco* in the sun on the glamourous industrial estate near work. I'm keeping my head under wraps in my new hat from Suburban Turban as my hair's so patchy I'm starting to look like some nutty professor. I'm certainly feeling the love, as there's a good crowd of us, all keen to know how I'm feeling and how I'm getting on.

Being a Thursday it's 'Fat Club'. My horrendously derogative term for Slimming World. I started on the 27th December last year.

Up until this kicked off, I'd lost nearly three stone through healthy eating and exercise. People were surprised that I was continuing to go but as I've repeatedly pointed out:

1. I'm not actively trying to lose weight anymore, as I'm pretty close to target and
2. now more than ever I need to fuel my body with the good stuff and not revert back to my shit old habits of inhaling a whole packet of biscuits at a time.

Now tonight is a special night because it's 'Woman of the Year' week. I'm one of the nominees. I knew this was coming, as our amazing consultant had already messaged me to say I'd been nominated and did I want to take part. I did query this at first as out of the nominees I've actually lost the least weight. This award isn't for the biggest weight loss, though, it's for someone who has inspired others. Apparently, I have! So, I'm up for it, not thinking for one minute I'll win it because the other nominees are all amazing.

My story isn't one of losing a shedload of weight. My problem has been the damn emotional eating that started many miles away from home at university two decades ago and the yo-yo dieting and ridiculous diets I've pursued ever since. I dread to think how many people I've lost and gained over the years. This time I've made small changes that I can actually stick to long term and, slowly but surely, I've nearly lost three stone. I've dispensed my tactics at group each week and shared the lovely meals I've been cooking. Okay, the lovely meals my personal chef (Darren) has been cooking.

Well, I only go and bloody win it! It is such an amazing lift to know that I've inspired this group of (mostly) women to vote for me. I get an awesome sash, certificate and bunch of flowers, but the adrenaline boost is amazing.

So amazing that I go home buzzing and declare to Toby that it's time to shave the nutty professor hair off!

Toby goes running around excitedly shouting, "Daddy, Mummy's going to shave her hair all off. Where are the clippers?"

Bless his little cotton socks, he then pulls the curtains closed in the bedroom to "protect my privacy", apparently.

The main event takes place in the kitchen at a quickly mocked-up barber shop. Toby is totally involved and finds it hilarious snapping pictures as Darren takes to my head. I'm pretty sure Darren's been looking forward to this moment and is taking too much pleasure in this.

First look is a mohawk. When that's gone, I'm left with a dodgy fringe that would easily qualify me as an extra for a *Mad Max* movie. And then it's all gone. Complete baldy. And do you know what? I don't look half bad bald. I've got a lovely shaped head I never knew I had.

Do you know what I do next? I feel the urge to do a rendition of Sinead O'Conner's "Nothing Compares to You", record it and message it to everybody! I don't even think about it, it feels right, and I just do it!

So, there it is. The biggest thing I was dreading, and I've done it. The hair is gone. It's really fricking obvious that something is going on with me.

Cancer Comms

Circle of Trust:

"You look awesome, I don't think you look like Russ, you still look like Em to me. P.S. awesome singing! Love you."

"I'm crying for a whole number of reasons with this, but the main reason… only you could present yourself in this style. xx"

"Hello, it's Skye. Auntie Emma, you look beautiful. P.S. you have an amazing voice. Love you sooooo much. xx"

"Oh, mate, so much love for you! With that video, you've made me

cry, laugh and burst with pride. You rock the Sinead look. Though still hotter than Russ (sorry Russ)!"

"She was gorgeous and fearless, and I was in awe."

"Think you've found your next karaoke song, mate, and actually I'm thinking, who needs a twat hat when you have a lovely head like that? You're pretty amazing, mate, you know that? Love you. xx"

"Why thank you. I'm getting the hang of this entertaining business! I won woman of the year at Slimming World tonight, so buoyed up on that the nutty professor haircut had to go. I think I rather rock an egg head. You are all amazing as well. You are my rocks and you listening to my ridiculous ramblings and humouring how I'm choosing to deal with this situation is what keeps me so positive. xx"

"Woman of the year. Well done, mate. xx"

"Oooooo congratulations, slim Jim! I really need to join again."

"Oh, woman of the year! Does that come with a trophy?"

"Funnily enough, I'd lost the least out of the four nominees, but people told me I inspired them! No trophy but a certificate, sticker and sash. I was so excited after that I thought 'fuck it, the shit hair has to go'. Toby joined in and we had a right laugh. I experienced lots of haircuts, mostly resembling a cast member of *Mad Max!*"

"I reckon that was the best thing to do, whip it off! Look at Toby's face. To make such a hard thing to do as a woman into a fun experience for you all is definitely the right choice."

Massaging Mummies:

"Ah, Em! Well done, chick! You've faced your fear. You are rocking it! Please can we have a rendition – 'It's been seven hours and fifteen days since you took my hair away'! Big love Mrs Lumpy arse kicker. xx"

"Alec is so happy he's got a buddy to discuss how to best polish his swede with! So proud of you for sheer unadulterated courage and

humour when stuck in the shit sandwich. Great voice too – another career option maybe?!"

"Seriously, I need to talk to Alec about egg head care. Where do you start with products? X"

"I will quiz him later for you, Em, and let you know. You're my woman of the year in every sense. You've certainly rocked every look. Massive hugs. xx"

"Crying with laughter and a tiny bit of anger at the sheer unfairness of it. You got some good voice on you, bird. I reckon Fester Adams is more the look rather than Andy. Woman of the year. Love you. xx"

"Emma. Wow just wow! Words can't really describe how amazing you are! Karaoke down the ship again, I think! Love you and your beautiful bald head. Who won the sweepstake?"

Shits and Giggles:

"Oh, my pal! How can you have me sobbing and laughing all in the same sixty seconds?! I love your head btw, it's a lovely shape and makes your eyes ping."

"You look gorgeous! I knew you would. You are such an entertainer. Very good rendition. Congrats to woman of the year. xx"

Local Yocals:

"You look fucking amazing. xx"

"Fantastic, Em. I'm impressed you know all the words. Can we make weekly requests?"

"I'm emotional and teary but yes you look fab and yes nothing compares to you."

"Taking bookings now."

"You bloody lunatic. Still managing to make us smile. Thanks for sharing this next step with us."

"I think I'm enjoying this rather too much!"

"It's your journey. We are 100% here to ride along with you! Embrace the bloody adrenaline highs!"

"No way! Well done Wonder Woman!"

"Yes, Emma! You absolute QUEEN!"

ED Fan Club:

Sending my work colleagues my Sinead O'Conner video – Nothing compares to you.

"You're beautiful, bird. Lovely to see you today."

"You did it! Go girl!"

"Is there no end to your talents? Love it, you're awesome. Fab to see you today."

"It was so lovely to see so many people today. The ongoing support from you all is amazing."

"Whoop whoop, well done! U defo rock it. x"

"Good decision, you look beautiful."

"Legend."

"Very clever, Sinead."

"Woman of the year too. You are so fabulous it hurts. xx"

"Honestly, that's got my vote for Eurovision next year, ED! Who won the sweepstake? You rock this look btw, you utterly inspiring lady! So sorry to have missed you today."

"Well done on so many levels, Emma. I hope your Friday tomorrow feels more like a Thursday and the happy times from today keep you buoyed up. xx"

"Fab U Lous, darling – and most definitely woman of the year – you are such an inspiration – I've moved away from my Crunchie. xx"

"You are amazing, Em, I salute you! You inspire me and I am so proud of you. Also, you have been hiding your singing voice… you are beautiful inside and out. Love you. xx"

Nicola:

"Ah love you so much, you're truly amazing, beautiful. And yes, there is deff a Russ look!"

Jo S:

"I fucking love you. Well done for taking the plunge. You have a very nice shaped head, proud of you. xx"

Friday 23rd August 2019

The day after the night before!

OMG, in the cold light of day, did I really email a shed load of people with my new bald look badly impersonating Sinead O'Conner? Oh well. Can't take that back now and I don't have time to dwell on it, as I'm off to the breast unit for my first scan.

There's a strange calm about this visit. Yes it's my first follow up scan but then logic dictates to me that 1) because I can't feel it anymore and 2) the consultant seemed impressed, lumpy must already be retreating from the lovely cocktail being pumped into me.

And retreating he is. He's shrunk by two thirds. The radiographer is really impressed with how deflated he's looking. She explains the picture to me, and he looks like a rather deflated balloon.

After the scan, I go off for another mammogram. So impressed at the shrinkage is the radiographer that she invites me back into the room to show me the comparison pictures.

I leave feeling totally elated. The plan is working. The feeling pants is worth it. Me and my 'overachiever booby-bug-killing body' have got this.

No rest for the wicked today, though. After the usual date with my PICC line care nurses, it's off into town with Toby to attempt the school uniform shop. I fear I've left this a little late in the day as we make our way into Thomas Moore to make my credit card cry.

It's whilst I'm delving through the logo'd jumpers that the most random encounter with a stranger happens:

"What's that on your arm?"

Turning around, **"Excuse me?"**

"What's that bandage on your arm?"

Um, it's covering up my PICC line.

"What's that?"

Now this is where I could have nipped the conversation in the bud, but so taken by surprise was I that I just continued answering questions!

"I've got cancer. It's where the medicine is put in."

"What cancer have you got?"

"Breast cancer."

"My cousin had bowel cancer."

"Oh, I'm sorry to hear that. I hope they're okay."

"They died."

Okay. Good chat. And with that I politely repeat how sorry I am to hear that and say I need to get back to my shopping.

It's not until later that evening that I think how random and personal that conversation was. I wasn't prepared for it and just didn't know how to respond.

Equally disappointing was the fact that I wasn't able to get everything I needed, which will require another trip into town!

But that doesn't dampen my day. Hell, my week. It's been an amazing week this week and I'm not feeling too ropey today.

Cancer Comms

"LUMPY STATS:
1ˢᵗ scan 29mm x 15mm

Today 10mm x 4mm
Adios little bugger!"

Circle of Trust:

"*Amazing! And ladies I can confirm the bald beauty looks amazing in real life too. xx*"

"*Freaking amazing! You are kicking ass. Cancer messed with the wrong chick. Xx*"

"*Wow! This is amazing Friday news! Well done, my beaut… smashing it. xx*"

"*Just told Frank the awesome news and his response is 'Die lumpy, die'! So American.*"

"*Will you still need second lot of chemo? If it carries on like this there'll be nothing there!*"

"*This is amazing news. So happy about this. You really are beating this. xx*"

"*Well, that's just the best news, mate. And that's quite a shrinkage! Well done, my love.*"

Saturday 24ᵗʰ August 2019

Tonight, me and Darren are taking the new car out for a spin and heading to Exmouth (local beach) as there's a Car Cruz on. Yes, you heard me right, a Car Cruz with a 'Z'. Now I'm properly in mid-life crisis mode as we head off to relive something we used to do in our kevved-up boy racer cars in our early twenties.

To be honest, we don't get involved wandering around looking under the youths' shiny bonnets or admiring their sound systems. We just park up and go for a little amble along the sea front. It feels so good to be out in the fresh air. Just me and Darren reminiscing about younger, easier times. When the 'youth' move on to location two (McDonalds!), we opt for a quick drink at a pub on the way home.

This week has been amazing. The cherry on the top will be spending time with family tomorrow for a BBQ at Mum's house.

Monday 26th August 2019

I might possibly have consumed the best cream tea ever with my neighbours Becky (G) and Rachel today at The Angel Tea Rooms in Babbacoombe. Quite apt that our WhatsApp group is called "Cake. Always Cake". I don't think I've ever consumed a cream tea quite like this one. I think I've eaten my own body weight in cake, scones and sandwiches. I'm feeling a bit of a traitor to all the women who voted for me at Slimming World last week!

We're in Babbacoombe, Torquay and it's gloriously sunny. As we're sitting on a bench overlooking a beautiful view, a lady stops to ask me how I'm getting on with treatment. She says she recognises the bandage over the PICC line, has recovered from breast cancer herself and without intruding on my privacy just wanted to say something to offer me hope and encouragement.

I'm really rather taken aback by this and chat away with her about her own personal story and where I am with mine. A much better interaction than the one whilst school uniform shopping.

Tuesday 27th August 2019
– Chemo Round Six

> "My courage is stronger than my fear."
> (YESmum card)

Kelly was my amazing 'chemo sitter' today. Full lowdown on her entertainment to follow but it was another amazing session of laughs and catching up.

Straight after chemo, I was picked up by Darren and the kids

159

and we made our way down to a cottage at Bovey Castle to spend a couple of days with my mum and Gary. We were all supposed to be in Menorca this week with my brother and family. We're swapping sun and cocktails for drizzle and a cuppa but it feels great to get away.

I'm feeling a bit tired today, but Toby wants to go out to explore, so we head out with Mum. It's so beautiful and peaceful. We walk around the castle grounds. We see a deer. Toby runs off to explore whilst Mum and I slowly amble around. This is what it's all about. Slowing down. Spending time with the people who matter the most to me. Just talking about normal day to day things and how this time next year we'll be on our sun-kissed holiday.

A tea of pizza and once the kids are asleep a cheeky G&T or two and catching up.

Emily and Tracey's Little Jar of Cards

"You are an amazing friend. I remember when I was made redundant and you drove me home to Exmouth to make sure I was okay. xx"

Cancer Comms

"Session number six of my chemo fix.

Just a quickie update as we're heading straight off on a little holibob for a couple of days and I'm turning the phone to flight mode. Don't want my radio silence to spark worry so full update to follow.

In the meantime, session six, halfway there and lumpy has decreased by two thirds and isn't looking so lumpy anymore. More a deflating balloon."

Circle of Trust:

"We have a winner!"
"I forgot it's Tuesday, feel it's Monday! How you getting on, Em? Looks fun, always love a bit of bingo. xx"
"We're having a great time. Bingo, fruit platter, cheese scones."
"Thanks for the update my love, I would have been hounding you had you not sent anything lol! All sounds very positive and heading in the right direction and rocking the turban too. Have a lovely few days away. xx"

Massaging Mummies:

"Whoopie. Something happened today that made me think of you in a random way. Austin and Sandy came to work with me and in the middle of the reception at the busiest branch, Sandy says, 'Mummy I have a tummy ache... Oh, Mummy, I did a fart that was actually a poo.' OMG. This is why you shouldn't take your kids to work! Have a fantastic family holibob, enjoy every moment with each other! Big love to all the Davies clan!"
"That's amazing news, babe. Absolutely amazing. So pleased for you all and especially you, bird. So proud of your strength. Paula, that is brilliant. Did she actually poo?"
"Amazing news, Em, Keep kicking lumpy's arse. Have an amazing time away together."
"Just so happy for you, Em. Lumpy chose the wrong girl to mess with! Enjoy time away with team Davies. You deserve it. Massive hugs. xx"

Strong Randy Ladies:

"Wow, that's amazing news. Soon the little fucker will be gone. Have a fantastic few days' break."
"Amazing news! Have a lovely few days. xx"

Local Yocals:

"Hope you have a lovely few days away! Fantastic news about the lump too. xx"

"That's great news about the lump shrinkage, Emma, have a lovely time away too."

Cake. Always Cake:

"Right, just dropped off two of the RD&E's finest cheese scones and I think the ward clerk may be swearing at me as I left as she said they're gurt lush! On that note, may be worth bribing with scones for earlier appointments. X"

"Or flat as a witch's tit! Have a lovely relaxing few days away. xx"

ED Fan Club:

"When you're fifty, your whole boob looks like a deflated balloon (apparently)."

"But you still manage to trip over them in the morning (apparently)."

"After children I've said mine are like empty socks with buttons on the end! Apologies if that's too much info for the lads!"

"Great news, Emma, and enjoy your holibobs… empty socks and all."

"Man present…"

"Are your boobs like socks?"

"Not just yet. At the rate I'm overfeeding myself it won't be long for sure."

Jo S:

"Happy chemo day. Hope you haven't been too poorly. Hope today's is swift enough you get away to Bovey in good time. Look forward to the update later, big love Strudders. xx"

"Happy holidays, love. Switch off and enjoy, fabulous news lumpy has shrunk so much too. xx"

Thursday 29th August 2019

A few nights away in a cottage in the middle of nowhere sounds like just what you need to recharge your batteries, doesn't it? Throw in a six-year-old and sharing a room with a two-year-old and I'm shattered. It's been so great to get away and we've not even overdone it. We visited the Miniature Pony Centre and a motor museum! On the way home today, we stopped at the Cat & Fiddle pub for a family lunch and for the kids to play in the ball pit. I'm knackered. It's a struggle to keep my eyes open. It's time to concede defeat. I need to go home to sleep.

Cancer Comms

"Session number six – the full chronicles!

Latest chemo sitter Kelly came in strong with a fruit platter, healthy juice drink and bingo. I love a game of bingo and won a bottle of gin on two lines and took a candle for the house. Nurses even said they'd turn a blind eye to the gin if I didn't get leery!

We have toyed with the idea of employee awards – chemo sitter of the month. But to be honest, everyone has been amazing.

What a week. Unexpectedly voted 'Woman of the Year' at Slimming World. Fuelled by adrenalin I raced home and did a Britney, shaving my nutty professor looking haircut. Darren enjoyed giving me a mohawk and various looks of extras from *Mad Max* before we ended at egg head. Toby joined in and we all laughed through what could have been a sad scenario.

Most of you will have seen the Sinead O'Conner tribute that quickly followed. In the cold light of Friday, I realised you might have thought I was a bloody lunatic for that! Quite empowering to spontaneously send something in the moment instead of analysing the shit out of it. Might do that more often.

So, in terms of the sweepstake, the winning date, albeit aided by me, was 22nd August. Emily and Charlotte are my winners. You are welcome round for a rub any time, ladies.

Taking requests for next week, I've already had Right Said Fred – I'm too sexy for my shirt (Hair)!

Hit me up with your hair-related best gags. Indeed, I can now just 'Wash & Go' – thanks, Mum. And yes, I will make great savings on shampoo and conditioner.

How have I been feeling? Just a couple of nose bleeds, dodgy tummy and tiredness to contend with. Hot sweats leave me wanting to get my kit off and run outside, but so far I've abstained from this, as I've enough on my plate without adding a criminal conviction and referral to my regulator into the mix!

LUMPY STATS (perhaps the most important update):

1st scan 28.06.19 29mm x 15mm

2nd scan 23.08.19 10mm x 4mm

Not so lumpy now, are you booby bug?

So, this week we were supposed to be in Menorca. Sadly, we had to cancel that, but instead of wiggling my toes in the sand I'll be wiggling them on my new carpet for the foreseeable that the refund financed! There's always next year and this week we've had a little break at Bovey Castle and visiting the Miniature Pony Centre.

So that's it. Bit of a busy week. I thought the messages might have tailed off a bit by now but that's not been the case. I clearly have an amazing tribe of people around me

and I truly believe it's all this positivity that's helping with this quick progress. You are all amazing. Xx"

Circle of Trust:

"Another update filled with positivity and humour that only you could deliver. Yes, it's a shame you couldn't go to Menorca but the carpet will last much longer and, you're right, there is always next year. Hmmmmm, hair gags. Gonna have to think. The Wash & Go would probably have been one but you beat me to it. Glad you had a nice break away. See you soon, my love. More chocolate deliveries maybe? xx"

"I think you need that German shampoo. Plantur 39? For women over forty with premature hair loss! You are awesome. Sending lots of love. xx"

"No bald jokes yet, but I'll get thinking! I have a tune, though: 'Hey you over there, what's it like to not have hair, is it hot or is it cold. I don't know 'cause I'm not bald'. Fab update as usual and ladies I have a pad of bingo tickets. Thought we could have a get together and have a game, all bring three prizes. We all love bingo and this way we can have a proper chat in between as no old ladies to tell us off. xx"

"Totally up for an in-house game of bingo. xx"

"Amazing update and amazing chemo buddy with the gin prizes! As and when there's another ladies' night let me know. xx"

"In-house bingo sounds fantastic, totally up for that!"

"I'm totally up for in-house bingo. Shall we see if we can get a date in September? xx"

"Amazing, it's in the diary. Don't go mad, cap it at £10 for all three. I did a choc bar, mini gin and a smelly candle."

"Halfway through first sesh, Em, well done, my lovely. I'm up for 20th for a bit of bingo. It'll be lovely to catch up with you ladies."

Shits and Giggles:

"How's your holibobs?"

"Exhausting! Nothing like sharing a room with a

toddler! No, it's been lovely to have some time away, but thank goodness we're going home today! Xx"

"*You have my admiration. As someone who has refused to go abroad this year for that very reason!*"

"**Although I'm gutted I'm not in Menorca with my brother and family, I'm kinda thinking I dodged a bullet! Two nights away in a holiday cottage and I'm so ready for my own bed.**"

Local Yocals:

"*Yes, Emma. Goodbye booby bug indeed. As usual, handling it with strength and humour, you're brilliant. So pleased it's on its way out and aside from minor side effects you're okay. Love you.*"

"*Emma, this is brilliant news! I so admire your approach to this journey. You are INCREDIBLE and I feel so privileged to be your friend. Keep going. You will beat this. Love you. xx*"

"*Oh, Emma, after all the tears at the start and the unknown, what will you write next? Keep it coming. Sometimes I shed a tear, sometimes I absolutely belly laugh out loud. You have this cracked, girl, and booby bug is doing one! WE love you loads and keep up that positive on life, and listen to your body: if it needs to rest let it. Shout if you need us.*"

"**Thank you for your kind words. I so appreciate your support. I'm quite conscious now that this is my journey and I don't want to 'go on about it' but lovely friends are still genuinely interested. I hope by doing it all in one weekly update it strikes a balance between updates and overkill. xx**"

"*It'll never feel like overkill, Emma. I for one certainly think of you daily and wonder how you are doing, so never feel like you're going on about it! We are here in full support.*"

"*Hear, hear. Never overkill. Tell us everything. xx*"

"*As the others have said, the communication/updates you share with us are always welcomed. It certainly helps me to understand where you are on your journey without feeling like I need to bombard you with communication."*

ED Fan Club:

"Well done, Strudders. You're kicking the shizzle out of lumpy Mcdouchebag. xx"

"That's an amazing decrease in size – goes to show how strong your chemo cocktail is. Hope you enjoyed your quiet time with the family. xx"

"Morning. I personally don't think the Sinead O'Connor tribute was lunatic. I think you are more sane than she is reported to be these days. Anyway, I thought you were rather brilliant. Glad the lump is doing one. That's impressive shrinkage. Enjoy the carpet and the car too. xx"

"Great update, Emma, and I loved the singing. Plus, you rock the new do!"

"Fab news – Menorca or Bovey Castle? Bovey Castle every time. Although not been to either. I think the Miniature Pony Centre sold it. x"

"Woohoo, I will come and claim the head rub soon! And I may also rub my toes in your new carpet! So glad to hear that lumpy is considerably less lumpy, sounds like its days are numbered. Glad you had a lovely break with the family. Who doesn't love a miniature pony?! x"

Darren's words

When I was finishing this book (May 2020), I asked Darren if he would like to write a paragraph about how he felt now that it was all over. As I was trying to cook soup from scratch (not something I ever attempt!), my phone pinged. He'd written this whilst we were on our mini holiday cottage break, so I thought here would be the best place for it. He's not one for sharing his emotions, so this left me crying into my soup.

My wife has cancer!

Just writing it down sounds weird; trying to comprehend it is even more difficult. I know it's happening; I've been to the doctor and surgeon appointments. I've sat through chemotherapy sessions and none of this makes it seem real.

Other people get cancer.

We lost my nan to it seven years ago and I refused to accept that until the end.

Now Emma has cancer. Some days I feel sad. Some I feel angry. Others I feel distant, almost out of my body, then I feel angry again. Not at her having cancer, but at myself. I feel selfish for feeling this way because Emma has cancer, not me. I'm fit and healthy(ish). It's my time to pick up the slack and there are days when she is knackered and a little bit irritable. And we snap at each other. In those moments, I forget she has cancer and me being me I snap back at her and then I feel bad again (I would never admit it, though). But I think we've been together long enough now to know it's not a real argument and normality resumes.

Some nights I lay awake trying to make sense of it and trying to figure out how she is staying so positive throughout. There have been a couple of wobbles due to badly timed doctors' letters, but on the whole – on the outside at least – she is doing awesomely.

I'm not a great one for showing my emotions (I was a bit of a wimpy kid and I think I used up all of my emotions then), which I think annoys Em, as she can't gauge whether I give a shit or not. Some days I feel knackered when I go to work after sleepless nights thinking about all this. I refuse to tell people this and just say Chloe had another sleepless night and knock back a can of Monster and crack on as normal.

The few work friends I have told about this I try not to talk to about it more than is necessary because it's not their problem. Why should I drag them down too? Even when they ask, I hear the voice in their heads saying, 'Here he goes again, banging on about his wife's cancer, I only asked to be polite'.

I know this is probably all in my head and then we go full circle, back to me lying in bed overthinking things again. And now it's two in the morning and I'm lying here writing this poorly punctuated dribble.

Doctors have estimated six months(ish) to deal with this lumpy little shit. I keep telling Em six months in the grand scheme of things is nothing, but in reality it seems like forever despite the fact the weeks seem to be flying by.

Everyone has their own way of dealing. We've resorted to a really dark sense of humour towards the situation. Some days I think I've pushed it too far, usually after a couple of beers, but Emma has never been one to pull any punches when calling me out on my behaviour, so hopefully I'm okay.

Friday 30th August 2019

When you find out that your child's new school isn't going to be open in time and the Autumn Term start date is put back three days to 9th September.

Am I feeling #blessed to be gaining an extra three days with my cherub or do I hold my head in my hands and weep?!

Cumulative side effect nasties after six sessions:

- General tiredness and feeling achy. Particularly on a Friday and Saturday.
- Spotty teenager skin.
- Hair loss resulting in the bald egg look.
- Dry skin (cream me up baby!).

August – Looking Back

I think any owner of small humans would look back at August and be proud of surviving the school holidays! Constantly living up to the daily expectations of *"What are we doing today – Mummy?"* and *"Can we go to soft play?"* and *"Can I go to x's house?"* and *"I'm bored, what can we do?"*

I've had another four poisoning sessions, five other hospital appointments, including scans and consultations, and five visits to the community nurses.

I started the month with a full head of hair and ended it with a bald shiny egg head.

My family wall calendar with its five columns (even the dog gets one) has barely any space left for any further commitments. The pink and green highlighters to indicate hospital appointments and childcare have been fully utilised and as I look back at it I think I might be sick all over my legs. I'd really recommend you get some kind of system in place to keep a note of all your appointments and a folder for all your letters.

How on earth did I get through all that? One day at a time and with a lot of help from my amazing husband, Mum, family and friends. On the days I've felt really under par I've not been afraid to listen to my body and ask for help so I can rest, instead of waiting for people to notice and offer or feel bad about asking.

I'm halfway into this first round of twelve chemo sessions and I'm feeling so optimistic about the long-term goal. I feel like I've come so far, and I've really settled into this new weekly routine. I also feel like having this madness happen with young children has helped focus my mind, as I don't have time to stop for long. I just have to keep on going.

It's always good to have a light at the end of the tunnel, though, and I'm now not so secretly glad that the Autumn school term will be starting soon.

September 2019

Monday 2nd September 2019

Ham, egg and chips for tea tonight. I finish it then realise I didn't taste any of it. I guess that's the sense of taste gone then!

Tuesday 3rd September 2019 – Chemo Round Seven

"I am not afraid to ask for help and lean on those who love me."
(YESmum card)

My chemo neighbour today was a guy called Paul. He runs his own building business and turned up in his work clothes to plug in and get his drugs flowing. I was particularly enjoying his banter with the nurses when they had told him to relax and he informed them he'd only been filling skips that morning.

His cancer was discovered early because he received a leaflet sent to all men over fifty inviting him for a scan. He took up the offer, not because he had any symptoms, but he thought it was a good idea, and they discovered two small shadows. Because of this early detection, he will be all done and dusted before Christmas – amazing news. What's the moral of the story here? Get it checked, take up these offers. It could save your life or prolonged treatment.

I know my smears are up to date, so there's nothing going on in that downstairs department. I used to hate going for them. I was probably guilty of not keeping on top of them in my twenties. I used to be really embarrassed about someone looking at my lady garden, but after the awareness that Jade Goody raised about the importance of cervical smears, I've been on it like a car bonnet. I watched the documentary about her journey with cancer early on (perhaps a bit too early on) in my own journey. After having kids, your dignity is left at the door and I think I forgot to pick it back up on the way out, so I don't even bat an eyelid at this now.

Something I must get better at doing when all this is over is having a proper grope of my boobies. I do have a bit of a feel in the shower, but I don't do it religiously on a monthly basis.

Anyway, back to my chat with Paul. We talked about the fantastic treatment we were receiving at the RD&E and also the fantastic work of FORCE. Neither of us have utilised the discussion support groups but we discussed how important they would be for people going through this on their own. We haven't used them as we're both fortunate to be surrounded by loads of supportive friends and family. We get our fill of cancer-related chat on our chemo days and various appointments and personally haven't felt the need to discuss it in another forum.

Emily and Tracey Little Jar of Cards

"Love you."

Cancer Comms

"Session number seven: 'Chemo heaven'.

Today I was very much looking forward to four and a half hours of drugs and peace. Excited even. Flying solo, I was going to read and sleep, sleep and read and drink hot cups of tea that someone brought to me.

Imagine my disappointment when they were super

efficient and I was done in a record time of three and a half hours. They did offer to draw the last flush out for me, but I decided I'd treat 'Dad's chemo cabs' to a swift one in the pub instead.

He made me laugh. We drove past a local hairdressers on the way home and he genuinely asked, "Where do you get your hair cut?" I just looked at him and we both fell about laughing when he realised. He also compared me to ET last week.

Kelly popped in on her lunch break today and we were brainstorming Halloween options. I'm stuck on Uncle Fester or Hellraiser. Suggestions please.

So tonight's update is brought to you by the letter 'T' (tired) and the letters 'VT' (very tired) and 'VFT' (insert own word) and the hashtag I can't believe Toby's school isn't finished and whilst every bugger else is over the finish line our term starts next Monday. I am not feeling at all #blessed at this extra time.

I loved our time away last week but it actually did me in to the extent I had to just take myself off to bed for hours on end, curl up in a fluffy dressing gown and just have a kip. I've got to start learning to take it a bit easier, but it's so tricky during the periods when I feel fine.

So, a much calmer week. No spontaneous activities. I just realised that my monobrow hasn't grown back in weeks, neither has much other hair. For a dark-haired person like me, who has shaved every other day for forty years (literally out of the womb), this is a game changer. I feel as smooth as a seal (are seals smooth? They look smooth). With all the creaming up I'm doing pre-bedtime, I should get some satin sheets and start up a bedtime routine of 'slip 'n' slide'.

So, here's to over halfway through phase one and all of you awesome lot. I now have four family birthdays coming up in the space of five days."

Circle of Trust:

"Can't believe you're over halfway! I'm gonna sound old now but how quickly do the weeks fly by?! Listen to your body and take those naps – remember happy to lend you a bed for quiet time away from home where not so easy to be off duty! Hope you all have a fab time celebrating Merv's seventieth birthday. Send him birthday wishes from the Yeos."

"Nice one, mate, another one in the bag! Can't believe Toby's school is still not done but Monday isn't too far away! Take it easy on yourself and rest when you need to. Halloween... what about Gru from Despicable Me? We could be your Minions. I'm jealous of your 'smooth as a seal'ness. I think they are smooth, yes. Enjoy the birthday celebrations, my love. See you soon. xx"

"Happy Birthday, Merv! Birthdays = cake. How come you were flying solo today? You should have said, and I would have taken the day off to come with you. If you have any other free sessions just let me know, I think there is only one Tuesday this month I can't take off. It's been said already, but it's okay to rest, your body is working its butt off to bust Lumpy, sleep is not giving in, it's preparation for the next round! If there is ANYTHING I can do to help, I will. You are such an inspiration, Em. You've got this. Love you. xx"

"My fault, Becks, I was rostered in but work refused cos my work buddy was off."

"Awww no, that sucks but can't be helped. Em, if you get a cancellation again let me know and I'll do my best to be there. xx"

"Thanks ladies. Amanda, I think you dodged a bullet yesterday as I was proper tired. I even had forty winks. I'm so grateful for all the continued support and there is absolutely no obligation to take holidays for me. I will, however, message in future if I need a chum.

As for the bingo, I'm happy to host the evening. I'd like to cook or order takeaway as a thank you for all your amazing support over the past couple of months. xx"

"Sounds good to me. BTW ladies, don't overthink the prizes. Just little token things. Choc bar, scatch card, mini bottles of booze, etc."

"Sounds amazing. I have my prizes sorted too. Really looking forward to it."

"Thank God I read this. I must have missed the message about prizes. xx"

Shits and Giggles:

"Evening. Gosh they were quick today. I think it's got to be Hellraiser myself. Uncle Fester always seems a bit humpbacked to me, and you are beautifully straight backed. Not like me and my posture – I would make an excellent Quasimodo. Plus think of the challenge of applying the needles! Hope you're all well, anyway. Get some rest and offload Tobes if you can for a day or two. I offloaded mine today, before they go back tomorrow, and I feel much more on top of things. xx"

"Happy over halfway through phase one, Em. Hope the second half goes as quickly and treats you kindly."

Strong Randy Ladies:

"Wow, I can't believe it is Tuesday again. The weeks are just flying by and what with the summer I feel totally fucking head screwed and all out with days and timings. Totally knackered but best not moan as my knackered and yours are probably completely different levels of 'I'm fucked'. My advice: rest whenever you can as fuck me you have the best excuse and you are hopefully never going to have this excuse ever again, so make the most of it and chill when you need to. There are no medals for running yourself into the ground, are there? That's what we need to learn, and accept help when it's offered. On that note, if there is anything I can do ever please let me know. I appreciate I'm not the easiest option as not on your doorstep, but always here if you need me for more than the routine bum chat. Anyway, glad to hear that all is continuing well and look forward to our catch up soon. xx"

"Well, you are amazing, and over the halfway mark. Glad this week has been slightly less eventful. If you need anything, including a free babysitter so you can rest, you know where I am. I do look forward to your updates, although not under these circumstances – you are an inspiration – and then followed shortly by Emily's entertaining essays. I'm afraid my replies are a bit boring as my life is less hectic at the minute. Looking forward to our catch up soon. x"

"Boring is so not boring. I'm happy for you with the boring as you've had more than enough activities in your life of late. Actually, a bit jealous of your boring! Thank you, ladies. It's these replies that keep things normal and that's more help than you'll ever know. xx"

Local Yocals:

"Yay, Em! Love you and your updates. It's always tricky balancing life, others' needs and listening to your own body. Sounds like you're still in tune with yourself and responding to the need to go slowly at times. Can't believe you're halfway through! You're doing a fantastic job, my friend. Xx"

"I've literally laughed so hard at this week's update. Slip 'n' slide. Hope they don't cut our time short next week! Mind you, I'd happily challenge myself to sit quietly if you need some zzzzzz's. Love you to bits, Em, you are doing so amazingly well it blows me away every week."

"Well done, Emma, you are doing amazingly. I think the treatment is doing what it is supposed to do, slow you up a little, listen to your body and get rid of lumpy, so sounds to me like it is working. Love you, Emma. Keep up the positive vibe. x"

"Week seven – this in itself blows my mind that we are closer to the chemo finish line than the start. Every week I get a little bit excited when I see your message pop up on my phone and I truly love reading every installment you send us! Keep listening to your body, especially with busy days ahead, I certainly advocate 'slower days' whenever possible – my kids though are not so keen. Kicking that cancer's backside – you got this."

ED Fan Club:

"*Good work, ED, video of slip 'n' slide please.*"

"Hmm, I feel that may be oversharing a step too far with work colleagues!"

"*I love your updates, they make me smile. You are one funny onion (I don't know if people use that term here in the south west? Or whether it's a midlands thing, or whether I made it up myself). I'm rubbish with Halloween suggestions, so you'll have to rely on others for that! I look forward to your next update.*"

"*I like you and your dad laughing as he put his foot in it (so easy to do, innit?). Reminds me of when I had chicken pox when I was seventeen and my dad kept making 'hilarious' jokes and I was just feeling ill and grumpy. We were at a point of being a bit huffy with each other and he put the radio on, and a jolly old song was playing called 'Spotty Mulddon'. It broke the tension and we both laughed until it hurt. You're doing brilliantly – thanks for your updates and positivity. xx*"

Wednesday 4th September 2019

Denied!

Autumn Term was supposed to be starting today. With Chloe in nursery and Toby back at school, I'd booked a few things in for me this week. Looks like I'll be juggling it up again and calling on backup.

With Dad drafted in to look after Toby, I'm off to my appointment with an oncology physiotherapist at FORCE. We talk about diet and exercise and keeping myself in the best possible shape whilst undergoing treatment. Essentially, the more I look after myself, both in terms of resting and the fuel I put into my body, the healthier I will remain and the easier this treatment journey should be.

I also mention that I've had a pain in my shoulder for over a decade, no doubt caused from slouching over a desk for donkey's years. I can tell that the weather's turned because I can feel it in my shoulder, elbows, wrists and knees. God that sounds like an old person thing to say! Truth is, my body is starting to feel like it's taking a battering. It's taking me a little longer to get going in the mornings and the achiness is starting to kick in a bit sooner, and last a bit longer, after each session.

The physio knows a musculoskeletal physio who will give me a free assessment if recommended via FORCE and recommend exercises. I'll absolutely take her up on this.

FORCE can also make a referral to a local gym where a fitness instructor specially qualified to train cancer patients can write me a program and offer me a weekly coaching session free of charge. I'll also bite their hand off for this opportunity.

Cancer Comms

Massaging Mummies:

"Em, what can I say. This is such positive news and so so pleased you're halfway through. Yes, you definitely need to rest more but you know your own body and when it's had enough you've listened, so massive brownie points. When are we meeting up? You are such a busy woman for someone with cancer lol (just as it should be). Love you all millions and hope we meet up soon. xx"

Thursday 5th September 2019

This week, whilst checking what take-home meds I needed, the nurse asked if I needed any pills to help stop diarrhoea. Initially I declined because I haven't been experiencing problems in that department. She asked again and pointed out that with the cumulative effect of the chemo building I might start to experience new symptoms. Better safe than sorry I took them and thank goodness I did because today I could shit through the eye of a needle. These suckers are good, though, and after an initial dose of two I'm plugged back up.

Cancer Comms

Circle of Trust:

Send them a bald head shot in my fluffy dressing gown. **"Amanda, if you're Professor Snape, I reckon I'm Voldemort."**
"Another option for Halloween."
"We could do the whole Harry Potter gang between us."

Friday 6th September 2019

Every Friday follows roughly the same routine. Drop the kids to their respective places, get my PICC line care done, do some shopping on the way home and then see how the day pans out. I don't really feel the best on Fridays, so I don't have any expectations of myself. Today I realised that this is hitting me as it takes me one and a half hours to do a food shop that usually takes thirty minutes. I'm knackered by the time I get home and it's all I can do to drag the bags in from the car. I'll have to pay more attention to how I'm feeling and appreciate my new limitations.

Physio appointment this afternoon. How's that for service? Turns out the shoulder pain I've been enduring for years can be assisted with a few simple exercises, wearing layers of clothes to make sure I keep my muscles warm and utilising a tennis ball and a Nora Batty stocking to self-massage!

Another example of why it's important to get yourself sorted out so you don't suffer unnecessarily.

And now time to chill out because September is our ridiculous month for birthdays and anniversaries where we annually teeter on the edge of bankruptcy and exhaustion.

Saturday 7ᵗʰ September 2019

The old man is seventy today! I say old man, he's probably in better nick than me at the moment.

Today's celebrations are twofold. Breakfast at our local Wetherspoons this morning where he'll be pleasantly surprised that some old friends and his brother have travelled from miles away. Then a family meal out this evening. Usually I would relish the logistics that come with such event management, but it's been a bit tiring, and also I keep forgetting stuff! Good job my brother is on board with this joint venture.

It's an amazing day for him and amazing to be with all my family. Understandably, I'm having to have repeated conversations about my treatment with people I've not seen for a long time. But at least I've got good news to tell them and their genuine love and concern is very warming.

Chemo brain

I think this is starting to kick in now. I'd heard people mention 'chemo brain' and compare it to 'baby brain'. Essentially, I'll be screwed then because I don't think I've ditched my baby brain.

Now, my 'baby brain' was caused by a combination of severe sleep deprivation from two babies who just wouldn't stay the hell asleep and trying to process too much 'stuff'. 'Sleep when the baby sleeps', they tell you. There are no wise words of wisdom if the buggers don't sleep.

I remember muddling my words (like spork and foon instead of fork and spoon), constantly forgetting things and forgetting how to do basic tasks. One highlight (or lowlight really) was forgetting how to make a cup of tea and pouring milk into the kettle. A couple of times I found my purse in the fridge.

I would also start a conversation and then have to stop as I didn't have a clue where it was going or indeed what I'd been talking about.

Life would become a game of Articulate. I remember once trying to tell someone I'd been in a Jacuzzi but couldn't think of the word. I went with one of those ponds at a spa with bubbles!

I joke about all this now but when this first happened to me post small human I was very scared, thought I was losing the plot and wondered how the hell I would ever work in a professional capacity ever again. I found that I could remember long-term memories, e.g. the barcode from a Cadbury's Crème Egg from all the years I worked in retail (5020 1600 – go on, google it!) but I was damned if I could remember what I had for breakfast or what I'd done the previous day. I found that having a calendar was useful.

So, when this started happening to me again, I just went with it. I'd warn people that we'd quite likely have the same conversation multiple times during our catch up, and subsequent catchups, and to not worry that I was losing the plot.

*Spoiler alert, I'm typing this particular topic in April 2020 and I'm pleased to report that both chemo and baby brain have retreated into a distant memory. I do, however, reserve the right to pull them out of the bag as and when necessary as an excuse for any forgotten birthdays!

Monday 9ᵗʰ September 2019

Happy birthday to Darren today and Happy Toby going back to school today! What a double celebration.

I think I'll take this opportunity to tell you about Darren. It's not all about me. Well, I know he'd argue it probably has been for the thirteen years we've been together, and throughout a process like this you do have to be mindful about how you're feeling and what you need, but put quite simply I couldn't have done it without him.

I'm not going to refer to Darren as my best friend or soulmate. Nor will there be a full PDA (public display of affection) because (1) he would kill me and (2) it wouldn't be very authentic as that is just not how our relationship works. Some people might look at us constantly taking the mick out of each other and think we have quite a dysfunctional relationship but it works for us and thirteen years [anticipates joke about getting less for murder] down the line we must be doing something right.

His proposal has to rank up there amongst the most romantic. We were travelling around Australia with such a selection of beautiful places he could have chosen to pop the question. He chose ladies' night at a hostel on Magnetic Island. If the blokes dressed up as women, they also got free drinks, so at the end of a night of dancing on tables, with a jelly Haribo ring and wearing my clothes, that's how the grand gesture came about.

With the arrival of children, the dynamic clearly shifts. From the carefree boy racer days of our twenties when we used to drive the streets at all hours in our kevved-up motors, listening to the latest Clubland compilation to now me being in bed by 9pm most nights. From weekend after weekend of clubbing/pubbing to owners of National Trust memberships, movies and a bag of kettle chips on the sofa.

I know I'm not the easiest person to live with, yet this chap has stuck by my side through it all, especially the hard times after our first small human, and again now as we navigate this new and unwanted illness.

I did say no PDAs, but it has to be said that, although he can drive me nuts sometimes, which I'm sure is reciprocated, he is a fantastically supportive husband. He's an awesome father to the small humans and we all love him very much. So even with the romantic range of a Neanderthal caveman he's a keeper.

We will get through this together. We communicate well. I tell him if I'm having a wanky day and need to take myself off to a dark room. I notice if he needs some downtime down the pub with his mates. We still try to grab some precious alone time together in-between the treatments, down days, children and life 'stuff'.

And on that note, we're off out for a meal tonight at a posh pub that's going to cost an arm and a leg for a meal that I won't even taste, but I can't wait.

Loss of taste

So, it's been a week since my sense of taste has thought 'bugger this for now and off I go'. I'm a real foodie person. I love eating and take great comfort from it, so when you can't actually taste what you're eating it takes all the joy out of it.

The imperial mints and Werther's Original in my chemo cupboard are coming into their own now. I constantly feel like I've got a bit of a 'claggy' mouth. Drinking water doesn't really seem to help. Squash is better. Having something to keep in my mouth and suck is best. (Sounds dodgy just typing that!)

I lost my appetite initially. Not because I felt sick from the side effects but because I just didn't really fancy eating. I found I needed to put sauces or gravy with food to give it more of a wet texture now that I couldn't taste it.

183

I could still taste strong flavours: salt and vinegar crisps and Snack a Jacks, pickled onions and piccalilli. For a moment it was like being pregnant again! Also, strong curries and chillies. The only downside of those was that they would now give me the squits!

I could still tolerate fruit and veg, even if I couldn't taste it much, and actually started to enjoy food again by how it felt. My mates took the piss and suggested we could play a game of 'guess the food' just from the texture. I didn't trust them enough to do that!

Tuesday 10ᵗʰ September 2019 – Chemo Round Eight

"I have a lot to offer the world."
(YESmum card)

Given that I'm a frequent flyer on Cherrybrook, I'm building up a good rapport with the staff, but today was great. It was a quieter day than usual, so I really got to have a good chat with them. Given my job, they were interested to know about the types of cases I represent nurses in and we had a good chat about drug errors and dishonesty. I have now run out of 'I love nursing' badges but on the promise of some pens, I've secured myself another 10.30am appointment for next week. Always pays to get in with the ward clerk and it is not beneath me to bribe my way there.

I also brought in cupcakes today to share with my 'chemo chum' Dawn. It was her last session today, so I wanted to mark the occasion with cake and chat. I've really enjoyed my chats with her and her brother and the camaraderie we've built up in a short time.

Emily and Tracey's Little Jar of Cards

"Poo, poo, poo. Why do we always talk about poo?!"

Cancer Comms

"Session number eight of phase one – tick.

Featuring today's chemo sitter – Pippa (ha, autocorrected to Pitta!) with her lovely manicure, friendship bracelet making, chatterbox making and homemade chocolate brownies. Not to mention a good old catch up. These chemo sitters on their zero hours contracts are really making my day with their thoughtful activities and gifts but please, there is absolutely no pressure to bring/do anything. I am just grateful for your time and company.

Also, massive thanks to Paula who is en route to cook my tea, provide a pedicure and keep me company. I was a little sad to give up my pretty nails but now I'm all set with a new alternative.

Talking about missing things, never take your nose hair for granted! I used to get fed up of mine poking down but turns out it's quite useful when your small human kindly infects you with a cold. It stops your nose running like a tap into your mouth. Nice! Or sometimes I don't even feel it and catch myself in the mirror looking like a little dog with a wet nose and mouth. I might take the string off my tampax and shove them up there. Practical alternative use.

What else has gone? My sense of taste. Chemo or cold? Who knows? But it's amazing how you can find enjoyment through the sense of touch, how it feels and of its warmth.

I'm hoping it might curb my need to inhale whole packets of biscuits in one sitting.

Memory. That is currently **MIA**. So, if conversations become painfully awkward just smile sweetly. I will get there eventually. We'll likely re-visit the same topic multiple times and if you like Articulate schedule in a visit with me for an impromptu game. I can, however, still remember the barcode of a Cadbury's Crème Egg (I know you want to check: 5020 1600).

So, this week was all about me getting some stuff sorted. Oncologist physio, private musculoskeletal physio, referral for a private gym PT and massage, all free via Force. They are frigging amazing, and I can't sing their praises highly enough. I feel so lucky. They also provide great services to friends and families, so if any of you are feeling affected by this please give them a call. And talk to me because I don't want you sad.

I also received a lovely orchid this week. I had thrown my last bunch of dried up flowers away and after two months thought I was going to have to purchase my own!

Thank you once again for all the continued support. In answer to the **FAQ**s, no you're not bothering me, yes I still want to hear from you, yes you lose hair from **EVERYWHERE** – even down there – so it now looks like an old leather sofa, further suggestions of Gru and Voldemort under consideration for Halloween.

So, with that nice visual burnt into your head, I bid you farewell until next time. Have a fab week. Xx"

Circle of Trust:

"Is it wrong that I look forward to your weekly updates? You always manage to make me laugh with your escapades! Eight done is awesome, that's two thirds of the way through, you are totally kicking ass. You could try testing your taste changes. Can you now eat things you didn't like

April 2019 – joint 40th birthday celebrations with Mel

June 2019. Chemo sitter Michelle (before she knew about chemo sitters, the week before she knew about breast cancer)

July 2019. New haircut and locks posted to The Little Princess Trust

Modelling 'The Darren': new headwear with the girls (The circle of Trust)

All the cards!

Feeling like all my birthdays and christmases have rolled into one

My beautiful niece Skye Strudwick (10) who cut her long locks, donated them to The Little Princess Trust and raised over £200. Legend.

Aug 2019. The 'massaging mummies' meeting all my catering needs

The 'Nemo Chemo' bag of treatment essentials

The amazing chemo sitter Jo

Toby's excitement at the mock barber shop. "Daddy, Mummy wants to shave all her hair off!"

The mohawk

The '*Mad Max* extra' look

Matching hair cuts with my brother Russell

Sept 2019. Still just a mum in their eyes

Happy anniversary to us on 'Happy chemo Tuesday'. The amazing chemo sitter and husband – Darren. Xx

The amazing chemo sitter Kelly bringing the bingo

Rocking it in my fancy dress wigs

The 'Circle of Trust' girls bringing the bingo, gin and laughs

Oct 2019. Mum going all out on her chemo sitter duties.

Amazing chemo sitter Emily bringing the 'breast' cake I've ever seen

Amazing chemo sitter Paula and her beauty set up

Amazing chemo sitter Jo bringing the childhood games and sugar

Baking fun for the McMelon
Coffee morning with Toby

Amazing chemo sitter Helen
and her spotty bag of treats

Happy
Halloween

Nov 2019.
Amazing
chemo sitter
Becky on
her birthday

Down in Wookey Hole caves, the only strange looking creatures are me and my brother

Dec 2019. Not short of headwear for the festive season

Amazing chemo sitter Charlotte and the last festive themed poisoning

Magical fun on the Train to Christmas Town

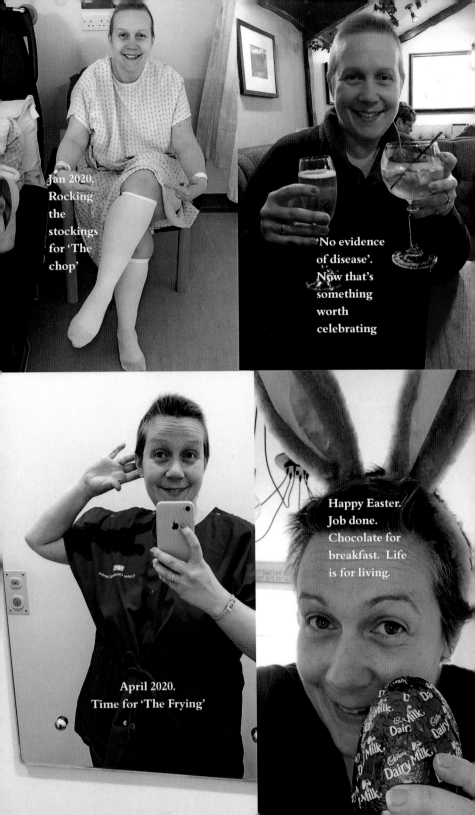

Jan 2020. Rocking the stockings for 'The chop'

'No evidence of disease'. Now that's something worth celebrating

April 2020. Time for 'The Frying'

Happy Easter. Job done. Chocolate for breakfast. Life is for living.

before? How about hot chillies? Hope the cold passes soon and you can start to feel stronger again. Remember, if there is anything I can do to help, please just say! xx"

"Ah man, homemade brownies on the week I was on leave! I bloody love FORCE and what they do for people and their families. I'm glad session eight is done. I wonder what lumpy is looking like now, the little loser! Hope the cold does one soon. xx"

"Try Vaseline on your nose, Em, stops it from streaming down your face. I use it when my hayfever is bad. Old leather sofa, lol, what a lovely image! Well done on the completion of week eight. So proud of you. Just reading your texts and talking to you, you'd never know what you're actually having to go through each day. And it makes me happy that there is so much support for you outside of your friends and family too. FORCE sounds pretty brilliant. Looking forward to bingo next week. Take it easy, mate. Xx"

"I'm looking forward to bingo and I think we should also have a game of 'guess what you're eating?' When do you have your next scan to see how big/small the little fucker is? Take it easy, my beaut. xx"

"Vaseline on my nose and Vicks on my arse, is it? (A longstanding joke. A little but as you can appreciate disappointingly painful mistake for a small child to make?!) **I'm really looking forward to bingo. Any requests for food? Not sure when next scan is. I'd guess around week twelve. Next oncology appointment next Friday but not sure what more they'll need to say to be honest. It's at 8am, so I'm guessing I will drag my ass out of bed at 6.30 for a ten minute appointment where they won't be able to feel anything and repeat what they told me before! xx"**

Massaging Mummies:

"Is it so wrong and weird that I look forward to these messages on a Tuesday, sorry! You just have me in stitches, Em. I'm sure Pippa was a good sitter. I can't believe your growler is now like a leather sofa. If only I

could see mine. I can't believe how amazingly you've just taken this all in your stride. Super proud of you. I'll always be here for you all."

Shits and Giggles:

"Tell me more about your nails. Photo please. Your updates are the best. How are you both? x"

"Lovely to read your update as usual on a Tuesday, lovely. That free service sounds great and really well thought out – let me know how the PT goes! Always thinking about you even though I'm pants at messaging."

"Will do. I've had plenty of PTs in my time so it will be interesting to see how this differs and how he can reign in my 'go hard or go home' approach to the gym!"

Strong Randy Ladies:

"The visual of down there! OMG! Hilarious! I am a bit weathered for my usual response this evening. I am on a training course with our accountant tomorrow so I will attempt to come up with a witty (probably not so witty) response by end of week. Tuesday comes around so quickly I fear I am losing materials, but you, my friend, are still on fire. xx"

"Thanks for the visual whilst I'm sitting on my leather sofa! That made me laugh. I love it that you still know the barcode of a Cadbury's Crème Egg. I had forgotten that useful fact! Sounds like FORCE are amazing and great you are getting good support and making use of the services. Did we finalise chemo sitting on the 1st October?"

"We abandoned the 1st and went for the 2nd Tuesday in October. Is that workable?"

"Is that the 8th? I lost the plot on this, sorry."

"Of course we did. Although I've got my operation that week now so have to work the beginning of the week, otherwise I would be there like a flash on the 8th."

"I'm sure I will be able to sort something. There will just be more pressure on my own to live up to these chemo sitters. I'm shit at baking *so don't expect anything other than shop bought treats. xx"*

"Please don't worry, ladies. There are no expectations here. My mum has already booked the day off to come with me on the 1st and she really needs that visit. She's not coping too well with it. Em, if you can make the 8th that's fab and we can arrange another catch up with you, Trace. It's usually a 10.30 start but again you just come and stay as you can. x"

Local Yocals:

> *"An old leather sofa!"*
> *"Best catch up yet!"*
> *"Oh my days!"*
> *"Oh, Emma. You always articulate so beautifully!"*

ED Fan Club:

> *"TBH I am sad because you should be at work with us, not going through this crap. Great update. Thank you."*
> *"Keep being fantastic – because you are – you need to write a book – you'd be a bestseller. Big thanks for the update. xx"*
> *"Aw Em. You're an amazing human. I'm currently sitting on the train back to London from Exeter. A day trip unfortunately, but it was lovely to see some sunshine. My journey has been made so much better by hearing from you. Keep being you. xx"*
> *"OMG the barcode is right! Sorry, I'm sad – just had to check it – I think that highlights what a true Cadbury connoisseur you are. xx"*
> "You're sad? I think it's sad I remember that from my days in retail. These days I can't remember my own children's names. I'm also thinking of getting myself a bracelet 'If found, my name is Emma, please return me to Haven Day Spa!'"
> *"Definitely write a book. You could just pop your blog down in it."*

Friday 13th September 2019

"I do the best I can with the experience I have gained so far."
(YESmum card)

My mummy is broken.

She phoned me earlier in the week from work to say that she was being sent home. I spoke to her lovely colleague who told me that she was taking care of her because everything had just got a bit too much and she needed some time out.

Mum had an appointment with FORCE today to see how they can help her through this time. I knew she was anxious about parking, so I offered to drive to take that worry away. At first she protested and didn't want to put me out until I pointed out that I was quite happy to sit in the relaxed centre with a book and a cuppa whilst they got to work on her.

When she arrived at my house, it was heartbreaking to see her. The lights had gone out in her usually shiny eyes glinting with mischief. Even my usual banter didn't illicit a smile, so I knew she was broken.

That's the amazing thing about FORCE. Their services extend to your loved ones also affected by your cancer.

After an initial consultation, my mum obviously isn't miraculously fixed, but now she has a plan. She can access counselling and complementary therapies. She'll be signed off work for a while and if you look at the positive in this situation it means I'm going to be able to spend a lot more time with her. When the kids are in childcare/school it means we will be able to go for walks, for lunch and actually get the opportunity to talk to each other without interruptions from small humans.

I'm not going to share more of her personal situation here, but I just wanted to show how this can affect everyone who loves you. It can creep up on them. They also might be putting on a strong face for you and feel guilty that they are struggling with their feelings when it's you that has the cancer. I was gutted I hadn't realised.

Wanting to end the day on a positive, I decide to bust out the fancy dress box wigs! The horrendously 'dragged through a hedge backwards' quality wigs passed from pillar to post from many a party past. Do you remember that show from the eighties, 'Tonight Matthew I'm going to be…'? *Stars in their Eyes*! Well, tonight I was both Danny and Sandy (*Grease*), a dodgy Axel Rose (Guns 'n' Roses), a pink long-haired Katy Perry and some punk goth fairy with purple and black hair. I couldn't find the wings, sadly!

Emily and Tracey's Little Jar of Cards

"I remember when you taped me to my chair whilst I was on the phone to a client and I couldn't move. xx"

Saturday 14ᵗʰ September 2019

We were supposed to be escaping this weekend, just me and Darren, down to Plymouth for a Gin Distillery Tour and tasting session. Now that the taste has buggered off there's little point in that, so we'll rebook.

With the logistics of dog and childcare still in place, thank you Mum, she offers a house swap and off we go to Cullompton.

I never thought I'd type 'Cullompton' and 'amazing' in the same sentence, but it was. It was so quiet at her house I thought I'd gone deaf! The only other living things were the pot plants and they didn't demand too much attention.

We went for a meal at the local pub. I'm not sure why I felt the need to have three courses considering I couldn't really taste anything. I guess old habits die hard. However, I could taste the gin and chose a couple of exotic sounding flavours. We did amble up to one of the pubs but only managed a couple. I'm in bed most nights by 9pm, so I've done well tonight pushing the boat out to 10pm. I've only done this safe in the knowledge that there will be no 6am small human wake-up call tomorrow.

Monday 16th September 2019

I've got cancer but I'm still a mum. I still have a small human to entertain. Cancer doesn't prejudice and neither does 'soft play hell'. I take my good friend Sarah along for back up in the hope that our two small humans will entertain each other for long enough to let us at least drink a warm cup of tea.

Tuesday 17th September 2019 – Chemo Round Nine

"Today is a new day."
(YESmum card)

I've grown in confidence in the bald head department. I used to keep a hat by the door to quickly pop on if the doorbell went. Now my current source of amusement is to open the door and invite people into *The Crystal Maze*!

I answered the door to my neighbours who I don't really see very often. The husband exclaimed, *"Oh, are you braving the shave?"* I think he was mortified when I responded, *"I guess so, but I didn't really have a choice, the chemo saw most of it off!"* Of course, I fall about laughing and reassure him that I am now at peace with the situation and treatment is going well.

Emily and Tracey's Little Jar of Cards

"Do you remember Darren's dancing at Tracey's wedding? This memory has just made me lol!"

Cancer Comms:

"Session number nine, lots of love this time.

I won't lie, it was a rocky start. I broke Chloe's banana in half to fit in her bowl. **BAD MOVE.** She then lost it insisting I magically stick it back together. Like an expert magician I did achieve this by quickly swapping it for a freshly peeled banana number two. This was after a repetitive shouty rendition of Happy Birthday at 5.30am.

Actual chemo Tuesday went well.

It's our anniversary today. Lucky thirteen years together, eight years married. Can't say we saw this one coming, nor would a chemo ward at the RD&E and a cocktail of bloody expensive drugs rank up there in our choice of anniversary outings, but that's what we did and we had some right old laughs.

The funny thing about this scenario is that it actually forces you to look for alternative ways to pass the time. A round of I Love the 80s was comical and I would say questions who's the older one out of the two of us! I think we've spent more time together today on our anniversary than the past five years of anniversaries combined. And we played nicely.

So, a big shout out to today's 'chemo sitter' Darren, who's actually been with me every day of this journey. On the poorly days, the damn right fearful and down days (scary but luckily not too many) and for keeping me laughing. On the day he asked me if I'd grown a dick because I now pee like a bloke due to all the drugs. To the day he shaved my head and we all fell about laughing at the hideous hairstyles! To the day he held me in bed whilst I sobbed, afraid to go to sleep in case I didn't wake up. To the many hours of chats and downright dark humour that we have not inflicted on anyone else, but we find hilarious. And the many more days that have just been normal parenting days.

Thank you to everyone who has checked in with Darren and kept him smiling. Please continue to do so because I need my rock.

Right, PDA over, what's been occurring?

Usual side effects not causing me too much bother. New one is some days having a mouth as dry as Ghandi's flip flop, but I've got a stash of mints and other delights to deal with that.

We aborted mission on the gin distillery tour Saturday. I wasn't feeling the best, it was £150 to stay in Plymouth (not a chance!) and it involved tasting. Slightly pointless right now! So, we did a house swap with Mum. She got two small humans and a beagle and we got some pot plants. Great deal. Never thought I'd commit to text 'We had a lovely evening in Cullompton' but hey, don't knock it 'til you've tried it.

First night away for a break just the two of us. I spent ages looking for my bloody hairbrush to pack! Funny how old habits die hard.

You might have seen on FB that my amazing mate Paula is running a half marathon in a month to raise money for FORCE on one month's training. I am humbled that she is doing this for me and in memory of her lovely mother-in-law who sadly passed away last year. She's still a bloody nutter, though, but at least she's a bit of a fitty anyway. If

you could spare a few quid to support her that would be awesome – link on my FB profile.

So, we're going to spend the evening now drinking the treats Darren brought – champagne and Ferrero Roche. It was good enough leading up to our wedding and it's good enough now!

I'll go now and get out of your hair (thanks for that one, Kate!). Have a fab week and catch up next week."

Being our anniversary, I popped a post on Facebook of Darren and I sitting on the chemo ward, drip in arm with the following:

"Happy Anniversary, Darren. We've done some amazing things in our thirteen years together but don't think either of us would have thought we'd spend our eighth wedding anniversary on a chemo ward. Four hours of peace and quiet to chat, though, not all bad!

So, for better or worse, sickness and health, thanks for being my rock in this unexpected twist. Here's hoping next year is slightly less eventful. X"

I clearly didn't think that one through, did I, as my phone started lighting up like a Christmas tree again! I think this was one of my most 'liked' posts with the most comments. I'd been so used to talking about this with so many people I forgot that I hadn't taken to FB about it and now I'd just opened it up to a whole load of other people!

Some of my favourite comments:

"Happy Anniversary orange boy and bald eagle. Together you will knock this cancer wanker out of the park. You got this."

"Happy Anniversary you two lovely people. Hope you have a lovely restful day and manage stinky poos (OMFG predictive text for drinky poos!) together after the events of today. xx"

"Peace and quiet, with Darren. And they said it would never happen. Congratulations and much love to you both."

So, I had to quickly follow it up with another FB post:

"It just occurred to me that my anniversary post on here earlier dropped the 'C-bomb' on a load more people who would have been a bit shocked. I've become rather accustomed to our new 'normal', but I thought I ought to add a little context given my phone has been lighting up like a Christmas tree.

14th June: found a lump – unexpected time.

28th June: diagnosed with the booby bug but unsure what and whether it was in the lymph nodes – bloody scary times.

3rd July: correct medical term is a Grade 3 Mixed Ductal Lobular, not in lymph nodes, treatable – much more optimistic times.

Few weeks of tests, appointments and getting my head together. Not spread anywhere else – productive times.

23rd July: chemo starts – let's get this show on the road times.

Recently a scan has shown the cocktail of drugs is doing its job and 'lumpy' has shrunk by two thirds.

So, there you have it. Obviously not what I would have wanted for the summer of 2019, but it's meant I got to spend it all with the kids, family and friends. As a frequent flyer, currently on week nine of twelve weekly sessions, then moving to one every three weeks for three months, I can say the NHS is bloody brilliant as is the amazing support around me.

Don't mind your Ps & Qs around me. Continue with humour and inappropriateness. I wouldn't want it any other way. xx"

Facebook Comms (a lot of ass kicking, apparently!)

You incredible, awesome, brave and wonderful human being.

You are pretty inspirational, Emma! Keep up the fight and kick its ass! You know where we are if you need anything… However, we're not taking the kids on! **Hot tub and dogs, they'll love you guys. We'll set up a play date. I thank you in advance for your generosity.** *Oh, how we laugh… Puts house up for sale!*

Aww, Em, you're fucking awesome. You are a true inspiration.

It did come as a bit of a shock. Wishing you a speedy recovery. **Yes, not something you can casually drop into conversation, really. All good though. X**

Did you find your hairbrush, Sinead? Big love, Strudders. **Ha I did and then I thought 'what a tit', surplus to requirement.** *Maybe use it for your eyebrows while you still have them… you are amazing, Em. xx*

I had tears reading this post and then I thought, 'Why the fuck are you crying?' You are amazing and your positivity is inspiring. Get well soon my happy hardcore loving denim backpack school friend. You have got this. Xx **Sorry about that. Bit of a shocker, I appreciate. But it's actually easier to tell people now that I'm into a good routine and it's heading in the right direction. I am indeed still enjoying my happy hardcore but have ditched the backpack in favour of a sensible mum bag.**

You're so beautiful, Emma, and rocking your new look. I love how positive and smiley you always are. You're truly inspirational.

You did drop the C-bomb. But it's yours to drop. Thinking of you all and know you'll attack this in your usual Emma way. Always here to be inappropriate, obvs. **I look forward to that. You continue with your hair-larious comments, thank you please.**

You're awesome. I love your attitude, you've totally got this.

Hey love. Thinking of you. I had cancer too seven years ago. You got this girl and if you need anything or want to speak to another member of the club just holla. Xx **Yes, I am indeed in the club that no one wants to be in. Thank you so much for your kind offer.**

Cor, talk about wanting to be the centre of attention! Surprised you didn't take your hat off for more of an effect. **Well, you know me**

being the quiet introvert! I reserve the hat removal for big things!

Loving the twat hat.

You're beautiful and strong. Your positivity will get you through. I always say that our oncology patients are the best. They don't lay around feeling sorry for themselves. They get up, get their shit together and face what life has dealt them. Rocking the head scarf too. **Ah, thanks. Best thing to do is to keep going. Keeps the fatigue at bay and I want to stay in the best shape possible both physically and mentally.**

Love that you can still be inappropriate. Glad you can still be you. Keep fighting. **Nothing's going to change there.**

Keep rocking the headscarf, you look fab. So true! I actually think it's a trendsetter. Next time we meet up we will all be copying you. **I was a bit self-conscious to start with, as always thought I looked a bit of a nob in hats, but maybe scarfs are the way forward. I've got three new bits of head gear.**

Love that you're facing this with humour and a flick of the middle finger. You haven't changed. **Oh, lumpy definitely deserves a middle finger, intruding on my 2019 like that!**

Still an inspirational mother and woman as always. I love the way you tell it and tell it true. I love the fun, kick ass, survivor attitude you have to all of life. **I feel a bit of Destiny's Child coming on.**

Don't forget to hand my card to any hot nurses (female ones for me please). You know it makes sense. xx

Cancer Comms

Circle of Trust:

"Sounds like a great day. Massive kudos to Darren too. Have a lovely evening. xx"

"As ever, a lovely update. And like Amanda said, credit to the Ginger Boy for being your rock. xx"

"*Ginger Boy, she spoils you. Happy Anniversary, guys. Enjoy a nice chilled evening with champers 'n' choc after a day at Chemo Café!*"

"*Another fabulously written update, thank you my love. I challenge you to get the word 'plethora' in the next one. Something that reassures me about this whole cancer thing is that you have Darren. He certainly steps up to the mark, doesn't he, and I am thankful to him for that. And I'm sure he knows we're all here for him too if he needs it. Do you pee louder now, is that what you mean? Sorry you weren't up for the gin date, but at least you still got some quality time together. Very much looking forward to Friday. xx*"

"*I still can't hear the word plethora without thinking of you two! Keep up the awesome work, Em, lumpy's days are numbered. I echo everything that has been said above re Darren, the boy has done good. Looking forward to Friday and seeing the plethora of prizes on offer. Love you all. xx*"

"**I extend my gratitude and love to you guys (well ladies), as well. You've all been awesome collectively in here and in your own ways. I'm very excited for Friday. xx**"

Massaging Mummies:

"*What are we going to do when lumpy has fucked off and died? You will still have to message us every Tuesday with a life update. Happy Anniversary to you beautiful pair. What doesn't kill you makes you stronger… so does laughing, crying, sharing the good, bad, happy and sad. As always keep being brilliant and smashing this, Em. I'm so up for a gathering round yours again very soon. When do you feel up for it? Happy to buy the ingredients if someone helps me cook. Em's feeling rough enough. xx*"

Shits and Giggles:

"*Darren's a bloody keeper, but so are you too. Watch him with the champagne, though – he's trying to seduce you. xx*"

"Ah, you guys are just the sweetest! I love how much you love each other and are just the perfect match… inappropriate sense of humour included! Happy Anniversary to you both. Not how anyone would have predicted you would be marking the occasion, but thank goodness you have a rock and your rock has other rocks to support him. xx"

"You sick of texting tonight, Em? Going Faceyb public with your news has probably made your phone explode."

"It's gone fucking nuts, hence I had to post another one. But time is one thing I do have right now and I'm absolutely loving hearing from everyone about their lives."

"Your FB post is awesome, Em. You are a bloody superstar."

Strong Randy Ladies:

"Have you grown a fucking dick! That is going to make me laugh all the way home."

"Glad number nine went to plan. Happy Anniversary to you and Darren. Enjoy your champagne."

"Well, you rock as ever, and you even look happy about your day in hospital on Facebook. I did wonder whether the post earlier would spark the next wave. First official Facebook post, but you both looked in really good spirits. Glad today has gone well and hopefully you've managed to enjoy your anniversary too. xx"

"It feels like a relief. I was still having to retell the whole story, so this way, unless someone has been in Outer Mongolia, I think that's all bases covered."

Local Yocals:

"Big love to you, Emma, those moments which are very personal to you and Darren, thank you for sharing with us, we love you loads and are all with you through this. xx"

"No, you're crying. I am so happy that you have had Darren as your tower of strength and silliness over these past weeks."

"Excellent update as always, lovely one! So glad you have Darren at your side, made for each other, you crazies!"

"Oh, Emma, my pregnancy hormones couldn't cope with this week's update. I'm a sucker for love and romance! Thanks as always for your honesty and being so open with your journey. x"

Wednesday 18ᵗʰ September 2019

Cancer Comms

Strong Randy Ladies:

"That was a fun game! Flower delivery for Emma Strudwick at 31 has been collected from 30 and safely found its way to Emma Davies at 35. Thank you so much, lovely friends. They are beautiful. You girls make me feel so loved. xx"

"What a nightmare! As if you haven't got enough to deal with! I couldn't believe it when they said the delivery had gone to 31. You'll always be a Strudders to us. xx"

"Didn't you say the other night you were up for a treasure hunt?"

"Oh, I enjoyed it. Made me use my brain to solve the riddle! Indeed, I did. I must facilitate that treasure hunt."

Thursday 19ᵗʰ September 2019

First freebie massage with FORCE today. AMAZING. I can't begin to tell you how amazing it felt and how amazing I felt afterwards. If it's doctor's orders that I should indulge in more of this good relaxing stuff, then who am I to argue?!

I also had an introduction session at a local gym with a personal trainer specifically qualified to train people going through cancer treatment. I can see where I'm going to be my own worst enemy. I used to be a bit of a gym monkey and now I'm going to have to slow it right down. I can go to a special group session once a week, but unfortunately, it's on the one day when I'm likely to be feeling my worst, so I'm not sure this is going to work. If nothing else, it has given me some food for thought and it's a good free option if it does work out.

Friday 20ᵗʰ September 2019

Another oncology appointment with my consultant. She's happy that everything appears to be moving in the right direction and I look well. I tell her these 8am appointments on my crappy day are a challenge!

I also tell her about the hot sweats that are waking me up numerous times a night. At their worst it's every half hour. It's like being back in the sleep-deprived days of life with a newborn, except now I'm also a Sweaty Betty. Apparently, acupuncture could help with that. I've never had acupuncture before and never really entertained the idea of having pins stuck in me. I'll give anything a go, though, and know that FORCE offer acupuncture.

Tonight it's 'Girl's Night' at my place. Entertainment on the cards is a night of bingo with my bezzie mates and pizza. We've all brought three prizes for a line, two lines and full house. The highly sought after multi-coloured pen, toilet roll, coasters and alcohol. Charlene not winning anything for ages then winning wine and a pen, claiming, "I'm surrounded by c★nts!" I'm not sure what her work colleagues will make of that! Laughter, and lots of it. Another 'just what the doctor ordered' prescription.

Tuesday 24th September 2019 – Chemo Round Ten

"I am not defined by what I have endured."
(YESmum card)

Emily and Tracey's Little Jar of Cards

"Camel's Toe! Oh, the things I learned at SRL!"

Cancer Comms

"Session number ten.

I feel like this is becoming as repetitive as The Bedtime Hour story on CBeebies. I'm no Tom Hardy, but if you're sitting comfortably, then I'll begin.

Once upon a time, there was a forty-year-old baldy, who thought it was funny to answer the front door without a hat and invite people into *The Crystal Maze*. THE END.

And she also inadvertently cancer outed herself on FB with what is probably my most popular wedding anniversary shout out to date! My phone went NUTS! But, actually, it was a good thing because I could follow it up with a positive update. So, unless someone has been in Outer Mongolia or living under a rock for the past three months, I think everyone in my world knows and I don't need to continue to explain to shocked faces why my hair is MIA.

Epic chemo session today with Paula my 'retired beautician' (her allocated title) friend. I had a complete gel take off and colour, much to the amusement of the nurses!

We made pom poms, played a card game that required quick thinking (Paula, what were you thinking with our collective sleep-deprived minds?), homemade banana and choc chip cake and a tub of Roses to share with everyone on the ward. Another very 'Happy Chemo Tuesday'.

I think the cocktail of drugs has finally caught up with me this week. Three days of tiredness like I've never known it. I could have fallen asleep standing up had I shut my eyes Friday morning, but given I was in the middle of Sainsbury's, I decided to push on!

I'm firmly advocating two-hour midday naps, as they are sorting me right out. I appreciate it's difficult in a working day but I'm sure productivity would soar. If you would like me to put your case to your employer, let me know, as time is something I currently have.

And the hot sweats! Bloody hell, they are relentless now. I'm sure my core temperature is hotter than the sun. If anybody has any tips on how to keep these bad boys at bay, I will literally love you forever. I am quickly becoming bored of frequent night waking, sweating my arse off. I'm not sure I've ever been so grateful for cooler weather. Normally I'm moaning that I know the weather has changed as I can feel it in my joints.

This week I had a lovely massage with **FORCE** and the first of my **PT** sessions.

I also had a lovely and hilarious girls' bingo night in and some more lovely deliveries from friends. I'm trying to balance resting but still having some lols.

MACMILLAN COFFEE MORNING Saturday 5th October @ my gaff from 2pm.

Who wouldn't like an audience with me over cake to raise some dosh? Oh, and it's not on the actual day, and it's in the afternoon, and I'm splitting any money between Macmillan and Force.

So, if you'd like to come, bring some baked/shop bought (let's get real, mine will be bought and presented as if home baked) goodies and depart with a few nuggets. We'd love to have you. Bring any small humans to entertain mine please so I too can eat cake.

Hope you're all having a fab week and let me know what's up in your worlds."

Circle of Trust:

"Ah, damn it, the one day I don't pop down is the day I could have got my nails done and had some chocolate! Sorry I didn't pop down, was only in until one and had a bit of a busy one! Number ten, that's crazy, how has it been ten weeks?! No tips for the hot sweats I'm afraid, but maybe stick your feet in some ice water. xx"

"Lovely update, although I didn't see the word plethora... perhaps you missed my challenge to you. I remember an episode of Friends *where they talked about the joy of standing naked with the fridge door open... could try that. I reckon it would feel quite nice. Not tried it myself, but I might now I've thought about it! I'm definitely up for a bit of cake and raising some moolah. I might even bake! And I'm sure Casey will be up for it too. Well done for getting through number ten, my love. You're powering through them like a trooper. Take it easy and nap when you can. xx"*

"I haven't fully read the update but got an idea on the flushes (currently spoon feeding my cat): this is the fan I use and it's silent. I'll try to find a link and will read about today shortly. xx"

"No worries, Kel. I know you're mega busy, so I absolutely don't expect it. You can keep the choc safe, right? Mel, I would stand naked in front of my fridge, however, I'm slightly concerned that my neighbours would get more than they bargained for with all that glass. Unless I do it in the dark! Oh, good recommendation, Amanda."

Massaging Mummies:

"How did today go, beautiful lady?"

"All good. Amazing even. Paula was an amazing chemo sitter. All the fun and snacks. xx"

"Well done, Emma, for surviving another session, and Paula for entertaining and feeding! Sorry I can't be a sitter on a Tuesday, but I am still waiting to help out in any way I can on a Monday if you ever need me. xx"

"Glad today went well and to Paula for keeping you company. Sorry I can't support on Tuesdays. Must rebook a Wednesday at some point. xx"

"Why did Paula get a turn at this? I want a turn. Absolutely smashing this, bird. The tiredness is gonna keep coming thick and fast, so keep listening to that beautiful body of yours. I love a nap. There are some herbal remedies that are good for hot sweats, also lots of Vitamin D, apparently. Complete naked sleeping, cool material for pillowcases and aired pillows and just a cotton sheet over you. Anything is worth a try. It's all trial and error, babe. As always, I'm here as and when needed, my beaut. Love you, baldy (it autocorrected to badly, you wish!). xx"

"Well, book a Tuesday off work then! Wow, those are some amazing recommendations. I'm going to get right on those. I know you love me badly.

As for birthdays, I'm hoping to get away with a smaller affair this year. Just the thought of a massive gathering and I'm losing the will to live. Chemo – no problem. Thirty excitable six-year-olds – fuck that shit."

"I don't work Tuesdays, beaut. Book me in."

"Phase two starts 15ᵗʰ Oct – you want that slot?"

"Sign me up, baby."

"Right, I've written it on the calendar, so you best deliver! xx"

"I was late to the chat but Jo I'm pretty sure it's 'cause I'm the vet's wife that I got to go!"

"Ha ha, the vet's wife, piss off, you!"

"No, it wasn't that, or because you're Austin and Sandy's mummy, it was because you're pretty awesome in your own right, Paula Pattison."

"Ah, way to big me up! I'll give you the cash later."

"You can sign me up for phase two as well, Em. Just let me know the date. I think chemo is the perfect excuse not to endure a big birthday! I'm so anti I've booked every weekend away! x"

Shits and Giggles:

"Glad to hear you're resting up. Good luck at your coffee morning, we've got the school one today. xx"

"How are you feeling today, Em? Sounds like the drugs are giving you a hard time. xx"

"I'm okay, thank you. Just bloody tired a few days each week now. But that's okay, just gotta get the job done. No plans today. xx"

Strong Randy Ladies:

"Glad to hear that chemo is still as delightful (if that's the right word, or maybe just the fact you have fantastic companions… I am starting to feel the pressure). Must be nearly at the end of round one now."

"No pressure for your chemo stint. It's only twelve out of twelve! Seriously, there is no pressure. Treat it as time to relax and chill out with some peace and quiet. x"

"Emma, glad the chemo companions are keeping you entertained. Rubbish you're so tired, but daytime napping sounds good. I could have done with one of those today due to only having a couple of hours' sleep last night. Think I've got some kind of virus but holding the fort at work, so no sick days for me and sure it will depart shortly. Definitely won't moan when you're dealing with it all the time! Hot flushes are horrible, especially the night ones, I feel for you having them regularly. Keep going – you are amazing."

Local Yocals:

"LOVE YOU. Not at all repetitive and I genuinely look forward to your Tuesday hilarities! You've beaten some of us to it with the night sweats, so when someone shares their wisdom with you please be kind and share with the group, give us all the heads up. So good to hear you are taking the rest and still finding lots of ways to enjoy this time off. You are so courageous, strong and inspiring, Emma, keep going. You will knock this on the head and be holding the hands of many who will sadly face this journey in their lifetime too. xx"

"As always, look forward to your weekly roundup. We love you, Emma, and are so proud of you for dealing with it so well."

ED Fan Club:

"Lovely update. I'd like to come on the 5th and will bring something homemade and free-from everything, except nuts! Well, may contain nuts. I might bring a sprog."

"Another awesome update, Emma, can't believe this is sesh number ten! I would love to come and eat cake with you, but sadly I'm away next weekend (children free!). But I'll eat cake in your honour and expect pictures to keep me updated please."

Tiredness vs Cancer Fatigue

So, in my life so far, I've experienced varying degrees of tiredness:

The tired the next day after a self-inflicted heavy sesh. Mostly pre-kids, I could just fester in my pit and nothing a full English and an energy drink couldn't sort out.

Sleep deprivation immediately post small-human appearance. Bloody hell. If I thought I'd been tired before, that did not touch the sides. I literally felt like the walking dead for months. But my body adapted and if I could get chunks of sleep, I was genuinely good to go.

Tiredness during chemotherapy (written after I've finished). Well, this is a totally different ball game. I have never known tiredness like it, so I was relieved to learn that this isn't just tiredness but 'cancer fatigue'. This is an extreme tiredness and exhaustion. It has a cancer-related name, so now I feel fully justified in rolling this bad boy out when I need to rest. Unfortunately, though, having a good kip doesn't make it go away and you can wake up after a full night's sleep still feeling tired. This is a common side effect of breast cancer treatment and one I've been told can last for weeks or months, even when treatment has finished. Fortunately for me, it stopped pretty quickly after treatment finished, so again I offer that as a nugget of hope. Even though treatment has finished, I can still have days when I can be quite tired, but hell I've got two small humans, so that could be entirely contributable to them!

I found the following useful to manage my fatigue:

- Keep a fatigue diary. I recorded how tired I felt on a scale of one to ten, and also noted what I was doing that day. This helped me to notice any patterns and whether I had perhaps overdone it with the exercise or expectations on myself.
- DO exercise. It might sound a bit counterproductive, but actually I felt worse if I didn't get outside in the fresh air and at least attempt a short walk. I'm not talking marathon training, just walks around my block.
- Take a nap. I was encouraged to take a rest if I needed it, but try and limit any daytime sleeping to thirty minutes. There was a point where I found I was enjoying my daytime naps a little too much, which then meant I was turning into a bit of a night owl.
- Complementary therapies. I was so fortunate to have some massages with FORCE. During the treatment, I'd feel really calm and relaxed, and it also calmed my mind.
- Drink plenty of fluids.

- Eat healthily. Keep fueling your body with the good stuff. I'd lapsed a bit by now, had put on a bit of weight and boy didn't I notice the difference.
- Accept help if you need it and don't be afraid to ask for it.

Cumulative side effect nasties after ten sessions

- Cancer fatigue. I could fall asleep on a washing line when the fog descended.
- Spotty teenager skin.
- Hair loss (current trend – the bald egg look).
- Dry skin (cream me up baby!).
- Chemo brain (sorry, what was I saying again?).
- Loss of taste and dry mouth.
- The squits (diarrhoea).

September – Looking Back

Feels more like 'shit got real' now. The side effects are clocking up and I'm more aware that my wonderful body is starting to protest. These are different to the cocktails I've pumped into it on my annual girly holidays. Similarly, both sets of cocktails may have made me feel a bit worse for wear, but these are going to ensure that I get to experience many more family holidays.

I've felt extreme tiredness this month and there have been days when I've struggled to get going. There have been occasions when it would have been all too easy to roll over and go back to sleep. I'm actually so grateful that I've had to get up and get the children off to nursery and school, as by the time I've done that and got home at least I'm up. Don't get me wrong, if I'd felt proper rough, I have amazing people who can step in and dispose (not literally!)

of the children for me to their respective places.

When I look back on September, I look at how busy it's been with family celebrations. With Toby back at school, I've grabbed the opportunity to catch up with friends and family over a cuppa or a pub lunch. I recognise now that I've been overdoing it and just meeting up with someone and engaging in conversation with them is quite tiring. I need to slow down. This is a new concept for someone who has lived their life at 100mph.

I'm so proud of myself, though. Ten out of twelve sessions done of round one, and the lumpy bastard is retreating.

October 2019

Tuesday 1st October 2019 – Chemo Round Eleven

"I am supported by people who love and care for me."
(YESmum card)

Emily and Tracey's Little Jar of Cards

"Argh the days of working with a hangover and sleeping on my sofa!"

Cancer Comms

"Legs eleven (thanks for that one, Jo), the penultimate phase one session.

Today I got the pleasure of my mummy for company. Now I know there's being competitive but when she got out of the car loaded with two bags, I knew that shit was getting serious.

GAMES: stack the emoji poo, Ludo, Snakes & Ladders, cards, guess the picture.

SNACKS: Jaffa Cakes, Ferrero Rocher (my staple Christmas breakfast diet), fruit.

CRAFTING: creating Petal the unicorn.

She'd even brought a box of Miniature Heroes for the nurses and told them they were her heroes.

I joked that we would need more time to get through all our activities. Well, my wish came true. Due to a blockage in my plumbing (PICC line) my stay on the NHS was five hours today.

The emoji poo game was epic, and we loaned it out to other chemo chums.

It was a long but fun session today. There was a real air of humour and happiness on the ward. Great to have my mum all to myself without the small humans demanding her attention. I know she was nervous about today, didn't know what to expect, but I think she was pleasantly surprised at how upbeat the whole process is.

Mum also came out with this gem she'd read:

"You are only promised two days. The day you are born and the day you die. The rest in-between is up to you."

I love a good quote but it's true, isn't it? You need to make the most of the hand you've been dealt and take control. I obviously wouldn't wish this situation on anyone, or myself, but statistically it's got to happen to me or someone I know. I've genuinely loved catching up with all my 'chemo sitters', and the fun atmosphere we create, and I look forward to the phase one wrap up party next week. No pressure, Emily!

Just two quickie updates as I'm not going to wang on about tiredness. I get very tired, I sleep.

I had loads of great recommendations for the hot sweats. My two-year-old friends recommended rocket ice lollies.

My other fav from Beagle Sarah:

'For the hot sweats at night I recommend putting your knickers in the fridge and having Darren stand over you with a big banana leaf fanning you. When you wake up, get him to nip to the fridge and grab the knickers and ice. Failing that, get him to buy you a Tempur mattress.'

Boringly, I'm making enquiries of **FORCE** about acupuncture.

And lastly, don't forget to pop round to my gaff this Saturday from 2pm bearing baked (home produced or bought, no judging here) goodies and dosh. I have bunting, games, prizes and look forward to catching up.

Hope you've had a good week and fill me in on the highs, lows and everything in-between.

Circle of Trust:

"Glad legs eleven was an entertaining one with Mum. Poo games are always fun! Nice that she thought of the lovely nurses that look after you. See you Saturday with some cake, which may or may not be home baked!"

Massaging Mummies:

"Good work, Mummy. They are the best, aren't they? Read: aren't we all."

"Loving the upbeat and positive vibes this session has given off and how much it's shown your mummy how well you've got this. Jesus, I've got to live up to my stint. I've even googled stripper prices. So pleased things are going as they should, my beaut."

Shits and Giggles:

"Your mum sounds ace. Idea – did you ever get those maternity pads you could freeze, so your lady garden calmed down nicely after giving birth? Would that work now? Freeze them and put anywhere that's hot!"

Strong Randy Ladies:

"Nearly there with phase one. Shame you had a five-hour stint today

but sounds like your mum did an amazing job. I recall that acupuncture helped with my hot flushes! I'm sure Emily has next week in the bag."

"Oh, fuck me, Emily does not have next week in the bag. Wishful thinking. After the high hopes of end of season party, I have failed massively as it's only next week now! Best pull my shit together, focus and plan! It's all fine, I'm not panicking at all (is there a finger biting emoji?)! Anyway, so glad you had a good day with your mum. I'm sure you both needed the quality time."

"Em, please do not stress about Tuesday. That is the last thing I want you to do. I've got loads of stuff I can bring and all I really care about is having some quiet time with my good friend to catch up. It's not the end anyway, so absolutely no pressure please. x"

Local Yocals:

"Happy Chemo Tuesday — one more less to go. xx"

"Eleven! Boom. Enjoy the time with your mum. x"

"Another great week, Em! So grateful to you for being so open about the treatment and how you're feeling. Keep it coming! Love you. Xx"

"Aww, that is so lovely about your mum. Have you tried one of those crazy cooling pillows for the sweats? The Darren with a leaf image is great."

"How lovely that you got that time with your mum today and she embraced it all so positively, especially when expressing her anxieties about it. All us mums — we are made of strong stuff when it comes to our children. Thanks as always for the update and including us all. I'm already waiting in anticipation for next week's installment! xx"

"Can't believe you smashed eleven sessions, Emma. WELL DONE. I was thinking of you and your mum today. I know she's understandably been finding this hard, but anyone who gets the privilege to come to a chemo sesh with you would be hard pushed not to enjoy themselves! You are incredible and clearly so loved, by us lot but also by everyone taking the best care of you. Reminder to call out if we can do anything at all for you. Big or small, we are always here to help. Love you to bits. Xx"

Cake. Always Cake:

"A poo game? Bloody marvelous! How's your mum getting on? Has she managed to get to chat to someone?

"I frigging love the emoji poo. Yes, mum is utilising FORCE more than me! She's having regular counselling and weekly therapies! She's getting there. Xx"

"Glad your mum is getting support. We're here if you need to chat or not chat and just talk poop and other stuff!"

ED Fan Club:

"Glad you got some quality time with your mum. Every cloud, eh?! See you Saturday. X"

"Another great update, Emma – keep 'em coming! And have a great time on Saturday. Don't forget some pics please. Xx"

"Looking forward to Saturday. Will bring cake, cash and a three-year-old."

"Ged on, Strudders!"

"Great update. Sorry I can't be there on Saturday. Look forward to seeing pictures of all those squidgy cakes. Xx"

Wednesday 2ⁿᵈ October 2019

If my mum's quote from yesterday didn't get me thinking about how I spend my time here, going to Darren's Grandad's funeral today did. Ray has passed away from dementia after a fantastically long and full life. The crematorium was packed with friends and family, which I think is a wonderful testament to the kind and fun man that he was. The sun was shining, and it was a wonderful ceremony, followed by a fair few drinks to send him off down the pub. It was lovely to speak to so many of Darren's family but, as usual, I realised it's usually births, weddings and deaths that draw us all together. Are we so busy being 'human doings' that we forget to stop and be 'human beings'? I don't know, maybe all a bit deep due to today, but it's made me stop and think again about who I spend my time with and what I spend it doing.

Thursday 3rd October 2019

A work/lunch catch up with Becky (boss) down the pub. I use the word 'work' loosely because there really is no work going on. My head is all over the shop at the moment and although I'm looking well and smiling, I think it's apparent my sick leave is genuine. I can't string a sentence together let alone draft a half decent set of submissions. Hell, I'd even self-refer myself to my regulator if I attempted to go back to work.

These catch ups are lovely, though. Not least because I class Becky as a valued friend, but also, it's lovely to hear that people send their love. Not a case of 'out of sight, out of mind'.

I am also so lucky to not have work/finances as an additional worry during treatment. We agree that an occupational health referral will now be made to assist us all going forward.

Saturday 5th October 2019

Today is an exciting day because we're hosting a Macmillan/ FORCE coffee afternoon. Similar to a Macmillan coffee morning (or 'melon morning', as Toby calls it) but with our own twist.

I can't bake for shit and I don't suppose having got cancer and deciding to do some fundraising will miraculously change that. I have enlisted the assistance of my mum to help the small humans create bogey-free cupcakes whilst I attempt my speciality 'half cake'. It always ends up being half a cake because it doesn't rise enough, so I simply cut it in half and sandwich the layers on top of each other smothered in shop-bought buttercream icing! Except this time, I haven't let it cool enough, so it all starts sliding apart. Good job I've got some Macmillan flags I can use as skewers to keep the chocolate gooey mess together.

The kids also produce some fantastic 'just add an egg' shop bought mix cupcakes.

Then the doorbell starts ringing and for the next two to three hours I'm entertaining quite a full house-load of people from all different groups. Work colleagues, old friends, new friends, mummy friends, family… most have brought cakes with them. Homemade, shop-bought. No judging here. All give generously and after an afternoon of laughter and fun we've collectively raised £250, which I'll split between the two charities.

I won't lie, the day has absolutely knackered me out and it's another 7pm bedtime. So rock and roll! But it was worth it to catch up with so many people and I'm touched that they all showed up for me.

Cancer Comms

Circle of Trust:

"Your cake was delicious, Em. Your afternoon of cake was lovely. I'm sorry if Frank ate too much. I hope you managed to raise lots of lovely moolah for the peeps at Macmillan and FORCE."

Cake. Always Cake:

"Cracking cake yummies today, Em. Let us know how much money was raised. xx"

"Thank you so much both for coming, for baking and just being all round awesome and supportive."

"Lovely to see you both and today looked fab. Hope you've raised mucho pennies. x"

"It was lovely to see you both, however manic! So far £200!"

Tuesday 8ᵗʰ October 2019

"I learn from the past and live in the moment."
(YESmum card)

"Session twelve out of twelve.

Level one complete. Player one, please proceed to level two.

Oh no wait, what's that? Your name's not down, you're not coming in! Not today, anyway.

So, session twelve didn't happen today due to an admin error but my amazing friend Emily exceeded all expectations with the most amazing 'f#ck you cancer' cake ever.

Session twelve is booked for 2pm tomorrow if anyone is around to join me? For any of it. Did I mention there's an amazing cake on offer?

We still had an amazing day together having brunch at Darts Farm. We then took our entertainment to the pub and sat playing all our games.

So, the finale phase one update will come tomorrow but this is a shout out to all phase one chemo sitters, you're more amazing than a glitter farting unicorn."

I have seriously not seen a cake quite like this bad boy. It's pink, glittery and has a massive pair of boobs on the front. It takes all my self-restraint not to get heavily involved with it, but I want to surprise all the chemo nurses tomorrow.

As I've learnt with this illness, you just need to take each day at a time and sometimes you just have to roll with sudden changes.

Well, I'm certainly more than happy to roll with being taken out to lunch and then going to the pub instead of spending the day sitting inside. The patrons at the pub must have wondered what the hell we were up to with our bingo board and unwrapping loads of presents over a midday cuppa. The heavens opened on us as we were walking back to the car, so we got drenched. This will be one of the days that I will always remember during treatment, as it was totally unexpected and full of laughter.

Cancer Comms

Massaging Mummies:

"Good luck for tomorrow my lovely. Wish I could be there with you, but that little pesky thing called work keeps getting in my way. Wow, that is one amazing cake. xx"

"Oh pants! At least you had a great day by the sounds of things and that cake is pretty awesome! That cake's got bigger boobs than me!"

"Hey, beautiful lady. Shame about today's session but at least you made the best of it. I can't believe I'm worrying about our chemo sesh on the 15th. All these amazing things people are doing, how the fu*k am I gonna top them?"

"Firstly, don't be soft. I don't expect anyone to bunk off work to come visit me. And secondly, there is zero expectation of anything. I'd just be happy with the company and a packet of salt and vinegar crisps. Also, our session will be new territory. I don't know how long it will be, as it's the new drug, and actually think it may be a lot quicker. So, might be we can get the drugs in quickly then go to the pub. Who knows! x"

"I'm only joking, Em. I'm looking forward to being your chemo wing gal. Wish to God you weren't having it at all but nice that I can be there with you. It's so lovely to see the amazing friends and family love you *have too. That's how we get through our hard times. Oh, with a cake like that too. xx"*

Shits and Giggles:

"Wowzers, what a cake! Glad you had a different type of day."

Local Yocals:

"Twelve out of twelve, Davies! You, incredible woman, are rocking this. Love you. xx"

"Twelve out of twelve, can't believe it's here already! Looking forward to reading the final instalment of this chapter later! As with all the others, you've got this. x"

"How frustrating for you! Cake sounds lush. X"

"Oh, Emma, that is annoying. Don't finish work until 2.15 and then school run, otherwise I would have been there with you. CAKE WOWZER."

"Ah man, what a frustrating fuck up! I'm free for an hour tomorrow, lovely lady, I'd love to come and be with you."

"What a cake! I can imagine that definitely helped lift the dampened spirits. Pleased you are booked back in for tomorrow and you haven't had to wait an age!"

"Bit frustrating, but hey, what can you do? These things happen. And I still got a day with my mate. Pippa, that would be absolutely amazing if you'd like to pop in. You can take cake home! X"

Cake. Always Cake:

"Glitter farting unicorn? There's some mental imagery. xx"

"That cake is amazing!"

"Cake was gurt lush. Breast cake I've had in a while. And lovely to see you, Em. xx"

ED Fan Club:

"What a fabulous cake (almost) too good to eat. Did your friend make it? Shame re the admin error but glad to see your day didn't go to waste. Look forward to update twelve tomorrow. Xx"

"Awesome cake. Sorry, whilst I'd much rather be watching you eat that cake, London's calling, so I can't. xx"

"That is possibly the best cake I've ever seen."

Wednesday 9th October 2019 – Chemo Round Twelve

"I approach every situation expecting the best."
(YESmum card)

I did feel a bit of a tit walking onto the ward on my own with a mahoosive cake to rival a wedding cake. It went down a storm, though, and quite a few of my friends who work at the RD&E popped down to see me. Fickle buggers! I dished it up amongst the nurses and ward clerks. Fortuitously being a day late with treatment meant I bumped into chemo chums Gabbi and Lynn on their treatment, so I was able to share some with them. Emily, you are definitely the tits when it comes to 'snack production' for the chemo sitting shift. I don't know why you were so worried.

Emily and Tracey's Little Jar of Cards

"Did someone say badger?! A result of a drunk journey home when Paul picked us up."

Cancer Comms

"Session Twelve out of Twelve Take Two.

On the twelfth week of chemo, the **NHS** gave to me, my last dose before I move to **EC** (sang in the style of Twelve Days of Christmas please).

Level one is now well and truly complete.

The cake was the tits and went down a storm, so a massive thank you, Emily. I've had a lot of comments that the cake has better tits than they do!

So that's it. Twelve weeks of this particular drug cocktail has come to an end. No rest for the wicked and straight onto the new drugs next week. I understand it could be a bit nastier but remember I'm an 'ideal candidate' for chemo, so we'll just see how the cookie crumbles (keeping on the baked goods theme today).

This one is once every three weeks for four to six sessions. I have the first two covered, but any takers for any other sessions? They are likely to be much shorter, so could incorporate a pub visit after.

Cake + tea + friends = £250 going to Macmillan and **FORCE**. Amazing support by so many people, so thank you so much. That will fund the complementary therapies I'm having.

So, thanks for sticking with me on this journey as I move onto the next phase. To infinity and beyond."

Circle of Trust:

"I can confirm that cake was the tits."

"Yay, phase one down. Well done, maid."

"I'm just pleased I was finally able to get a booking. You're one popular lady! Now to start thinking of things for the Nemo bag!"

"Well done on the completion of phase one, my love. You've done us and yourself proud. Now go have a gin and chill. xx"

Massaging Mummies:

"Well done, Em. You've made the last twelve weeks look like a breeze! Fingers crossed your 'luck' continues for the next batch. Do you have another scan soon?"

"Well, I'm not sure I made it look a breeze, but I think it could have been a lot worse. Yes, towards the end of the month sometime. I'll be interested to see if the thing is still there anymore, as last scan was week five!"

"Well done, Em. So proud of you. Pop me in a sitting on round two, just send me a date."

"Well done, Em. The first big chapter is now behind you and on to the next. You are smashing it."

"So bloody proud of you, Em. Let's hope your next scan shows you well and truly kicked Lumpy's arse! Really hope the next lot of chemo isn't too gruelling. Fingers crossed it finishes the job. x"

"Get on, Em. Smashed it and blew that lumpy bastard way out of the park. See ya, lumpy shit balls face. Let's hope phase two stays just (sort of) kind to you. I'm in for the 15th. Are shot games frowned upon?"

Shits and Giggles:

"Great news on your coffee afternoon. I'd love to sit with you if I could. Especially with the pub afterwards."

Strong Randy Ladies:

"Argh, to infinity and beyond. Love it. You are a bit of a superhero. Glad the cake was enjoyed, and I wish my tits were that big rather than the boulder holders I've been blessed (not so blessed) with, which I have just flung from their support. OMG the feeling of taking a bra off is actually better than *sex. Well, I am more than happy to sign up to another fix, whether it be in hospital or out. But also want everyone else to get a go, so if you're inundated, I feel like I've had my moment to shine (seriously kidding). Be nice if me and Trace could come in together. Happy to stand aside so your love can be shared. Looking forward to seeing you both next week. xx"*

"You certainly are a superhero. Phase one complete – you smashed it. I'm up for keeping you company as well and happy to do a joint one with Emily. But if you're inundated with offers won't be offended if others have volunteered. Look forward to seeing you both next week. xx"

Local Yocals:

"Well done, Emma, on completing those twelve weeks. Put me down for a session. Lots of love. Xx"

ED Fan Club:

"Yay for the end of stage one. Well done in the fundraising. Have a chilled rest of week. Xx"

"Fantastic fundraising. I'll leave something in the office, or can I send it directly to you?"

"Lots of sloppy kisses. Well done. X"

"Well done ED, stage one smashed! Let me know what slots are free for me to come and bother you. I may not be able to stretch to a tit cake, but could I balance a couple of bourbons on my baps? Much love. Xx"

"Well, I'm sure that would prove entertaining."

"Aw, can we all come and watch that party trick, Jessie? Or is that a bit weird? Seriously, though, awesome work Emma, onwards to stage two. xx"

Thursday 10th October 2019

I always feel like I'm in trouble when somebody says, "Can I have a word with you?"

This time it's Toby's teacher. She tells me there's nothing to worry about (always appreciate that precursor) but (ah, there's always a but) his behaviour has been a bit disruptive in class and he finds it difficult to settle. I say I've also noticed this at home. She wondered if anything had changed and I let her know that it hasn't, so I'm not sure why he would be acting up other than perhaps the formal structure of year one compared to reception.

I don't make a big deal out of it but that night I have a chat with Toby to see if there is anything 'cancer' related on his mind. I choose my moment when we're calmly engrossed in making puzzles.

"Is there anything on your mind at the moment?" (I didn't want to put words into his mouth by asking if he was worried about anything.)

"No."

"What do you think of Mummy's bald head?"

"It's so smooth."

"Do you want to ask Mummy anything about her bald head or the medicine I'm having?"

"Nope."

(So then I ask:) **"Is there anything worrying you?"**

"No, why?"

"It's just your teacher said you've been a bit lively in class and have been breaking your pencil case."

"School is boring. We don't play as much anymore."

"What's your favourite thing to do at school?"

"Playtime running around with my friends and PE."

"What about the lessons?"

"Writing is boring."

I shan't bore you with the whole conversation but I don't think his behaviour is anything to do with what is going on with me but rather an energetic five-year-old boy who suddenly finds himself in a more structured class environment. He does concede that the project about Egypt is interesting, so I latch onto that and run with it.

Friday 11ᵗʰ October 2019

First appointment back with the booby doctor. I'm sure she would prefer 'breast consultant', but even booby doctor wins out over bum doctor.

Slightly premature as she thought I'd finished chemo, but it was a useful visit to understand the pending surgery prior to 'the poisoning' results.

On the assumption that lumpy has buggered off completely, she will insert a wire to remove the clip in my breast. This will also remove the area that previously housed lumpy and a biopsy performed to check for 'clear margins' (no remaining nasties). I will also be injected with radioative dye to detect the two nearest lymph nodes (so-called sentinel nodes) and these will be whipped out, biopsied for the same reason and all being well that will be that.

I said I was still awaiting the results from the genetics testing and was asked how I felt about that. To be honest, I've still not given it much thought. I'm still focused on my current treatment and can't really give careful consideration to what would be major surgery for a result that hasn't returned yet. We'll cross that bridge if and when we come to it.

I had a chat with my booby nurse about the information I'd just been given and she popped off to get me some leaflets, which I shall file away in my 'cancer admin' file when I get home. She asked if I had any concerns about the surgery. My only concern is whether I have to take my tongue piercing out or whether I could replace it with a plastic retainer as I don't want it to grow over. It's been a part of me (literally) for two decades now and I'm not sure I'm ready to let it go, even if I'm now in my forties and risk looking like mutton dressed as lamb. FYI a small consensus of friends still consider it fine to have a tongue piercing. I will reassess the situation at mid-forties.

After this morning's routine PICC line care, I have to take Toby to the surgery to have his flu vaccination injection. Whilst his mates have had the squirty stuff up their noses, I have been advised against that for Toby as it's a 'live' vaccination and I can't risk being exposed to it with my compromised immune system. My prediction is that Toby will go nuts following his last set of disastrous injections a few years back when he grabbed the needle and bent it in his arm. We've weighed up the options of the distress it will cause him against him/me being exposed to flu. It's heartbreaking to think that because of me he will be subjected to this distress, but I decide bribery is not beneath me in this scenario. Sure enough, he's all smiles to start with but when he realises what's actually happening he goes ape shit. I have to literally hold him down whilst the nurse administers the injection and God do I feel guilty. Bloody cancer.

Sunday 13th October 2019

The Great West Run. So, I thought I'd do a half marathon to raise some dosh for FORCE. Did I hell! Most I've ever managed was a 10k a couple of years ago. But my fitty mate Paula decided about a month ago that she'd like to join the FORCE team, so has been training her butt off. She's raised a nice tidy sum, so it's the least I can do to see her come over the finishing line in a very respectable time.

After we say our goodbyes, I realise my mistake in having parked up at the top of a massive hill. Slow and steady wins the race. I think it takes me the same amount of time it took Paula to run thirteen miles as it does me to get back to my car! I'm really feeling it today and that outing was just too ambitious. I'm also a bit of a grumpy bum, so apologies to Darren.

Tuesday 15ᵗʰ October
– Chemo Round Thirteen (the new stuff)

"I take each day as it comes."
(YESmum card)

Emily and Tracey's Little Jar of Cards

"A girls' night out in Exmouth but instead of being concerned for Emily when she was being sick, we phoned Paul to pick her up and fucked off clubbing!"

Cancer Comms

"Captain's log 15.10.19 session thirteen but number one of the new hard drugs. **Boldly going where I haven't been before with 'chemo sitter' Scouse Jo. Maybe her car not starting and slightly late arrival was a sign of unlucky thirteen, but other than that the red drugs went in without incident. They will also come out red, so I will have superhero pee. Have taken a pic of the red drugs going in, will spare you their exit appearance!**

Bit disconcerting to learn that I have to inject myself in the tummy for seven days each cycle. That was a bit of a shock. Surprisingly for someone with so many piercings and tattoos, I'm not a fan of needles, but I'm sure it will be fine once I've got over the initial one. Also have multiple packets of drugs. So, our new normal is injections accompanying the Muller yoghurts, packets of pills set out on the microwave with military precision timings and a medical sharps bin accompanying my Tupperware!

We had a hoot today. Good game of 'guess the animal'. God knows what the other patients thought of me and Jo sitting there with headbands on and animal cards. So much chocolate and retro sweets. The wards will function at optimum capacity today as the nurses are all sugared up.

One nurse couldn't believe the number of different 'chemo sitters' I've had and has never seen anything quite like it! That's a testament to the wonderful friends and family I have who continue to keep me smiling through this.

Bit of a mixed week. I think finishing phase one was a massive milestone. Then an appointment with the breast consultant to discuss surgery. Learnt some new bits that I wasn't entirely expecting but again nothing horrendous in the grand scheme of things. So tired over the weekend, but thankfully Mum and Darren were amazing with the children, so I could take myself off to bed. I was a bit (probably a lot) grumpy on Sunday, so apologies to Darren for that!

Was amazing to see Paula come over the finish line in the half marathon running for FORCE. She has raised over her target of £300 and is truly inspirational. My cake afternoon did nearly £250, so that's a cracking bit of fundraising.

Feeling much more chipper again today (maybe all the sugar from the retro sweets!). Just got to take the rough with the smooth.

So new goal is 17ᵗʰ December. That's the proposed last session of drugs. Hopefully done and dusted just in time for Christmas with surgery in January.

Massive hugs and love to you. I do really appreciate your ongoing support."

Of course, the first thing I do when I get home is to go for a pee, get excited that it's red and take a picture of it! Weirdo.

The excitement is short-lived, as this particular potent cocktail starts knocking me for six around teatime. Feeling a bit sick and sorry for myself, I take myself off for an early night.

Circle of Trust:

"Well done, my love. Sounds like you've got a right old cocktail of goodies to help you get rid of lumpy. So, you have a couple of weeks between each session now? Bit of a rest. Keep going, mate, but remember to rest up when you need it. xx"

"Mel will volunteer to inject you, she loves needles! Seriously, though, well done today, take it easy, don't make too many plans, rest up. xx"

"Um, can I just bring you more chocolate to help you through it?"

"You are incredible, Em, you're on the home run now and can totally do this. xx"

"I hope the injections go okay, reckon once the first one is done the rest will be a walk in the park."

"Thanks, dudes. Yes, thankfully I'm not back in now until 5th November when Becky is joining me. What a birthday treat keeping me and her mum company. I would say 'killing two birds with one stone', but maybe I should just praise her time efficiency. Mel, if you wouldn't mind coming round at 6pm from Thursday for seven days to stab me that would be great. You're a star. I'm off to bed now and feeling very tired and sick after that batch of drugs."

Massaging Mummies:

"Sounds like information overload, Em. Well done for getting through the new hurdles."

"In awe of you, bird. How you just take this in your stride. Today flew by and I was actually gutted I had to go. It's amazing what they all do up

there, the staff, the volunteers, the patients. I felt very humbled to be by your side. I wish to God you weren't having to go through it. Seeing all the love and support you have around is just testament to who you are. Think all that sugar has turned me soppy. I had the privilege of a pee coloured picture!"

"You are amazing, hun, and just take it day by day as you are. If you need any help with the injections just ask. I'm always around. xx"

Shits and Giggles:

"Hope the red drugs are kind to you, my lovely. Roll on 17th December so you can rest up over Christmas and deal with the New Year with Davies determination."

Strong Randy Ladies:

"Wow, busy day then. I have to say, injections aren't too bad when you get used to them. I found that the initial two weeks were the worst until I got so frustrated with Jamie injecting me, and hurting me, that I took it upon myself to take control of the shit I had been dealt and eventually stabbing oneself isn't quite as bad as first thought (although never a pleasure). I found that the fat sides of my stomach worked best for me and also avoided anyone seeing the bruises on my arms, which lead to some funny looks like, 'Are you a battered housewife?' No!"

"Glad everything went okay today. Sounds like a lot of drugs you have to endure but will be worth it. Glad you're feeling more upbeat today."

Local Yocals:

"Well done on ticking this first one off – can't wait to hear about the Tizer pee! What's happening with the surgery? As always, sending love your way. Xx"

"Here's to chapter two! Genuinely love reading your updates and knowing where you're at. Can't imagine the tiredness but so glad you are getting the rest in. If I'm not on shift 17ᵗʰ December I'm putting my hand up! Xx Love ya."

"Wow, chapter two sounds full on! Intrigued by the 'red' drugs concoction and the things it does to your body. I feel there is the potential for a superhero moment here. Always enjoy reading your updates and riding along your journey with you. If pregnant ladies are allowed to accompany you, I'd love to be a chemo sitter. Xx"

"Well, that threw me. Update was very early and wasn't ready to read and reply. Well done, Emma. Your wee will certainly clean the toilet. You are doing amazing and we are all really proud of you. Can you get Darren to inject? Always easier when someone else does it. You will always be my superhero. Xx"

Thank you, lovely ladies. I've only actually got three more Tuesdays to go and they've been snapped up. Helen is joining me on the 26ᵗʰ November if there are any more takers. Can't see why preggars people would be banned, as it's not as though we have catchable diseases, but I'll check next time I'm in.

I don't mind saying about surgery, it just wasn't what I had expected. The ideal is that it has shrunk to nothing. They insert a wire and take out clip and surrounding area to do biopsy. They also inject a dye to locate two closest lymph nodes and remove them for biopsy. That was the bit I wasn't expecting. Don't recall that being mentioned after they said it wasn't in the lymph nodes originally.

The injections also threw me a bit. I'll woman up, of course, but it caught me off guard and I don't like the idea of injecting myself. But then I didn't like the idea of giving birth and I managed that twice, so I think this pales in comparison.

So, there we have it. Moving forward. But bugger me I feel rough today, so I'm off to bed now.

**Hope you are all doing well. I've been thinking of you all
and the new additions to our lives. Xx"**

"Sleep well, lovely."

"Make sure you listen to your body, Emma, sleep well. xx"

*"Ah, Emma, thanks for updating us as always. Sorry it wasn't what
you were expecting but well done for facing it head on. Loads of love.
Xx"*

Cake. Always Cake:

"Can we get pissed at Christmas?"

"Let's do it. Xx"

**"I would very much love to get pissed at Christmas.
Xx"**

ED Fan Club:

*"Big love, Strudders. Thanks for taking the time to keep us all posted.
It's amazing how much strength you've managed to pull out from
nowhere and your perception on these things could give us all a lesson
on outlook. Thinking of you. Xx"*

*"Massive hugs to you. Am I the only one who wants a picture of your
red urine then?"*

*"No, I think I want to see it too… I have a friend who had to do the
same injections recently, so she came to the diabetic (me) to do them for
her as she was terrified of needles and guessed I was an expert. I wasn't
so keen to inject someone else but in for a penny! You'll be fine. Xx"*

**"I'll spare you the red wee. Just think first waz of the
morning after a heavy night on the beers. Thanks for all
the kind words. I'm feeling quite tired and sick now after
the new drugs so I'm off to bed. Take care. Xx"**

"Lots of love, ED. Have a good sleep. Xx"

Wednesday 16th October 2019

My turn for the flu jab. I've stopped feeling guilty now about Toby as I barely felt anything. Drama Queen child!

Cancer Comms

Circle of Trust:

"Two weeks of no chemo – yay. Let's celebrate with more bingo! I'm happy to stab you for the next seven days if needed… but I'm also sure after the first one you'll be fine. But shout if you need me to."

"Thanks, nurse. I'm sure you're right. Once the first stabbing has been dealt with, I'm sure the next ones will be fine. Thank feck the feeling sick has buggered off for the moment. Give me aches and tiredness any day but not sick."

Thursday 17th October 2019

I have to start with the injections today for seven days. I'm really apprehensive about this. Darren offers to do it for me. I'm sure he'd take some satisfaction in jabbing me, but I feel it's something I want to do myself. People living with diabetes have to do this all the time so I'm confident it's something I can get used to. Fortunately, I'm able to pinch more than an inch on my tummy, jab the needle in, and actually it's not anywhere near as bad as I'd worked up in my head.

Friday 18th October 2019

Tonight, I was supposed to be going to a tenth birthday party celebration for the Devon CILEX (Chartered Institute of Legal Executives) Branch. A branch I helped set up. I knew it was optimistic buying tickets for an event on a Friday. Additionally, this week I've started on the stronger shit and I feel rough as a badger's arse. I encourage Darren to still go as he knows a lot of the people going. He could also do with a blowout. Turns out they're excited he's still going and assure me they'll look after him. That means he'll be coming home at God knows what time tomorrow morning!

Saturday 19th October 2019

I do not feel good today. I've got this aching in my lower back and I find it quite painful to walk.

NB – At a later date, after actually reading all the gubbins that came with the injections, I learnt that it stimulated the production of bone marrow and it was likely this that was causing the additional pain and aching. The pain always coincided with the commencement of jabbing and would then subside once I stopped. It varied in painfulness and was never horrendous. I just learnt to take things easier and take paracetamol.

I started feeling quite faint and dizzy and decided to call the hospital on-call number. I don't like making a fuss, as I know they're busy, but this doesn't feel right. I have a lovely chat with the triage nurse who assures me that I am not bothering her. She tells me I need to take it easy. She also encourages me to pop bitesize chocolate in the fridge to eat to boost my energy levels if I'm feeling faint as my body is working really hard after the new drugs. Normally, I would jump at the chance to eat extra chocolate, but I don't like the taste of it anymore. It's a sad day in my world when I have to type that!

I'm to call back at any time if I feel worse.

I need to remain horizontal today.

"I surround myself with positive, loving, supportive people."
(YESmum card)

Sunday 20th October 2019

Cancer Comms

Cake. Always Cake:

"Aiming for 12.30 dinner if that's a winner? Xx"

"That will be lovely. My troop will be coming but I'm going to see how I feel. This round has knocked me for six and feeling quite poorly. Xx"

"Oh, Em, as much as we would all love to see you, maybe use this chance to have some peace and quiet. Xx"

"Oh, Em, that's pants, I really hope you're feeling better soon. If Darren gets called out, we can happily look after the small people and I don't mind coming to help you with bedtime too. I'll have to send you up Aron's homemade cheesecake, he said he promised you some at some point, so beware what you wish for. X"

"I'm around tomorrow if you want me to have Chloe. Xx"

"Ah, you ladies are kind. I think now I'm going to have contingency plans and just slow down. I have Mum on call today. Only Toby tomorrow as I can put Chloe in an extra day and my friend will take him. Now I've had a couple of sugary teas, I've perked up a bit. Maybe tea really does fix everything. I also think the promise of cheesecake has had a motivating effect!"

Monday 21st October 2019

Half term this week. Of course that would coincide with the week one change in medication and what I am now referring to as 'wanky week'.

I have quite literally felt like shit since the change in the consultant's choice of poison. I knew it was likely but bloody hell I underestimated how it might make me feel.

Tuesday evening (not so Happy Chemo Tuesday this time) I started feeling unwell. Darren said I looked like I'd taken something I shouldn't have whilst I sat at the table trying to get my tea in. I haven't been too sure what to do with myself this past week other than remain horizontal as much as possible and let my dear mum and husband swoop in to deal with the small humans.

The new regime of post-treatment medication was consumed, and self-injections administered. Like a lot of new experiences in this process, the injections weren't as bad as I'd envisaged.

So, thank God for my amazing mummy who turned up like Nanny McPhee to help with Toby and Chloe today.

Cancer Comms

Local Yocals:

"**Morning, lovely ladies. As much as I'd love to see you guys tonight, I'm not going to be able to make it. This new batch of drugs has really knocked me for six and I've felt really poorly. Thankfully I've turned a corner today and feel a lot better, but I've been going to bed shortly after the kids, so don't really feel up to being out and about late. Hope you are all okay and hopefully catch up soon. Enjoy the half term. Xx**"

"Really sorry not to see you tonight. Thankfully not too many of these nasty drugs rounds. Stay positive and anything we can do please shout. Xx"

"Absolutely. Completely understand, we will miss you. Loads of love. Xx"

"You will be missed tonight but completely understand. Looking after yourself needs to be the priority. Take care. Xx"

"Oh, Emma, so sorry to hear this next batch of meds aren't as kind to you. Will miss you tonight but totally understand. Please let us know if there is anything we can do, any time. Love you lots. Xx"

Tuesday 22nd October 2019

'Happy Chemo Tuesday.'

Oh wait, no it isn't. For the first Tuesday in three months I'm not frequenting a hospital to have my magical medicine pumped into me.

This feels amazing.

I instead spent the day at FORCE for my first session of acupuncture and a 'Look Good Feel Great' pamper session.

I've never really understood how acupuncture works, and a few years ago would have probably pooh-poohed the idea as a bit alternative and what good would it do? Given the multiple times I wake up at night sweating my arse off, I will try literally anything. I can't say I was excited by the prospect of having needles stuck into me, but the reality was pretty pain free. Once you see past the five other people sitting there with multiple orange pins sticking out of their ears, it was quite relaxing and great to hear that the mini ear stabbings actually reap results.

It was also lovely to meet new people my age who are slightly further through their respective treatments than I am. To hear how the acupuncture has helped them. To see that their hair is growing back. To hear how they're returning to work, and some form of normality.

Whilst we're on the topic of hot sweats I've forgotten to

mention about my amazing purchase from Amazon, my Chillow Pillow cooling pad. They come in various sizes and you can even buy big ones to sleep on. Think when you're on holiday, you've got a bit hot sunbathing and it's time for a refreshing dip in the pool to instantly cool off. Well that's what this does. You can lie directly on it or pop it inside your pillow case. When I wake up feeling like I'm in a sauna I pop it on my pillow for instant cooling gratification. And then repeat the exercise multiple times...

Anyway, back to today.

From 1–3pm it was time for the 'Look Good, Feel Great' pamper session. AMAZING.

Little bit of history. Thirty years ago, a celebrity in America, diagnosed with cancer, woke up one morning feeling a bit under the weather and asked herself what would she normally be doing? Usually, her make-up artist would be coming over and after being 'made up' she felt better and that was where the idea was born. It's been going in this country for twenty-five years and is utilised by 135 hospitals.

The room was set up with stations for about ten of us with little mirrors and make up bags, the contents of which contained approximately £350–£400 of make-up donated by the beauty industry. Five make-up artists then volunteered their time for the next two hours, talking us through the products and how to apply them.

Now, I'm relatively new to the world of 'cleanse, tone, moisturize (CTM)', and feared they would need substantially more than two hours to educate me on the various products. When I was thirty, I walked into Debenhams, sourced the least orange-looking beauty person, and asked if they could 'help me'. When asked about my skincare routine, and I looked at them blankly, she took pity on me and started from scratch. Ten years later, I am fully aware of the order that cleanse, tone and moisturise should happen, but not really any the wiser on how to create smoky eyes or contouring. I'm also only half committed to the process, as although I'll CTM in the morning, I then take my minimal make up off with a wet wipe in the evening. From the look on Martin's face, this revelation was the cardinal sin.

Luckily for me, I was picked quite a few times to be their 'model', which meant they applied the make-up to me. I felt great when it was all done with, but realised I might struggle to recreate the effect, as I'd had a professional make-up artist apply the majority of my make-up.

This was such a great session and really needed after the 'wanky week' I'd just had. I've even joked to my friends that if they receive random beauty products for Christmas it will be a bit of re-gifting on my part.

Wednesday 23rd October 2019

I'd used a visit to Wookey Hole as a bribe for good behaviour from Toby in the couple of weeks leading up to half term. The plan was for Chloe to go to nursery as usual and for Darren and I to take Toby on his own to get some quality time with him. Well, nothing ever goes quite to plan, does it? That would be boring. I have now developed a cold, probably lovingly shared by the smaller small human, and it feels like daggers in my throat. Chloe is also borderline not well enough to fob off onto nursery. Given that we will be driving one and a half hours away with no reception as we descend into the caves, I took the decision that we should take her with us. We are going with Russell, Charlene, Skye and Jake, so safety in numbers with older children should see us through this.

I think I was too ambitious! Chloe went slightly feral in the underground caves, wanting to run off. Standard behaviour for a nearly two-year-old, but quite exhausting preventing her from falling into cavernous pits. She seemed rather indifferent to the display of stalagmites (mites grow up) and stalactites (and tights come down!).

As we went deeper, I whipped my hat off and, accompanied

by my bald brother, we looked like the creatures from *The Descent*. Shit scariest film I have ever watched and thankfully hadn't thought about when I was booking the tickets. I'm confident that other than me and my brother there were no other similar looking creatures lurking down there.

I'd visited Wookey Hole as a child but it now has 'soft play'. Wonderful words to any parent's ears who want to let small humans run off some steam whilst you grab a hot cup of tea. Fortunately, Auntie Charlene was up for accompanying Chloe, so I could sit down and re-charge and catch up with my brother.

Having been fleeced in the shop, we set off home, stopping for a nutritious McDonald's tea at Cullompton services.

We'd done it. We'd had our day at Wookey Hole. The children seemed happy and now unconscious in bed, quickly followed by me. I can feel that I'm going to suffer for this.

Friday 25ᵗʰ October 2019

And suffer I did. Silly girl. I need to learn (I've already typed this before, so I'm not sure I will) that I just cannot keep up my usual pace of life.

My poor immune system is struggling to fight off this sore throat and blocked nose. My mouth is sporting painful ulcers, which is limiting my choice of foods to mushed up soft stuff. I had to pop into the hospital today as they wanted to check me over. I'd only phoned to update them on my current manky mouth/throat situation and to seek some advice, but they wanted me to come in for some observations. I had been popping pills like no one's business, and getting through gallons of Diflam (antiseptic throat spray), so had been doing everything they would recommend but I was informed in no uncertain terms that they needed to know if I was feeling like this. I'm quite accustomed to sore throats and snotty noses at this time of year but, as I was told, not under these circumstances. I considered myself told off and promised that I would be less Britishly stoic and phone sooner in the future.

"I find the beauty in every day."
(YESmum card)

Cancer Comms

Shits and Giggles:

"How are you doing, Strudders? Missed your update this week, although I'm sure you are pleased to not have to go every week now. xx"

"Hey lovelies. I've been quite poorly following the change in drugs and now my immune system is weaker I've picked up a bug that usually wouldn't bother me. Apparently, I mustn't soldier on like I normally would but stop. My ticking off from the hospital today! Had to go in for a little check but they're happy with me and gave me some meds. My mum has basically just done everything for me today. But mentally I'm good and focused on the end goal. You guys both okay? x"

"Ah, sorry to hear you've had a bug. Suppose it's inevitable with a reduced immunity but thank God for mums, eh."

Saturday 26ᵗʰ October 2019

Starting to feel more human again.

Toby's best mate Thomas is coming for a sleepover today. Although we will be outnumbered three to two on the small human front, I am confident that Darren and I can orchestrate the 'Halloween fun' I have planned. The pumpkin trail will wear the two bigger ones out with some physical scootering around. We will then carve pumpkins, draw Halloween-themed pictures and eat Halloween-themed goodies. And that was pretty much how the day panned out with the standard balance of excitement, moaning and repeated requests to 'calm down' and 'listen'.

I treated myself to a tub of Ben & Jerry's Cookie Dough ice cream with the justification that it would help my still recovering sore throat. In all truthfulness, it wasn't that rewarding as I couldn't really taste it, but the coolness felt nice.

Cancer Comms

Strong Randy Ladies:

"Hope you're all good, Em. I'm missing my weekly updates, although not wishing another treatment upon you!"

Monday 28th October 2019

I am fixed. Well, temporarily anyway. I am back to my normal non-feeling-like-shit self.

Update scan day today. Another appointment to bear my boob to another stranger and now I think nothing of it. I think I have got my norks out more this year than I did on my Club 18-30 holiday to Ibiza in my twenties.

28th June scan – confirms the existence of lumpy.
Fast forward four months:
28th October scan – little bugger fails to put in a show.
So, although this is not the all-clear (yet) and I need to continue with the treatment plan (three more sessions of chemo and surgery) this is exciting news for a Monday.

Okay, exciting is rather an understatement. I might have leaked from my eyes a little (a lot) after this news. Four months and the little bugger has buggered off. I feel beyond relieved and – given that this is week three (which I'm naming 'wonderful week') – I might even have a cheeky G&T in celebration.

I've updated Toby by telling him the lump has gone but mummy still has to finish the medicine and have an operation. He's happy the bad boob bug has gone but not happy about me having to keep having the medicine. He chose for me to read *Mummy's Lump* again this evening. Luckily, we didn't have any follow-up questions this time and he seemed satisfied he knew the current position.

With the combination of feeling well and today's good news, I'm back to my usual self of annoying Darren to which he exclaimed he thinks he preferred me last week when I was ill!

We also discussed his social life this month. Now I appreciate I had encouraged him to go out with his man friends to get some down time. However, I pointed out that I now thought he was perhaps taking the piss with not one but two cinema outings this month, a 'session' last weekend and him taking in a show with his mum this week! We're not even going to visit the topic of the Rugby World Cup final next weekend. How convenient that he will have to be in the pub for 8am in the morning. We can write off seeing him until Sunday. Phone call to Mum to check her availability for Saturday!

Cancer Comms

Circle of Trust:

"So pleased. Amazing news, dude, and I even forgive you for fancying Dr Nobhead."

"Yay, so happy to see this, especially after watching the Stand Up to Cancer Gogglebox last week, I'm still in trauma with that story. Such a good result for you, you'll be back to normal in no time. Keep thinking what's ahead is a damn sight less horrific than looking back. xx"

"Em, this is fantastic. Celebratory pre-school drink?"

"Always looking forward, never back."

"Woo hooooooo, best news ever. You kicked ass and will continue to do so. So pleased that little fucker has left the building. xx"

"Ah, Em, I couldn't be happier for you. This is such good news and I definitely think you should go have a pre-school pick up drink. You've done amazing and I look forward to the all-clear message. When we get that I think we should all go out for a celebratory drink. xxx"

Massaging Mummies:

Lots of whoop whoops and whooooo hooos.

"See ya, ya lumpy bastard. Don't come back, you prick."

"Great news and definitely a great start to the week. So pleased. xx"

Shits and Giggles:

"So freaking fantastic. Best Monday news ever."

"This is the kind of message I like a lot. Sorry it's taken me my usual twelve plus hours to respond, but I did read it just as I arrived at a conference yesterday. I sat next to a lovely psychologist who asked me if I was okay when he saw me well up. I said that I had just read a good news message that had made me very happy. He nodded understandably and said, 'Then today is a good day.' Spreading the love to Devon from Sheffield via the medium of WhatsApp. Over the moon for you, Em – lots of love."

Strong Randy Ladies:

"This is flipping fantastic news for a Monday. Hoorahhh!!! God you girls are the secret to all my emotions lately. I'm just so happy to read this. xx"

"Bloody amazing news. Made my Monday. xx"

Local Yocals:

"Aw, love, that is so brilliant. So pleased for you, Em. x"
"Yessssssss! Such good news, Emma! X"
"Emma, this is excellent news! So happy for such amazing progress and here's hoping and praying that the all-clear isn't too far away."
"Wow, Emma, that is amazing Monday news. Xx"
"Emma, that is great news. Happy Bloody Monday. Xx"

Cake. Always Cake:

"Fan-fucking-tastic news! I'm so pleased for you. Xx"
"Woohoo! Amazing news, you awesome person. Xx"

ED Fan Club:

"I was thinking of you in the shower this morning. As you do. Was about to text to ask how you are. This is great news. Xx"
"Fantastic news. Xx"
"Boom. Good work, ED. Xx"
"Frickin' awesome."
"This is beyond brilliant. Well done, ED. Xx"

Tuesday 29th October 2019

Second round of mini ear stabbings (acupuncture). I've actually noticed a difference already in the frequency of the dreaded sweats. They've definitely reduced from every thirty minutes or so to two-hourly. I'm encouraged to learn that this should only get better as the course continues. It's great to have a natter with the other ladies in the group.

Wednesday 30ᵗʰ October 2019

Facebook:

Does anybody have a long black coat I could borrow for Halloween tomorrow please?

I've decided to utilise my unusual gift this year and go trick or treating with the kids as Uncle Fester. Lord Voldemort has a funny nose and I draw the line at plastic surgery just for the occasion. Pinhead from Hellraiser seemed cool but although I'm getting into my acupuncture all those needles in the head seemed a bit too much effort.

"What about Dr Evil?"

"Fabulous idea, though you're far too gorgeous for Fester."

"Nice try but you're too pretty! You're going to need a LOT of makeup! Funny though!"

"Get some bin bags round you, bird. Absolute legend you are xxx"

Thursday 31ˢᵗ October 2019

I love Halloween and dressing up. Pre-small humans we threw some awesome Halloween parties at our old gaff. One year, Darren covered the outside of the house in cardboard and turned it into a castle. The next it was a crime scene. I think you get the gist of how we go all in on this.

I'm excited with my costume this year. A long black coat kindly loaned to me by Petra, some dark eye shadow and with my bald head I'm good to go. Easiest costume ever. I meet another Uncle Fester out and about and receive a nod of appreciation from him under his fake bald hat! Downside is it's bloody chilly around the swede, so I have to wear a woolly hat for some of it.

So, cancer has afforded me a unique opportunity this year and I grabbed it.

Cumulative side effect nasties after thirteen sessions:

- Cancer fatigue. I could fall asleep on a washing line when the fog descends.
- Spotty teenager skin.
- Hair loss (current trend – the bald egg look).
- Dry skin (cream me up, baby!).
- Chemo brain (sorry what was I saying again?).
- Loss of taste, mouth ulcers and dry mouth.
- The squits (diarrhoea).

October – Looking Back

I'm bloody tired this month and it would appear still not totally heeding my own advice to slow the hell up. It's not that I'm in denial about what is going on but I'm just finding it difficult to not just live life at a slower pace but at a *much* slower pace. I feel shit so I rest. Then I feel fine again. Do what I think I can manage and then feel a bit shit again. And repeat!

It's been another month of good progress. Finishing one lot of drugs, straight onto the next. Hardcore. Lumpy running scared. Adjusting to a new treatment regime. I realised I had become quite dependent on visiting the ward every week. Now I'm down to every three weeks I feel a little bit lost, like my safety blanket has been pulled away a little bit. I have all the numbers to phone if I need them, but I guess it was just the little extra bit of security knowing I was going in to see those specialist nurses each week.

Surviving half-term with a lot of help from my mum and not missing out on doing fun family stuff. I've so wanted to keep things as normal as possible for the kids and to a certain extent I think I'm still managing to do that with extra help. Thank you to everyone, but especially Mum, Dad and Darren. Xx

November 2019

Friday 1ˢᵗ November 2019

Ah November. The month of a million birthdays. If September doesn't push us over the edge, the month before Christmas makes a second attempt!

Both our children are amorous Valentine's Day babies, after a night on the drinkypoos, born four years apart with birthdays within a week of each other. Toby is a vodka baby (24ᵗʰ). Chloe a gin baby (17ᵗʰ). I have, however, stopped calling them this out loud after Toby asked me, *"Mummy, is Chloe a vodka baby like me?!"*

Throw this on top of Russell's (brother – 16ᵗʰ), Charlene's (sister-in-law – 14ᵗʰ), my good friend Becky's (5ᵗʰ) and four other small human's birthdays, that's a busy month.

Christmas doesn't get a mention in this house until after the 24ᵗʰ.

For the past couple of years, Toby has had a big birthday party with a ridiculous amount of sugar-fueled excitable friends in attendance. I don't have that in me this year and suggest he might like to take a couple of friends out for a treat and something to eat instead. He can choose what he'd like to do. Anything.

Of course, he chooses swimming. The one thing I can't actually do because I have to keep my PICC line dry. I mention this to him, thinking he might like to do something else, but he's adamant on swimming.

"Mummy, you can watch. I'll keep getting out and coming over to check that you're okay."

Ah, bless him. Okay, swimming it is then, but I'm going to need to enlist the help of additional big humans to help Darren whilst I watch from the sidelines. I'm secretly pleased, as the new size twelve cozzy I bought for our holiday back in the summer would now only fit one leg, as I've popped on a bit of timber.

Another oncology appointment today. I've tolerated the treatment well up until the change, but I tell the consultant that it left me feeling proper shit for the first week. I'm glad I told her this because she says she can reduce the potency by 20% given that it appears to have shrunk away. Lesson here, never suffer in silence. If they don't know there's something wrong, they can't help you.

I also show her my zombie nails that are turning yellow and black and raising off their nail beds. I thought I'd got away with this. They'd hung in so well, but this new red stuff is even too much for them! She refers to some oil you can buy online for £50 that someone told her about, but she can't attest to its effectiveness. A cheaper option could be wearing purple or black nail varnish. I think I'll give that a bash.

PICC line care done, it's out for lunch with Dad.

Monday 4ᵗʰ November

Amazing news today. The results from the genetics clinic are in. The test found no evidence of a defect in either my BRAC1 or BRAC2 genes, so it is unlikely that this is what caused my cancer. Once I'm done with treatment, I just need to remain breast aware and to attend follow up annual screenings by the breast care team. So, no decisions about removing bits have to be made. I'm beyond relieved.

Cancer Comms

"Just had my genetics tests back and there is nothing wrong with my genes, so I was just unlucky. What a relief. If one in eight ladies get breast cancer, we can consider this as me taking one for the team and we're all good now. xx"

Circle of Trust:

"Whoop whoop! That's great news."
"Awesome, great news for little Chloe."
"Fab news and thanks for taking one for the team! xx"

Massaging Mummies:

"This is bloody brilliant news, but I'm gutted anyone had to take one for the team. They did pick the wrong one to mess with, though. Love you to bits. Always here. Xx"

Local Yocals:

"Wahoooooo. Such a beaut. X"
"I'm really hoping I can make Friday. If I feel the way I did last time, I'm afraid I won't be able to. But the consultant has reduced my prescription by 20%, so I'm optimistic I'll feel 20% less shit. Xx"
"Aw hun, fingers crossed. But don't worry at all if you can't or just want to stay an hour or whatever. How have you been the last few days? X"
"Bloody amazing the past week. Back to my normal self, until tomorrow! But only three more."
"20% less shit! Love it. Here's hoping."

Tuesday 5th November 2019 – Chemo Round Fourteen

"Courage, dear heart."
(YESmum card)

"Remember, remember the 5th of November. Cupcakes, laughs and plop(?!) The latter being a card game of Top Plops (like Top Trumps). What does it say about me that there have been a number of poo-related activities during my chemo sessions?

It's been a three-week gap since the last poisoning. Loads has happened. Go grab a cuppa, sit back, and here we go...

So, I merrily updated that everything went in fine at the last update. Well, the new concoction rendered me feeling pretty shitty the same day for about a week. Darren said I looked like I'd taken something I shouldn't have. Imagine your worst hangover when you can't lift your head off the pillow but lasting a week. This trumped my holiday to Ibiza in my twenties, and I thought I'd done some damage then. I will admit I did start feeling a bit sorry for myself. That was week one in this new cycle, which I'm naming 'wanky week'. Thank goodness for my lovely mum who swooped in like Nanny McPhee and kept the wheels turning.

Week two might have been better had I not overdone it with a half term day trip to Wookey Hole. It would appear I'm still not learning to take it easy and traipsing through damp caves trying to stop a one-year-old falling into the abyss was challenging. I did have fun whipping my hat off and looking like one of those creatures from *The Descent*. I thought one day would be fine, I was wrong, and succumbed to the nasties lovingly passed on by the small humans. Had to pop into hospital for some checks but all okay, accompanied with a slap on the wrist for not phoning sooner.

Acupuncture commenced in an attempt to stop the hot sweats. Little group of us all sitting with ten orange pins sticking out of our ears. Surprisingly relaxing.

Injecting myself went well. It was only a little prick in the end. So many jokes to be had, but I'll leave that there!

'Look good, feel great' pamper session was amazing and a real pick me up after wanky week. Five make-up artists volunteering their time for two hours with £400 worth of make-up gifted to each of us. I didn't even look like an Oompa Loompa when all done.

Halloween was great fun. Utilising the unique gift I've been given this year, Uncle Fester is a very cheap and easy outfit, if not a bit chilly.

My nails are protesting now and are starting to look like something that is past its sell-by date. I'm referring to them as my 'zombie nails'.

But saving the best for last, the great news is that lumpy is no longer getting on my tits as I've killed him off and there is nothing wrong with my genes. I'm beyond relieved that I don't have to consider having bits of me removed. So, I was just unlucky. In other ways, though, lucky as I'm getting a good outcome and ironically having this has given me some lovely unexpected experiences.

And week three has felt amazing. For a good few days, I've felt like my normal old self, just a lot less hairy. I even had two G&Ts on Friday. Party animal.

Back to my poisoning session today and my chemo sitter was Becky. On her birthday, she chose to sit in a hospital ward. Going the extra mile, or what? We had two and a half hours of cake, sweets, British Trivia quiz, Top Plops, would you rather game and laughs. I gave her a bottle of tequila as a present. Some of the patients and nurses were up for us cracking it open. I'd rather take my chances with the red cocktail of drugs. A reduced dose by 20%, so I'm hoping I feel 20% less shit this week.

So, there we go. Two of four in the old bird. I've had quite a few texts asking how people can help me. In terms of practical arrangements, we're very much sorted, thank you, but it's the text messages that are priceless, especially during wanky week, so please keep them coming. Xxx

Bonfire Night. I feel okay this time round, so we're off down to Exmouth with the kids to meet up with my brother and his family, grab some fish and chips and watch the fireworks.

I am so hot in the fish and chip restaurant that I actually take my hat off for the first time in public, revealing the smooth egghead. It felt like a big thing to do, I was a bit self-conscious, but everyone I was with didn't bat an eyelid and that in turn made me feel more confident.

The kids loved the fireworks as we all stood huddled up and twiddled their sparklers around. I'm so glad we ventured out, but as the evening draws to an end, I start to feel tired and achy. A little reminder that all is not well, and my body is adjusting to a new cocktail after the over-indulgence on the former one.

Cancer Comms

Circle of Trust:

"£400 worth? Jealous. But as always, smashing it, dude! And you are definitely nearing the chemo finish line."

"Tell me about it. Amazing company. I could have re-gifted had I not used a little bit of everything."

"Oh, mate I would have used all of it too! Though next time I see you I expect a full face of slap."

"*Great update, mate. All good news and glad you're getting something nice as well as the shite that's being put in you! Well done for completion of number two. The end is near.*"

Massaging Mummies:

"*Love you, Emma! You are a diamond. xx*"

"*You are amazing, hun. So proud of you. Love you. xx*"

"*What an absolute legend you are, bird. Fuck all those popstars, actresses and actors, any icons, even the royals. You are the biggest superstar in my eyes. Love you millions. xx*"

"Oh, I'm feeling the love. Jo, you're making me feel like a Z-lister. I might contact *Hello* magazine for a six-page spread."

"*I'll contact them myself, bird. Z-lister ahoy.*"

"*Well, one word for all that, 'Epic'. You've been very busy for a very tired person! The end is in sight. Fingers crossed for a less shit week. Big love! Here's to being the luckiest unlucky person. See, best type of cancer!*"

Strong Randy Ladies:

"*I've tried reading this three times and keep having to return to read the rest. Anyone would think this is all about you! Well done. Two down, two to go. Deserves a few whoops. Hope you are feeling okay this evening. Have a great time at the fireworks.*"

"*Whoop whoop from me. Amazing news this week with the gene results. Hope you manage to enjoy the fireworks and are not feeling too rubbish.*"

Local Yocals:

"*Ah, Emma, what a great update, thank you for taking the time to share with us. How are you feeling after today's treatment? Fingers crossed your prediction of 20% less shit comes true. Lots of love to you. Xx"*

"At the moment I feel fine. Just penning my thoughts for my *Sunday Times* bestselling novel! Going to the fireworks later in Exmouth, but even if the hard stuff has kicked in, I can just sit in the car looking like someone off their tits! Big love right back. X"

"Emma, you are literally incredible. Also, I'm crying with happiness and relief at the results of your tests and the fact that lumpy is being dealt with. I'm sorry these new drugs are knocking you sideways, it sounds really awful, so badly hoping you manage to keep your chin up the way you have done to this point right to the end of this insane journey. You are very much loved."

Cake. Always Cake:

"You're an absolute trooper, Em, truly. So glad that your genes are sound. Hope wanky week was a one-time wonder and you don't feel so shit this time. And any time you want to crab dance past my window, carry on."

"Merryn had her jabs today and chose this as her treat (princess plait). Feel free to borrow it anytime, Em. Love you, bird. X"

"Oh, I like that. I think I might need to also borrow one of Phoebe's amazing headbands to attach it to, though. Crab dancing my way through life! 'Mummy, who's that at the window?' 'Oh God, don't look, darling, she'll get bored and go away in a minute!'"

"Didn't realise you could lipread."

ED Fan Club:

"Another fabulous update. I loved the fancy dress btw. Massively relieved that lumpy is no more but sorry the drugs are anything but recreational. Please learn to take it easy. Xx"

"Another awesome read, Emma, so much chuffin' excellent stuff in amongst the tough stuff. Hoping this week is much less wanky for you. Sending lots of love. Xx"

Becky's words

I've known Becky since I was thirteen and have lived with her a number of times! I imagine we'll be friends forever as we've got too much shit on each other to fall out! Here's what the birthday girl has to say on all these goings on:

I woke up on Friday 14th June, looking forward to a catch-up lunch with Emma and Nicki, and while getting ready I get a text:

"I might need to ask a favour please! I've had to take an urgent GP appointment at 11:30am this morning and could use a hand with Chloe. I found a lump under my breast and just want to get it looked at ASAP. xx"

I wasn't concerned, it was going to be nothing, maybe a cyst, but there is no way it's going to be cancer, it can't be. Emma and I are the same age, we've known each other since we were at High School together, there is no way she can have cancer.

When Em was back from the appointment and said she was being referred, I still couldn't believe it was anything terrible. We kept it light, made jokes about getting new boobs if it was anything serious, fully believing that that could never happen, but it did.

I remember exactly where I was when the message came through that Emma had had her appointment and was given the news. I was driving to an appointment in Taunton and it flashed up on my watch. Emma had cancer. Fuck, no, she's joking, right? I parked up and read the message fully on my phone. I couldn't take it in, not Emma, she can't have cancer. It took quite a while to really understand that it was real, it really was happening, and when I got home that night I remember sitting in bed and it hit me; I cried.

We are a very close group of friends, there is no way she was leaving us, and we leapt into action. What can we do to help her through this? We arranged a surprise catch up, thought of all the things we could get her to help her through and bundled these together (twat hat, moisturisers, herbal teas, boiled sweets…), we talked about which days we could help with things such as childcare between us all, and we even discussed all getting the same tattoos to show our solidarity (reading this is probably the first Emma knows of that one!). Whatever Em needed, we would be right there for her.

Em's positivity throughout all this clearly helped her to cope, but it also helped us all to cope too. One of my favourite evenings was spent at Emma's playing bingo with our friends. We all brought prizes to win, which varied from beautiful handmade coasters through to a toilet roll and, of course, wine! We had so much fun and laughed a lot and, even though by this point she had lost her hair, she wasn't Emma with cancer, we were just hanging out with Em.

It sounds awful saying this, but I started to look forward to the humorous weekly updates, the latest instalment in the adventure. We would also try to respond with humour too, it's what Emma wanted. I would read them out to colleagues, and they were all inspired by her strength and humour. So many responded with, 'She should write a book!'

Then came the call for chemo sitters! I wanted to be there to support but the sessions were always on a Tuesday when I work. They filled up so fast that the ones left I couldn't take leave. I felt so bad not being able to be there during the first round of poisonings, so when the dates came in for the second round I got in early. Em gave me a list of dates to pick from but left one out, "Aren't you having a session on the 5th November? I could come with you that day." But it wasn't listed! It was my birthday, so

Emma didn't think I'd want to spend my birthday on a chemo ward, but she was so wrong. I wasn't spending my birthday on a chemo ward; I was spending my birthday with one of my very best friends!

There had been many chemo sitters before me, each one bringing different exciting games and activities to pass the time – oh Christ, what do I bring?! So much pressure to meet the standards set by others! Poo, it has to be something to do with poo, so Plop Trumps it was. Also, Would You Rather, which was aimed at kids but posed really interesting questions like 'Would you rather have unlimited toys or unlimited sweets?' and other such questions, which now as an adult you would have a very different perspective on. And, of course, cake; it was my birthday! It sounds like a really strange thing to say but I had a great time in hospital with Em. We talked and laughed and I totally forgot why we were there. We could have been anywhere and when the nurse came and told Emma she was done, I was almost sad that we couldn't stay there longer (sorry Em!).

Wednesday 6th November 2019

As part of my 'ongoing care pathway', I'm invited to attend a 'Well-being Clinic' today. I'm a good way down my treatment journey, so I'm already familiar with the earlier steps of diagnosis and treatment. It's really useful to hear about diet and exercise and the importance of both. I have to admit I've put on rather a lot of weight and it's not wholly attributable to the medication. The Trust run a healthy eating workshop, which I'll be signing up to next year once I've had my surgery. With access to a dietician and a physiotherapist, it would be rude not to.

Friday 8th November 2019

Cancer Comms

Local Yocals:

"I am sorry but as the day's gone on, I'm absolutely shattered (having done nothing!) and think I'll be going to bed before you even get going. Hope you have a fantastic evening, ladies. Xx"

"Aw, Em! Obviously gutted but of course understand. Maybe next month we should do breakfast meet up prior to your treatment and a little closer to Grace in the hope of a full house? Miss you. Xx"

"Aww, Emma, yes we totally understand. That's a fab idea, Pip. Xx"

Saturday 9th November 2019

Cancer Comms

Massaging Mummies:

"Hi girls. I'm really sorry but I'm not going to be able to make tonight. I'm really wiped out again after this last lot and my blood count is low, so I'm feeling proper knackered and sleeping a lot. Darren has braved soft play on his own! Hope you have a fantastic night and I look forward to catching up soon. xx"

"Will miss you. We will need to do it again once Emma is done and dusted with chemo! Hope you have a relaxing night .x"

Sunday 10ᵗʰ November 2019

With both Toby and Darren staying out last night with their respective friends for 'boy down time', I enjoyed a night with just the girls – Mum and Chloe.

I gave poor old Mum a fright today. I really wasn't feeling very well when I got up. At one point I was sitting on the loo and had to call out for her as I just felt so strange, like I was going to pass out. As the morning went on, I started to feel really short of breath and really strange. I telephoned the hospital and they asked me to come in so they could check me out. Poor old Darren had to cut short his eagerly awaited lie in and fry up.

Mum dropped us to the ward. By this point I was feeling utter shite. Very cold, short of breath and like death warmed up. I hadn't felt this ill in a long time, but it was the dizziness and disorientation that was worrying me. The nurse who took my observations was lovely and popped some antibiotics into my PICC line. They decided to keep me in to monitor me, which I was extremely thankful for.

I was already in a side room, but they said they had another room I could use. Blimey, talk about winning the jackpot. I was taken to a room they use for young families. It was amazing. Xbox, TV, tea making facilities, en-suite wet room. There was even an outside garden with wind chimes. Darren also thought he'd won the jackpot, as rather than parenting slightly hungover, he now got to sleep the day away in a reclining chair.

Throughout the day, I was checked on by various nurses and doctors. I was fed and watered and everybody I met was absolutely lovely. If you weren't required to be poorly, I would check into these facilities again!

Mum dropped in a few more bits for me later in the day, as I hadn't been expecting to stay overnight. Toby had put a picture of himself in the bag, *"So mummy doesn't forget what I look like."*

Cancer Comms

Circle of Trust:

"So, me thinks this isn't the usual hospitality on Yeo ward! PlayStation, TV, tea facilities and a garden! Just getting checked over, not feeling too great. Bloody drugs. Nothing to worry about. xx"

"Sorry you're not feeling too great again, hopefully it's just wanky week and nothing to worry about. xx"

"Oh no, hope you're not in there too long, my lovely. Well done for being sensible and going in, though, my beaut. xx"

"I'm being very well looked after. Catching up with X Factor. Just a bit shaky and funny feeling. Sure the drugs will sort me out. I get a free stay tonight."

"Oohh nice, have a peaceful night. I say 'oohh nice' not in a 'have fun' way, bye, obviously not nice. BTW not bye! Don't pass away or anything, not ready for byes yet! xx"

"Not planning on it anytime soon, you pleb!"

"Oh, mate, look at it like a dodgy spa stay!"

"Dodgy spa? This room is lovely. I have my own garden! Room service will be coming in a moment with my pasta!"

"It does look lovely. Looks like you hit the jackpot with that little number. Can you eke it out for a week? Just get Darren and the kids to pop in and see you, but leave so you can have a peaceful night's sleep all week."

"Deffo feel like I've hit the jackpot. It's been so peaceful in here today. Maybe I was just proper fucked and needed some peace!"

"It's amazing what a bit of good peace and quiet can do. I'm glad it's made a difference to how you're feeling with wanky week. x"

Monday 11ᵗʰ November 2019

I was actually looking forward to a good night's sleep without being woken by small humans. Well, think again. Hospitals don't appear to sleep and neither did I. The wind chimes weren't so lovely during the night! The wards are also quite busy and then there's observations and medication to be given at unsavoury times.

I get visited by some of my hospital chums. Kelly brings me and Mum a bacon sarnie.

I'm knackered but I feel a damn sight better than I did yesterday. I get taken down for a chest X-ray, which shows there's nothing untoward going on there. As I'm wheeled down the corridor, I'm regretting my choice of slippers – pink sparkly fluffy things with ears!

Blood results come back all fine, so there's no infection to indicate why I felt so pants yesterday. Later in the day, I'm discharged home to just take it easy.

"I begin and end each day with gratitude."
(YESmum card)

Cancer Comms

Circle of Trust:

"Pleased to report I'm very much alive!"
"I've been worried I cursed you with a goodbye and you would have taken it literally! Happy to see you made it through the night. xx"
"I was contemplating how I could shit you up about that!"
"So glad you're still with us! Are you feeling better today?"

Tuesday 12th November 2019

Cancer Comms

Strong Randy Ladies:

"Hey ladies. We need a date in the diary. Emma, how have you been feeling? I hope wanky week has been a bit less wanky with the 20% reduction. Do you fancy meeting at George and Dragon for a change, if Emma feels up to it? Could do 25th so it's before next chemo? x"

"Sounds fabulous to me. Hope you're both okay. Do you know it's six weeks until Christmas? That's six bloody weeks, argghh!"

"Hiya. Yes dates. Little lights at the end of tunnels is what I need. I've popped that in the diary and hopefully I'll be good. Been quite poorly again and had to have a little twenty-four-hour stay in hospital on Sunday. They never got to the bottom of specifically what was wrong, but I was so short of breath and felt really weird. Anyway, I got my own room with an en-suite, TV, tea making facilities and a garden! I was the luckiest poorly person on that ward! Having now read the side effects from the injections I have to self-administer for seven days post treatment, I reckon it's those buggers and not the chemo making me ill. Anyhoo, just relax, nearly there and this short-term pain is much better than the alternative of pushing up the daisies! Hope you girls have a relatively stress-free day. xx"

"Bloody hell, Em, sounds like this round is taking its toll. You and your usual humour, though, 'pushing up the daisies!' You do make me laugh. Well, if you need anything at all, let me know. Even if it's just a 'come make me a cup of tea and fuck off again as I'm tired', I'm amenable to that. Hope you are feeling better soon and look forward to our next catch up. xx"

"Sorry to hear that, Em. Sounds horrible. Sending lots of love. If you need anything, let us know. xx"

Sunday 17ᵗʰ November 2019

A hat-trick of birthday celebrations.

Charlene's birthday was Thursday. We went for a family lunch yesterday for Russell's birthday and today is Chloe's second birthday.

Thankfully, I'm feeling much better, having rested all week and literally done nothing.

Chloe's birthday is a small gathering of a couple of neighbours with small humans her age and immediate family. She doesn't really know what's going on, but is excited to have lots of attention and new toys. I think I'm more excited than she is and just happy that I feel well enough to enjoy it with her. I even managed to home bake a chocolate 'number two' cake (using a shaped tin) with lines of smarties. I made the same cake for Toby's second birthday, so was determined that she would get the same 'mum attempts to bake at least one birthday cake in their lifetime' treatment. I've treated them equally and now feel happy to shop buy all future cakes.

We have a little birthday tea with all the usual beige food that children enjoy with a token plate of peppers and cucumber thrown in and rejected. Of course, the jelly and ice cream goes down a treat.

It was an amazing day. Once again, all my friends and family stepped in, meaning I didn't need to try and be the hostess with the mostess, and for that I am so grateful.

Tuesday 19ᵗʰ November 2019

During acupuncture today I tell Cath that my thermostat appears to be broken. My internal thermostat that is. In general, the hot sweats have greatly reduced, but in addition to feeling hot I can now feel very cold. Apparently, this is normal and should start balancing itself out, so that's reassuring to hear. I'm very grateful that after only two sessions I can already see a marked difference.

Friday 22nd November 2019

Oh 'wonderful week', what a great week you've been.

Other than the usual 'ongoing side effects' that are just part and parcel of this deal, I've felt bloody amazing this week. Could this be due to the fact that I've been a 'lady wot lunches' for four days out of five?

I've also had an early Christmas shopping amble around town with Becky G where we 'mooched' about. Yes mooched! I can't remember the last time I just mooched about in the last six years with no agenda or a small human telling me they're bored after five minutes. We even had a festive Christmas dinner.

Keeping with the festive theme, I met up with some of my besties tonight for the Christmas markets. We didn't actually bother looking around the markets but headed straight for the mulled cider tent. It was packed. They were trying to convince me to whip my bald head out and look forlorn to see if people would give up their seats for us!

After that we headed to the cinema, stopping first to purchase contraband of chocs, sweets and mixed tins of G&T before settling down to our Christmas themed film.

Whilst I had lots of energy this week, I was determined to make the most of it and I was so thankful to feel well.

Saturday 23rd November 2019
Special Days and charities

Today I post my application to The Willow Foundation for a

Special Day. Set up by Bob and Megs Wilson in 1999, in memory of their daughter Willow, who was determined to live a full life despite her cancer diagnosis, they provide special days to seriously ill young adults. I'm cutting it fine with the forty-year-old cut off and certainly don't consider myself very young at all! I feel like I'm in the body of somebody a lot older.

I've come to find that there are various different charities that offer special days or discounts on an array of different products/services that can make you feel better.

I've decided to ask for a trip to Legoland. Not an all-expenses paid family break to Denmark but the UK one. Toby has repeatedly asked to go one day and, seeing as we had to cancel his 'sunny holiday', I think he'd be up for this.

Initially I felt a bit of a fraud putting in the application. I'm sure there are plenty of people who are a lot more poorly than me. But then I thought about the impact this has had on our family, on our plans, and I thought 'why the hell not'. I might not even get selected, but you've got to be in it to win it.

The application is quite straight forward. I just had to complete one page. Darren, as my carer (ha!) had to complete a page, as did my booby nurse to prove that I did have the booby bug.

Contact details: Willowfoundation.org.uk

Sunday 24th November 2019

Another weekend, another small human birthday. Toby turns six today.

So, he'd chosen to go swimming with his best mate and cousins. Off we head to the English Riviera. After fighting Chloe into a swimming costume – I think getting a slippery eel into a pair of tights would be easier – I get to sit back and relax on the poolside. True to his word, Toby keeps popping over to check that I'm okay. He can be a right monkey, but he can also be so sweet and caring.

After swimming, we make like grockles (that's 'tourists' for any non-Devonshire readers) and head for the amusement arcades. We push pounds worth of 2ps into the slot machines to win tokens which will ultimately purchase a few pence worth of sweets and some plastic tat.

Then we head onto a local Wetherspoons for a birthday tea and cake. It's a long day, but an amazing day, and both the children have loved it.

I've loved it. Chemo has fallen in such a way that I was able to be totally present and enjoy both the children's birthdays. That to me has been absolutely priceless.

Tuesday 26th November 2019 – Chemo Round Fifteen

"I allow my thoughts to be calm and peaceful."
(YESmum card)

Cancer Comms

"The Penultimate Poisoning!

We're nearly there, folks, so thank you for sticking with the program.

It's really weird having gone from weekly to three-weekly. It gives me more time to think. When it was weekly, I was in a good routine and the weeks were flying past. Now I look back and think, 'Wow, I've had a lot of shit pumped into me, well done body!'

Latest casualties are my eyebrows and eyelashes. They've hung on valiantly but have now thought 'fuck this, we're off'. Funny (well not really funny) how they really change your appearance and I feel a bit generic-looking

with my bald head. A bit like a plucked chicken, so that's quite timely to accompany the Christmas turkey. If you've got time, google 'awful eyebrows' and share your favourites. I might go for some straight ones as I could just use a ruler and get an even look _ _

For once in our relationship, Darren now has more facial hair than me!

Just as they're departing, my head hair appears to be making efforts to return. It's like a little fluffy coat a newborn animal would have. I'm told it could grow back completely different, maybe curly, maybe grey. I hope it's the lovely silver colour twenty-somethings pay good money for. I fear I'll end up with a wiry grey curly situation looking like a lady garden on my head.

I've also packed on the timber a little (well, a lot, really). I'd like to blame it on the steroids. I rather think it's the 'go on treat yourself' approach every time I catch up with someone. The pitfall of being so popular!

So, wanky week was proper wanky this time round, to the extent I had a brief hospital admission. Nothing too untoward, as it turned out, but I was feeling proper sorry for myself. I was very jammy to bag the family room, so I had my own TV, computer, en-suite, garden and tea making facilities. That was before I even dropped the 'I'm a lawyer defending nurses' into conversation!

Wiped out for about a week but then I started feeling better. Thank goodness because it was back to back birthday celebrations with the pink small human reaching two years and the slightly bigger blue version reaching six. He chose to go swimming, the one year I can't, but swimming he did with me watching from the sidelines. So now we can relax... actually no, Christmas now.

If anyone was thinking they might gift me a bobble hat

this year that's extremely kind but I'm bobble hatted right up with an impressive range, thank you.

So, back to today, and the penultimate chemo poisoning. My chemo sitter was Helen, who has been amazing through this journey, having undertaken her own thirteen years ago. The day after my diagnosis when the arse fell out of my world, she restored some calm, talking me through her experience. She came equipped with snacks in her Mr Tumble's spotty bag and her own game 'getting to know you'. We've known each other for six years because of babies/children, but have never really properly talked about ourselves whilst keeping an eye on over-adventurous children or interrupting conversations with 'stop playing with your willy', 'take that out of there'. It's good to talk and I really enjoyed our time today.

So, there we are. One more left on the 17th December and I'm suitably informed by Charlotte that it will be Christmas themed and I'm to wear a Christmas jumper! All wrapped up nicely in time for Chrimbo and a new start for the new year.

I'm going to quietly take myself off for wanky week now and see as many of you as possible in the run up to Christmas. For the many of you who still feel that you haven't been doing anything, I shall repeat that your texts mean the world to me. To know I haven't dropped off your radar and you are still thinking of me really makes me smile and keeps me positive, so thank you. Xx

Start receiving lots of photos of dodgy-looking eyebrows!

Circle of Trust:

"Sorry I gave you another hat! Three down, one to go, you've almost made it my lovely and you are doing so well. Maybe we could get you

some stick-on eyebrows? If you need anything during wanky week, just let me know."

"See you on the other side, mate (of wanky week, not the afterlife). So close to the end now and we can eagerly await the new hairdo of 2020. Holla if you need anything."

"Close to the finish line, my love, and you are most definitely winning, despite wanky week being... well... um... wanky! I'll do a bit of eyebrow research and send you my findings. xx"

"No, I love the purple hat and very appreciative of it. I just don't need any more going forward. Funnily enough, I'm getting a lot of responses offering stick-on eyebrows. That'll be the next thing coming through the door!

Jesus, there she goes again, talking about pushing up the daisies!"

Massaging Mummies:

"I both love and hate these updates at the same time. You really are a fucking legend, babe. Smashing on like an absolute warrior. I'm signed off for another week, so if you're up for a lay on the sofa and watch a shit movie (non-cancer-related) then I'm all yours next week. Xx"

"You are amazing, hun, as always. So proud of you. Just focus on getting through this week then one more treatment to go. So close to the finishing line. If I can do anything, please just ask. Big hugs. xx"

"I'd love that. I can do Tuesday or Thursday, but I warn you I might not be great company. A film that doesn't involve cancer would be great. The last three books I've read there's been three cancer-related deaths – joyful! X"

"I don't want you to be great company, darling. I can just sit in silence (fuckin' be like a bush tucker trial for me that, ha ha) and hug you or wipe your sweat. You can be whatever, and I'll just be with you. To be fair, you're not that great company when you're not fighting this cruel and bastard illness!"

"Sit in silence! I'll believe that when I see it!"

"Well done, Em. So nearly there. I can't even imagine the shitty shit week feeling. You are awesome for keeping your sense of humour throughout! Wish I could mooch on the sofa for the day, but I guess I'll just be grateful for my health. Xx"

Strong Randy Ladies:

"Hope the next week isn't too wanky. See you on the other side of this wanky period for some of these (drinks)."

"One more to go, Emma. Sending lots of love and hope it's not too bad for you. xx"

Local Yocals:

"Absolute privilege to have spent time with this trooper today, love you Emma. X"

"Lovely photo of you both."

"Strudders, your way with words is an absolute gift and I love reading every installment you kindly share with us. See you on the other side of wanky week. I will hopefully have a new addition and a good story of my own to share with you. Look after yourself. X"

"Oh, Emma. So lovely to read and so glad you had a lush time with Helen. Really hope wanky week isn't TOO wanky and so looking forward to seeing you on the other side. Loads of love."

ED Fan Club:

"Another fabulous update. I've missed your weekly writings, so it's even better to hear from you. I'm sorry you've had a bit of a shit time but glad you were able to 'enjoy' the sproglets' birthing days. Why do we celebrate them whilst our nether regions go uncelebrated? Who made the real sacrifice? Miss your face. Hair or no. xx"

"Pleased to hear you are nearing the end of your treatment. Sorry to *hear you've been feeling rough. Fingers crossed you'll be feeling great by Christmas. X"*

"I've missed writing them as they always produce a flurry of messages. Tonight, I'm enjoying eyebrow recommendations. Xx"

"Surprise! ALL the time."

"Bow brows?"

"What's work's dress policy when I come back sporting bow brows?"

"Try it! As if anyone's going to say you can't."

"Any objections and I'd have to speak to the resident employment lawyer. Surely I get protected status now and if the bows are good for my well-being then…"

"Ha ha, yeah, I'd be up for arguing that bow brows are a reasonable adjustment. Just don't go with the painted-on slugs."

"See, it's not what you know, but who you know."

"Lovely update, Emma. Thank you. Hope you're feeling better soon. I'll hopefully be down in the new year, if you fancy a leisurely lunch. Big love. Xx"

"Another fab update, Em. Let's hope the wanky week isn't quite so wanky this time around. I'm preparing for the grand finale on the 17th. The festive theme will be in full force. Xx"

Cumulative side effect nasties after fifteen sessions:

- Cancer fatigue. I could fall asleep on a washing line when the fog descends.
- Spotty teenager skin.
- Hair loss – BUT it's coming back. Current trend – little fuzzy chick.
- Dry skin (cream me up, baby!).
- Chemo brain (sorry what was I saying again?).
- Loss of taste, mouth ulcers and dry mouth.

- The squits (diarrhoea).
- Zombie nails (turning black and yellow and raising off their nail bed).
- Bye-bye eyebrows and eye lashes.
- Weight gain.

November – Looking Back

In the words of Elton John, "I'm still standing."

We survived November. Two more potent poisonings. An all expenses stay on the NHS as a result of the wonderful 'red stuff'. Two small human birthdays. A girly night out and a fair few 'ladies wot lunch' catch ups.

Just when you think you're getting used to something, it's all change. But that's the nature of the beast. I've quickly learnt to take the rough with the smooth. Although there are patterns as to how I'm feeling dependent on treatment days, this can also vary. I'm very much living in the moment and taking each day at a time.

There have been tears of happiness when I've seen how happy the children were on their birthdays. There have been tears of sadness when I've struggled to lift my head off the pillow. The fear came back when I had to go into hospital because I felt so strange. That was then replaced with relief and then happiness when my mum popped in to see me.

And with all this going on, I'm still a mum. They mean the world to me and to them I am their world. When I'm feeling shite, I think of them. I hear their laughter (and bickering!) from my bed on the bad days and it reminds me how precious life is and that I WILL get through this.

December 2019

Sunday 1st December 2019

With both birthdays out of the way, the countdown to Christmas can now begin.

It's the middle of 'wanky week', but miraculously I'm not feeling too wanky this time round, just a bit tired.

I send Darren up into the attic to retrieve the Christmas tree and decorations. In my head, we're all going to have a lovely afternoon putting the decorations on the tree (which I'll re-decorate when the kids have gone to bed) listening to festive tunes. In reality, it was carnage with the kids arguing over which baubles they wanted and a few casualties in the process (baubles that is, no humans were harmed!).

I won't lie, I was a bit disheartened that the afternoon hadn't gone quite to plan. I love Christmas and it felt really important that we all had fun this time round. But then I remind myself that they're just kids and these were scenes no doubt repeated up and down the country.

No time to dwell, as I've got to position the bloody Elf with Toby's reward card. And so starts the twenty-four day countdown that feels like a couple of months.

Cancer Comms

Local Yocals:

"How is everyone? Emma, how is wanky week? xx"

"I'm okay thanks, Helen. Really tired and 'weak' feeling but not ill this time, so I'll take that. Xx"

Wednesday 4th December 2019

I don't know if it's just me, but each cycle of injections I'm so hungry I'd consider eating my own arm if nothing else was available. Today I'm meeting my friends Paula and Jo at Jo's house. True to form, Jo has got held up, so whilst I'm sitting in the car, I manage to inhale a good load of the lunch I'd brought to share! I can't seem to get it in my face quickly enough!

Jo is always one for her hilarious stories. She tells me that she woke up 'mooing' from her recent surgery under general anaesthetic. Apparently, it's not uncommon and people can wake up making all sorts of noises or saying weird things.

As always, it's a hilarious catch up. Jo's mum (Lin) also pops in. Lin saw breast cancer off last year. Without realising, Paula and Jo have retreated to the other room whilst we launch into our own stories. It's not often I get to talk to someone else who has 'walked the walk' and it's fascinating to hear her story and how she looked for the positives, just like I'm doing. We exchange numbers and I know we'll keep in touch.

Sunday 8th December 2019

THE TRAIN TO CHRISTMAS TOWN.

In our house, it's an annual tradition to visit Santa and his helpers at Otter Nurseries (a local garden centre). We've been doing this for years with my brother's family and Mum, but this year we decided to do something different. We're going to Okehampton to take 'the train to Christmas town'.

I'm so excited about this. I can't wait to see the kids' faces.

We all head down in convoy, dressed in our PJs, as per instructions. We're really early, so we all traipse around a garden centre to kill some time as the heavens open. I'm dressed in stripy PJs with my new head gear – a Christmas pudding hat.

The train station is heaving with excitable families as we're greeted and entertained by Santa's helpers. Then the conductor calls us onto the train and we're off. Decked out with Christmas bunting and glittery tables each carriage is entertained by helpers who sing and read stories. We're given hot chocolate and cookies as we make our way to Christmas Town. The kids are loving it. We're all loving it and fully immersed in the Christmas magic.

Santa boards the train and works his way through the carriages, asking Toby and Chloe whether they have been good and what they would like for Christmas. Then it's back again with more singing and dancing.

It's such a magical afternoon spent with my brother, his family, Mum and Gary. We've made so many memories and got so many pictures of everyone with huge smiles on their faces. Once again, the timing in-between treatment worked out well and this was another one of those magical times that just for a couple of hours I forgot about all this other stuff and was just 'Emma the mum'.

Tuesday 10th December 2019

Today is my last session of acupuncture for the year. I've had five sessions now and I'm really starting to notice a massive difference in the hot sweats department. They've gone from every thirty minutes down to maybe every couple of hours to now only a couple of times a night.

It's a great positive session because we're all in good spirits. I've made a new friend in Adriana, who is just coming out the other side of ovarian cancer. We have children of a similar age and, with a mutual friend, we have a lot in common. It's great to talk to someone who is pretty much going through the same thing at the same time. Then there are two other ladies, one and five years post breast cancer respectively. Sitting there with their full heads of hair, listening to our concerns and reassuring us that what we are feeling is completely normal. I look at them and think 'that's me a year from now'. It's not so long.

The last session is next week but as that's 'Happy Chemo Tuesday', I say my farewells and wish them all well. Amazing the positive impact a group of women talking and sharing can have on your mental well-being. To just say it how it is with people who aren't your friends and family, so you don't even have to think about sugar coating it a bit.

Wednesday 11ᵗʰ December 2019

I'm fed to the giant polo (CT scan) again tonight. I don't feel too anxious about this scan, as everything seems to be moving in the right direction.

It's also Mum's last session of counselling today. In preparation, her counsellor had asked her to think about how she might look back at this period in her life a few years from now. My immediate reaction when she mentioned this wasn't one of sadness but one of happiness. Of course, I'm not going to look at it through rose-tinted glasses. There were moments of pure fear for both of us, as we both reacted in different ways, and tried to put on a brave face for each other.

I remember when I had to take Toby for a scan because of a lump on his neck. I was petrified. I was convinced he had something awful and would cry uncontrollably just at the thought of what it might be. Luckily, it was nothing untoward, but I remember the pure fear I felt in that moment. Just because I'm forty years old, doesn't make it any different for Mum. I'm still her daughter. She seemed fine, but I found out she was just putting on a brave face.

It was when we truly accepted what was happening, how we were both feeling about it and dealing with it (very differently!) that we were able to do something about it.

I will fondly remember having my mum all to myself properly for the first time in... when? Since before my brother was born! Before all this, my mum was round for tea most weeks but the first couple of hours were spent with the children vying for her attention and the chaos of tea, bath and bedtime. By the time that was done, I probably snatched a quick catch up before they had to go home.

These past months, we've been given the gift of time. We've spent hours alone in each other's company. We've spoken about anything, everything. We've sat in silence just reading, or Mum watching the TV whilst I snoozed. We've had lunch out numerous times where we could actually have a full conversation without keeping one eye on the children. And on my darkest days all I wanted was my mum and just knowing she was in the house I felt safe.

I know this is only a temporary situation and as I'm getting through this there will be a time, in the not too distant future that she will be well enough to go back to work. I think I'll get withdrawal symptoms. I think the children think she lives here now! They love having her around; I love having her around. I think having this opportunity to care for me has also helped her put herself back together.

Mum's Words

Quickly jumping forward to April 2020, I asked my mum if she would like to write a paragraph about finishing counselling. I got far more than a paragraph and she's letting me share that with you. I think this is the best place in my book to share her words with you. WARNING – it might make you cry. I did.

June 28ᵗʰ 2019, the day my world was rocked, my life turned upside down and my heart was broken. My daughter, my child (it doesn't matter whether they are four or forty, they are still your child, your flesh and blood) was diagnosed with grade three breast cancer. That word, that horrible word, it was so wrong that my daughter should have it. I would have changed places with her, it was just not right that she should have it. As a mother, you'd do anything for your children to keep them safe, and now there was absolutely nothing I could do to stop this and that made the feeling of helplessness even worse.

Once Emma got over the shock, she immediately seemed to become so strong and positive and adopt the attitude of, "Right, let's get on with this and do what I have to do to get rid of lumpy."(Her name for it.) I, on the other hand, was struggling to come to terms with the situation. I carried on at work through July and August but was on autopilot. My friends at work were very supportive and knew when I rushed to the toilets, as I just wanted to cry, to leave me a little while before coming to see if I was okay. I always thought of myself as a strong character, as I have gone through some rough patches in my life, but this was the hardest emotion I had ever experienced. To have to watch your daughter lose her beautiful long hair. For Toby to be so proud to show me his mummy's long plait that she was going to donate to The Little Princess Trust. For the conversations with Toby when he said he wished his mummy didn't have to keep going into hospital and having the medicine. Also asking if younger people sometimes died before older people. To try and keep it together in front of him and answer as best as I could when all I wanted to do was cry.

At last, on Monday September 9ᵗʰ, I broke down at work completely and was a blubbering wreck. I knew once I walked out of the office on that day, I would not be able to go back until Emma was better. So, I now could help Emma, but it was in fact Emma that helped me. It was Emma who took me to FORCE for my first six-week pamper sessions. This included back and head massages and the chance just to talk in such peaceful surroundings. This is an amazing charity and I cannot thank them enough for their part in putting me back together again. They also provided six counselling sessions. I had never been to a counsellor and really did not know what to expect. I have never had trouble talking, but this was something very different. My counsellor helped me to see that over the years when bad things happen, we may not really address what the effect has been on us and we put that memory away. I liked to think of putting them in different sized boxes (depending on the gravity of the memory) and storing them in a large wardrobe. After a while, the wardrobe is full, and it just takes one more thing before all the boxes come crashing out. He helped me to revisit old bad memories, put things into perspective and look at how I was dealing (or not dealing) with this horrendous event now. Before my last session, he asked how I would look back on this and how would my relationship with Emma be changed in any way.

So, having watched at first hand my brave daughter having her chemo, having seen her curled up exhausted, asleep on the settee with her bald head and pale face, it made me feel very proud of her but also so devastated. Emma never complained or said 'why me'. I have always had a close relationship with both my children, and this has brought us all even closer. It really makes you appreciate life and family. When I look back, it makes me realise that you can even find good in something as horrible as the big C. I got to spend time with Emma and all my grandchildren. It does you good to slow down and have to take stock. Work out what is important and what you want to keep in your life and what needs to be let go. Be kind to yourself and make time to do something that is important for you, even if that is just reading a book for fifteen minutes or going for a walk. As my counsellor said, "It is okay not to be okay," and to know when to ask for help. Emma has taught me so much this last year as she has fought and won her battle with cancer. I myself have had to fight my own battle of going to pieces, picking myself up (with the help, love and support from my husband, family and close friends) and hopefully, like Emma, have come out the other side a stronger person. So that is behind us and now on to LOCKDOWN!!!!!

NB: If you don't know what LOCKDOWN is, google it! 2020 – the year another big C made an appearance in our lives.

Friday 13th December 2019

What a week! I know I'm on steroids, but it appears that Christmas is as well!

Just the children's Christmas social calendar alone is ridiculous: Take food for class Christmas party, choose school Christmas lunch option, remember Christmas jumpers, Christmas crafting (with parents welcome).

I appear to have taken full advantage of 'wonderful week' and have scheduled in a catchup with someone every day. I feel really good this week. Physically and mentally. Maybe it's because I've only got one poisoning left.

It's my last visit to the wonderful community nurse team at Whipton. I've taken Christmas biscuits with me today as a Merry Christmas and thank you. I feel quite emotional as I walk out. Yes, I know it's a good thing I won't be requiring their services anymore, but this has been my routine every Friday since the PICC line was inserted. I've got to know them well and enjoyed our banter. If I've had any questions or concerns, they've been another little safety blanket cuddling me (not literally) with their advice and recommendations.

This is another layer being removed from the treatment process. What am I going to do with myself next Friday?!

Tonight is my work Christmas do, even though I haven't done a day's work since June! We're going for pizza – as you do. It is so fantastic to see everybody and to feel part of the team again. I just slip into conversation with my usual banter and it's as if I've never been away from these guys.

Saturday 14th December 2019

We're off to the big smoke (London) with our good friends Michelle and Russell to see Pete Tong and guests accompanied by a classical orchestra playing Ibiza classics anthems. This was booked back at the beginning of the year before all this cancer madness started. A whole weekend away in London, just the two of us!

The timing is perfect with the last poisoning due in a couple of days, so I'm feeling as good as I can be. Michelle has organised it all, and they're driving, so we really do get to sit back and relax. When we arrive, we pop some bubbly and having forgotten any glasses we drink it out of mugs.

That night, we make our way to the O2 Arena. It's huge! The warm-up DJ gets us going and then the main event. It is amazing. I feel amazing. I completely lose myself as I'm taken back into my twenties. Memories of various girly holidays come flooding back with each tune. Memories of simpler times, crazy times, the best of times.

I look around and the place is packed with people of all ages conducting their own invisible orchestras as they stretch their hands into the air. Lost in their own moments, no doubt.

I love music. I love listening to dance tunes. I played my clarinet in an orchestra for ten years, so to listen to a classical orchestra play some of my favourite dance tunes is electrifying. To share this moment with Darren and some great friends at the end of the most ridiculous year of my life. At some point, the senses become overwhelmed, the emotions come flooding in and I cry happy tears.

I will remember this night and these feelings for a long time to come.

Sunday 15ᵗʰ December 2019

A lie in. OH MY GOD no small humans waking us up.

Today we're heading into Central London and to Hyde Park to visit the Winter Wonderland. It feels so Christmassy. It's cold but the sun is shining. Without the children in tow we just mooch about, eating, drinking and playing on the fairground stalls for a few hours.

When it's time to hit the road home, I'm very much looking forward to a sit down. It's been a great day, a great weekend, but blimey I'm tired.

Monday 16ᵗʰ December 2019

Toby's school nativity today. It's only when we're near the front of the queue with Darren, Mum and Dad that I realise that I've actually booked tickets for the right day, but the wrong school! I promised Toby we'd sit right at the front but now it would appear that that promise won't be fulfilled, and the early queuing was rather a waste. My name's not down, I'm not coming in! Well, we can come in but instead of seated tickets we're going to have to loiter at the back. I'm using chemo brain as my excuse for my lack of attention to detail. Normally an anally organised person, I know I'm not going to live this one down.

As expected, Toby is less than interested and fails miserably to hide his facial expression, which screams, "I'd rather be anywhere else but here." I love it. Other than not being at the front, I've made it. Half promised.

Tuesday 17th December 2019 – Chemo Round Sixteen

"I believe in myself."
(YESmum card)

Cancer Comms

"**To be sung along to some festive classics…**
On the seventeenth day of Christmas the NHS gave to me,
My last dose of chemotherapy.

You better not cry, you better not shout,
Today they took my PICC line out,
No more lovely cocktails to down.

Once in Royal Devon & Exeter,
Stood a row of IV drips.
Lots of psychedelic poisons,
Not a drop would pass their lips.
Even though it made them ill,
It got the nasties against their will.

Today's chemo sitters were Darren and Charlotte. I feel they were handed their theme and what a way to mark the final sixteenth poisoning all wrapped up (see what I did there?) for Christmas. Sitting wearing Christmas jumpers and sparkly Santa hats, we had mince pies with clotted cream, chocolate coins and sprouts, lucky dip presents in a stocking for all the nurses (the syringe pens went down a storm), festive paninis and a fun general knowledge quiz game. Oh, and lots of laughter. With a little time to spare,

we all toasted to the end of the poisoning with a cheeky one down the pub.

Thank you to all my chemo sitters who have gone above and beyond with their time and generosity. You are amazing.

That's me done (on the poisoning front). Like the film *WALL-E* when he finds a single green shoot evidencing new life, the black chin whisker indicates to me that life is returning, and I ought to locate my hair removing paraphernalia. I haven't missed that.

Quite an emotional day. So glad the chemo is over and the PICC line is out, but I will miss the team of nurses on Cherrybrook and the community nurses who have been bloody amazing these past five months.

All that remains is for me to thank you all sincerely for your continued love and support this year, wish you all a very Merry Christmas and here's to a healthier 2020.

And so, the end is near,
I faced the final chemo.
My friends, I'll say it clear,
I'll state my case, of which I'm certain.
It's been six months of ups and downs,
But awesome people, my thanks to you,
Because you let me do it 'my way'!"

And just like that, I'm sitting typing about the final round of chemo. Sixteen rounds of drugs pumped into me. Goodness knows how many hours sitting hooked up to an IV drip. Hundreds of pills popped. Hundreds of thousands of NHS money spent on just me. Hundreds of messages wishing me well. WOW. PAUSE. REFLECT.

It's not until you stop and look back that you realise just how big something was, but how you got through it anyway. That's how I'm feeling today. Just wow.

Cancer Comms

"Thank you to all of you for your kindness along the way. I literally have an army of people who have kept my spirits up and I couldn't have done it without you all. I am a very lucky girl to have you all in my life. xxx"

Circle of Trust:

"Ah, mate, I'm so pleased that's it! You've done us all proud with your positivity and humour and got through this like a real trouper. I'm sorry I wasn't brave enough to join in with the chemo sitting, but let's face it, the minute they hooked you up I would have been on the floor, no use to anyone! I hope that this last dose doesn't make you feel wanky and that you're able to enjoy Christmas with your family. Love you lots. xxx"

"Awwww, Em, I must have PMT or gone soft in my old age as that's got me in floods of tears. You've only gone and bloody done it, you've kicked its arse, you've laughed the whole way through, and you've kept us laughing along with you. The only way is up from here. You're a superstar. Love you. xx"

"Where am I going to go now for my Tuesday treat of chocolate and cake? Echo what Mel and Becks said. Well done, mate, you smashed it. The op in Jan will be a walk in the park compared to the poison. Have a fab bloody Christmas, you deserve it."

"Well done, bird. Long journey with ups and downs but you did it. And now it's a memory. xx"

"We'll send our invoices in the post."

Massaging Mummies:

"What a wordsmith! Brilliantly fitting. Well done, lovely, smashed it! Never has a chin hair been so positive. Are we still seeing you on Friday? Celebrations overdue. xx"

"Deffo still on for Friday play date. Unless I'm feeling shit, then one of you can take Toby off my hands!"

Shits and Giggles:

"Wahey. Chemo is over. xx"

"A big congratulations from me. Here's to a bloody marvelous 2020. xx"

Strong Randy Ladies:

"You're hilarious. Thank God it's nearly over. Is it just a small op to go now then? Have a bloody fabulous Christmas. I have nearly survived this year too. What a bloody hard one. Here's to a very happy, healthy and prosperous new year. And, of course, to Venice. Have a good one, all the Strudders. xx"

"So glad you're through the chemo, Em. You are a superstar and have been so brave. Hope you both have an amazing Christmas and also sending lots of love for a healthy and prosperous new year. xx"

Local Yocals:

"You are just the best, Emma. So happy for you. You've been amazing throughout your treatment. Love you!"

"Hurrah! Well done, you hilarious and bonkers woman. Absolutely thrilled for you that it was the last one today, love you to bits. X"

"Ah, Em. So emotional. What a day it must have been for you and what a feeling. You are amazing. It's been an honour to be brought along the journey with you. Loads of love and cheers. Xx"

"Oh, Emma, that was the best finale ever, so happy for you that the poison is now done, we are here for you every step of the way. Sending you loads of love and here's to an amazing Christmas and new start to 2020. X"

"YES, EMMA. A beautifully written festive finale! So happy for you

to have nailed the final chemo session and as usual you do it with such spirit and positivity. Thank you for including us in your journey. It's been a privilege to be a part of it with you. Here's to a peaceful Christmas and a positive start to 2020. X"

ED Fan Club:

"Excellent news, Emma."

"That's amazing. You're amazing. Time to put that behind you and enjoy the festivities. Here's to 2020 and much healthier times. Xx"

"Brilliant news. I prefer your versions of all these songs. X"

"What a great start to Christmas."

"Fantastic news, Emma. Love the song lyrics. So pleased it's all over in time for Christmas. Hope you have a lovely Christmas and look forward to an amazing, happy and healthy 2020. Xx"

"This is amazeballs. So happy for you, Emma. Have an amazing Christmas and New Year. X"

"Such amazing news, ED. Well done for kicking ass. X"

"Fantastic news. The lyrics are brilliant. Have a fantastic Christmas and cheers. Xx"

"Emma, what a brilliant update. I hope you all have a fun, restful, peaceful, sparkly Christmas. X"

"What a fabulously festive update to wrap up 2019. Thank you for taking me along on the ride for the final dose. Merry Christmas, one and all. Xx"

Tuesday 24th December 2019

Cancer Comms

Yocal Locals:

"Merry Christmas to you all. Hope you have a wonderful few days with your gorgeous families."

"I'll drink to that. I think 2019 has been rather a momentous year for all of us. Not sure we'll get two babies, a divorce, a uni degree, the not so big C and whatever else I've missed (!) packed into another year! And we're all still standing. We are an amazing group of women, stronger together, and I'm so glad I've got you in my life. Here's to a wonderful Christmas. Xx"

"Well said. What a year it's been. I feel so lucky to have been lovingly engulfed by you wonderful lot. You are all such a blessing to have in my life and I wish you all a peaceful and restful Christmas. X"

"Aw, absolutely, Emma. So glad to have you all. Beth, you were very easy to engulf. I am just counting down the minutes to stick on the Christmas music, have my mulled wine and a mince pie, and when I do I will toast to you all. Merry Merry Christmas wonderful friends. Xx"

"Couldn't be more thankful for the friendship of every single one of you. Love you to bits. Xx"

Tuesday 31ˢᵗ December 2019
Christmas 2019 and looking back

I didn't keep a journal from my last chemo session (17ᵗʰ December) until the end of the year. I just wanted to be me and a mum and a wife over Christmas. In my head, I'd just done all this hard work and I didn't want to be thinking of cancer. There was nothing that needed to be done on that front until next year.

We had a great Christmas. Wanky week wasn't too wanky, and when I got tired I just took myself off for a rest with nobody batting an eyelid. We went to my mum's for Christmas Eve. Her 'I'm just doing a few bits and bobs' turned into its usual extravagant spread. The afternoon was spent in the company of my brother's family with the kids playing nicely (in the main). We even managed to orchestrate the grandchildren photo, sitting on the stairs descending in age, which has inadvertently become a new family tradition. The adult children also managed to pull the same photo off!

Christmas Day was spent with Darren's family. We were waited on hand and foot and again nobody batted an eyelid when I took myself upstairs for a three-hour sleep!

Too much food and drink was consumed, but to be honest, it was pretty peaceful and calm and so easy (and cheap!) spending it at other people's houses. I reckon we've missed a trick holding it at ours, so might have to see what excuse we can come up with next year!

The children loved all the presents and spending time with so many different family members. I loved being around everybody and this year it really did seem rather special.

Cancer Comms

Massaging Mummies:

"So much illness. Hope everyone is coming out the other side and here's to a healthier 2020. We're going out out. I've had a nap in preparation but not confident in my staying abilities! Thanks for being awesome this year. As you have in all years but your kindness and humour has been especially appreciated this year. Love you all. xx"

The demise of the cumulative side effect nasties after sixteen sessions:

- Cancer fatigue. Not as bad as it was and rest and sleep is making a difference.
- Spotty teenager skin.

- The hair is returning. Current trend – little fuzzy chick.
- Dry skin (cream me up, baby!).
- Chemo brain (I can now converse like an adult).
- Loss of taste – this is starting to come back.
- The squits are no more. All seems to be back to normal in that department).
- Zombie nails (turning black and yellow and raising off their nail bed – thank goodness for my lovely friend Paula who keeps them nicely painted).
- Eyebrows and eyelashes are starting to grow back.
- Weight gain (any ongoing weight gain to be blamed on Christmas indulgence!).

January 2020

Wednesday 1st January 2020

HAPPY NEW YEAR.

So, I had cancer last year. I don't have it this year. Well, I obviously haven't had the official sign off, but I'm still hanging onto the radiographer's comments: *"There's definitely no cancerous lump in there."*

A lot of people have asked me recently, 'How are you?'

So, how am I?

Physically I don't feel too ropey at the moment. Achy and tired, but hell, that's probably all of us after the over-indulgence of Christmas coupled with hyperactive small humans. The extent of the tiredness fluctuates on a daily basis and whether or not I've overdone it a bit. But I'm trying to listen to my body and rest if I need to. At least there was no New Year's Eve bender hangover to deal with this year. So, in comparison to previous years (pre-children), I'm probably starting the new year perkier.

Emotionally, I'm still okay in the main, but I've had some wobbly moments when I've thought 'shit the bed, that was full on'. Sometimes I also can't quite believe it has happened to me at this time in my life. I've never got angry about the diagnosis or questioned 'why me?' With one in two people developing cancer at some point in their life then why not me, really? Why do tiny children have cancer? Why do fit and healthy people who run marathons get cancer yet other people who are desperately unhealthy don't? I can't let myself go down that rabbit hole because there are no answers. Rather, I allow myself to acknowledge that it has happened to me, that it is a big deal, but we got on with a shit hot treatment plan and it's working. I try and keep myself grounded in the present and not worry too much about the future. I say try because sometimes I do wonder if my time has been cut short. I sneak glances at my children and wonder if I'll see all the milestones as their little lives turn into adulthood. I wonder if Darren and I will go clubbing with our Zimmer frames, as we always joked we would. But nobody knows when your number is going to be up and, thankfully, I'm usually able to push those thoughts aside.

I also consider myself lucky. Not lucky that I got cancer. I wouldn't wish that on myself or anyone. Lucky that I live in a part of the country that has an amazing hospital and that I could access treatment less than a month after diagnosis. Lucky that the treatment appears to be working. Lucky that the chemo didn't wipe me out completely. Lucky that I work for an amazing organisation, which affords me full pay so I could stop work to get my head together, and attend multiple appointments without having any financial worries. Lucky that I was able to spend extra time with the children over the summer holidays and pick Toby up from school without using the afterschool clubs. Lucky to have been afforded the gift of time to catch up with so many friends and family. I think I've probably seen most people I know in the past six months! Lucky to have experienced such an outpouring of love and support from friends and family. I knew I had a fab tribe around me, but bloody hell this experience has made me realise just how wonderful and selfless they all are.

So that's how I'm feeling, actually. Pretty damn grateful that this tribe of people have supported me through what I think (and I hope) is the worst of this process.

Normally we try to get out for a walk on New Year's Day. Start the year as we mean to go on and all that. But today the heavens opened and so I don't think we got dressed until after lunch. Today was a quiet, slow day and it was very welcome.

Saturday 4ᵗʰ January 2020

Cancer Comms

Massaging Mummies:

"How are you doing, Em? Emotionally and physically. Anything we can do? Xx"

"Not too bad, thank you. Physically I'm feeling quite achy and a bit tired. I think I'm just knackered from Christmas and life in general to be honest, but I guess the weeks of poison have played a part, plus the weight gain. I look like a bloke in a dress now with my GI Jane hairdo! Emotionally I'm pretty good still. Now chemo has stopped I've had a chance to breathe and think 'fuck me that was actually something quite big'. The achiness worries me sometimes, but I just have to trust in the process and I quickly banish any negative thoughts. xx"

"It still hits Mum now, Em, at times. It's a poison at the end of the day. It's fucking crazy when you think about it. You need to give yourself a few years, bird. That's what friends and family are for. I pissed myself at the bloke in a dress. Sorry, I've always looked like the bloke. I weigh more than some rugby players and my shoulders are wider than some of them too. You clearly don't look like a bloke in a dress. Although drag queen could be your next career."

"Trust me, Em, I look more like a bloke in a dress than you! I know the chemo is over, but the road to full recovery is still a long one and we will still be here for you. So proud of the way you've coped, but it's okay to let us know when you're struggling or having down days."

"Thank you very much. Indeed, I will let you know if I'm in need of some 'pull yourself together' talk. xx"

"Em, you are amazing in all ways. It's all been a whirlwind for you and now you can breathe and have time to think about it all and what

you have been through, and still need to go through. The first big part is done and onwards to the next. It will be a rocky road for your emotions and physically with ups and downs along the way. But all completely expected. Try and take it day by day as you are, and we are all here for you as always whenever you need us. You are no bloke in a dress, gorgeous. Love you all. Big hugs. xx"

Sunday 5ᵗʰ January 2020

We are now Crealy Adventure Park annual members. #livingthedream

Bit chilly to be ambling around our local adventure park with our lovely neighbours, but everyone enjoyed it. It was one of those days that just felt like a normal day, like any other family out enjoying themselves. For a day I forgot everything.

Part 2: The Operation 'The Chop'

Tuesday 7ᵗʰ January 2020

Pre-op assessment today. This feels like the start of something new in this process, and after days of increasingly later starts, eating my bodyweight in chocolate and over exposure to the small humans, it feels like the start of a new routine.

I quickly stop off at Cherrybrook to drop off my sharps bin and other unwanted goodies (dressings for the district nurses) they gave me on day one. This is a nice feeling as it feels like the last of the chemo goodies are being returned and that chapter is well and truly closed. It also means my Tupperware boxes will have more room in their cupboard now the sharps bin has gone and my dairy items will no longer be sharing a shelf with injections that made my bones ache like I've never known before.

As always, the RD&E are super-efficient, calling me in before my allotted time. I've only been operated on once before under general anaesthetic, to have my tonsils out when I was eighteen, so I can't remember the drill. I only remember having to wear sexy pressure stockings, which was quite mortifying at that age. I couldn't give two shits at this age; whatever it takes. The process turned out to be pretty straightforward really, just checking I'm healthy enough to undergo the surgery with a few tests and questions.

Going through the long list of medical questions, and answering 'no' to the majority, it turns out I'm actually quite healthy apart from this cancer situation and good to go on the 21st. The routine for D-day is explained to me, but I'll save that for later.

The good thing about having many mates in the RD&E is that I can pop in to visit them. Quick trip up to Endoscopy to catch up with Kelly and bump into my booby nurse for a chat. I mention to her that now the chemo has finished, and I've actually had time to look back at what's happened, sometimes I feel like 'bugger me, that was big'. I also mention that sometimes the niggling doubt creeps in when I feel a bit achy: 'Is that normal for me still or is there something wrong? They scanned me and there was nothing else, is that still the case?' She gives me a paper by Dr Peter Harvey, consultant Clinical Psychologist, called 'After the Treatment Finishes – Then What?' I'll have a read of that later once the children have lost consciousness for the day.

I pop off to the restaurant with Kelly for a cuppa before my next round of mini ear stabbings (acupuncture). I share my concerns with her about the niggly thoughts and she reassures me that this is exactly how her brother-in-law felt after his treatment. I've mentioned this to two people today and already just sharing is banishing those niggles for the time being.

Off to FORCE and it's great to catch up with Cath. Just me and another chap today, who's having acupuncture for his dry mouth following treatment to his neck and throat. It's really interesting to hear another perspective as to how he's dealing with life and the after-effects following the end of treatment. I mention to Cath that the mini stabbings were working but unfortunately as the last session was the 10th December, and I've had another treatment and illness since, I'm back to quite a few wakeful nights sweating my arse off. All booked in for another session next week.

As I've mentioned before, these sessions are invaluable for two reasons: (1) the assault on my ears actually does work in the sweating department, but (2) it's a great opportunity to talk to others in the same position, share stories and advice and benefit from Cath's wise words. Today we chatted about life after treatment and for the third time today I mention how I've been feeling. I know that everybody is different and deals with situations in different ways. Hell, if this had happened to me five years ago, I would have retreated into the woods like an injured animal and given up. Well, perhaps not quite as drastic as that, but I wouldn't have dealt with it as positively as I have done, trying to put my own positive spin on the situation. I can see my companion is sceptical about the whole 'being kind to yourself' and 'not needing to be stoically British'. I'm forever wanging on these days about 'being kind to yourself' and needing to take time out to look after yourself, talking your concerns through with others. And I'll continue to wang on about it because when cancer came knocking for me, having spent a good few years practising mindfulness and working on my mindset, I was as best equipped as I could be to face this new challenge.

Before I leave, I book in another massage for next week. About time for another treat before the knives come out!

Now one thing that I do want to address now, and it starts today, is this additional timber I've put on to the tune of three stone. I'm done with the 'treatment and steroids wouldn't have helped' because I know that I have taken too much advantage of the 'go on, treat yourself' excuse. Yes, I know I need to be kind to myself and not worry about weight gain, but I also need to be kind to my body and start putting some better fuel into it. I'm not about to start some faddy diet but I am not happy at this weight, never have been, never will be, cancer or no cancer, so today I'll start creating some healthier habits and take one day at a time.

I laugh with my friend at Aldi at the fact my conveyor belt contains almond milk and chia seeds. I never thought I was a chia seeds type of person, or the owner of one of those flash smoothie bullet machines. Equipped with kale, spinach and frozen fruit, my intention is to whizz up a nutritious storm and not relegate the fandangle machine to the back of the cupboard come February. Stay tuned.

Once calm has been restored post small human bedtime, I sit down to read Dr Harvey's paper. He likens the diagnosis and treatment of cancer to a rollercoaster:

"On a rollercoaster, you will be strapped in and sent off into the terror, knowing that there is nothing you can do about it until you emerge, wobbly and battered at the other end. You manage by getting your head down and dealing with it as best you can at the time. It is only afterwards, when you are on solid ground again, that you can look back with amazement and view what you have experienced and marvel at your courage."

This is such a spot-on analogy and exactly how I have been feeling. I thought that I'd get through chemo with my jokey ridiculous sense of humour, have an op, maybe have radiotherapy and then 'get back to normal' as soon as possible and that would be the end of this blip on my timeline. Well, turns out this cancer situation is rather bigger than just a 'blip' and I'm likely going to have to find my 'new normal' having had a cancer diagnosis. I don't feel overwhelmed today, but I know that could change tomorrow.

I've had periods over Christmas when life has been slower paced and I've had time to think, done a bit of worrying, but then one of the children has done something silly, or more likely wound the other one up, and I'm snapped back into being a mum. I've had many days of doing nice things with friends and family when I've completely forgotten what I've been through, what I'm yet to go through. Equally, there have been other days when I've felt rough as a badger's arse, completely knackered, caught a glimpse of my GI Jane haircut and felt a bit sorry for myself, and I'm all too acutely aware of what has happened to me.

I felt a bit nervous booking our family holiday for August. Now I love my holidays and 'nervous' is never a word I would have used in the same sentence about booking a bit of 'sun, sea and sleep'. But eight months feels like such a long time in the future when I've been living day to day. What if I'm not fixed by August? What if there is something wrong? What if they didn't get it all and it's come back? Ultimately, I had a chat with myself, reminded myself that I have had 'a complete response', that surgery and radiotherapy will have been completed in plenty of time, and that I can allow myself to look to the future. I've spent the past couple of years focusing on the present, not dwelling on the past, and not allowing the 'what ifs' to cause unnecessary worry. It's served me well and I'm going to try and keep going with this approach. And if it all gets a little too much, I have an army of people, both professionals and friends/family, who I can talk to.

Wednesday 8th January 2020

My sleep is pretty horrendous at the moment. Can't get to sleep until late. Then when I do it's pretty disturbed and I can be wide awake at some ridiculous time.

Last night was no different. Normally I reach for my current read, but seeing as that's currently a legal thriller where the defendant is pleading insanity for killing his wife and three children, I thought I'd reach for something a little lighter at bedtime.

My lovely mum bought me a copy of *The Boy, the Mole, the Fox and the Horse* by Charlie Mackesy. This book only takes about ten minutes to read from cover to cover but it is the most beautifully illustrated book telling the story of this random group of friends. These are some of my favourite bits:

"Sometimes," said the horse. "Sometimes what?" asked the boy. "Sometimes just getting up and carrying on is brave and magnificent."

"We don't know about tomorrow," said the horse, "all we need to know is that we love each other."

"When the dark clouds come… keep going."

"When the big things feel out of control… focus on what you love right under your nose."

"This storm will pass."

"We have such a long way to go," sighed the boy. "Yes, but look how far we've come," said the horse.

I shall hopefully be sleeping better tonight as I got the good news that my work's Income Protection Policy will be paying out. I was on six months full pay but that dropped down to half pay as of 17th December for the next six months. Fortunately, the policy will top it back up to full pay. I am all too aware of how bloody fortunate I am that once again financial worries will not be on my agenda as I carry on with my treatment. I had started to think about how we would 'cut our cloth' accordingly if I did drop down to half pay, but I was quietly optimistic that my claim would be successful.

Thursday 9th January 2020

Well, aren't we on a roll with the good news this week? Another consultant letter. No need to google ridiculous medical terminology this time as: "I am pleased to tell you that your recent CT thorax scan has demonstrated no new changes or cause for concern," is rather self-explanatory. Thank you very much for that one.

Tuesday 14th January 2020

I seem to have commandeered FORCE this morning! Don't feel so guilty, though, knowing I did a good bit of fundraising for them last year.

The staff are so attentive and as soon as I walk through the door I'm greeted with a smile. They all know me now and I settle down with my cuppa and new read. Although it's a psychological thriller, I'm not sure *After I'm gone* is the best book to be sitting down with in this scenario, but I'm gripped!

I'm having a massage first and OMG what an amazing massage it was with Kayleigh. I've been disappointed at having to pay for 'tickles' at spas before but she got right in there. Just what my achy body needed.

Some more light reading then it's my last session of acupuncture. This was a sneaky seventh session when I was only supposed to get six, so I'm very grateful. This week it is just me and an elderly gentleman who finished his radiotherapy in October having been treated to the throat. I sit and listen to him explain how he is exploring acupuncture to aid his dry mouth. That he has lost three stone and is being predominantly fed through a 'RIG' (radiologically inserted gastrostomy) in his stomach. That he is able to swallow but he can only taste for a second before the food turns into a salty paste that is difficult to swallow. That nothing helps keep his mouth moist. That he's predominantly on liquid but is able to swallow soup and porridge. How food is a big part of life, his routine, and not being able to taste it or eat 'normally' has had a massive impact on his life, his life with his wife, his ability to go out and socialise. Everything revolves around food.

I appreciate everything is relative and my hot sweats cause disturbed sleep, but boy did this gentleman put things into perspective. I'll take my hot sweats any time in comparison and again I feel thankful that the path I've had to take has been far smoother than his. He's also a farmer and is working! He had amazing strength of mind and I was grateful to him for sharing his story in front of me.

Driving home I was feeling rather contemplative. We'd spoken again in the session about readjusting to living in the moment, rather than planning all sorts of things too far in the future. It's quite a liberating way to live and does slow life down as you're not constantly wishing the time away. As I walked through the door, I was still feeling a little sad from his story. The next emotion was anger as I thought the dog had shat on the floor until I realised that it was only Toby's fake poo. And with that, I'm laughing and getting back on with my day!

Wednesday 15th January 2020

Funny old day today.

First of all, I attended my first session of the NHS Eating Well Group. This was a small group of ladies who had/were going through treatment for cancer and wanted to get healthier/fitter/lose weight. It was held in a training room at our local Tesco. I wondered if we would have a tour of the aisles: 'Here's the fruit and veg section – fill your faces', 'Here's the chocolate aisle – try not to inhale so much of this stuff'! This was not the case, though, and we looked at the pros and cons of making changes and what we might like to achieve. The sessions are run by a nutritionist and a physio looking at healthy eating and exercise. We also get weighed. I'm quite glad I don't really understand Kgs because the number looked big!

After stepping off the scales, we stepped outside to go for a walk. It was great to get outside and also to chat to one of the new ladies I'd met. Equipped with my food and exercise diary, I'm now off to make some healthier changes.

So that was all really positive and upbeat. I then took the car to the garage and went for lunch at a nearby Sainsbury's. Whilst sitting there like a Billy no mates, I started scrolling through Facebook. I follow a number of cancer-related pages and started reading an article about a lady dealing with secondary cancer. That was where I should have stopped reading because then there was a link to symptoms and, just like that, I've diagnosed myself with cancer of the liver. I can feel the panic, it feels irrational, but it's very real nonetheless. I need to get out of here, I need to get home and I need to speak to somebody.

On the drive home I recall all the positive progress I've made. The CT scan results were just last week but I still can't get rid of the damn fear and the tears keep coming. Maybe I'm more anxious than I thought about the upcoming surgery. Maybe I'll rest easier when 'something' has been taken out of me. Maybe I just need to hear the words that the cancer has gone and it isn't in my lymph nodes.

I leave a message for my booby nurse and she gets straight back to me. Hers is the voice of reason that I needed to hear. She explains to me that these feelings are completely natural. I'm immediately apologetic for wasting her time as I know everything's heading in the right direction, but I just can't seem to push the fear back today. I even start that ugly adult crying where you blow snot bubbles. My booby nurse is amazing at what she does. She listens to my blubbings, points out all the progress that has been made to date and reassures me that these feelings are all completely normal.

The good thing about having a young family is that there are pick up times and clubs to deal with. And with that the school run begins and swimming club.

I make sure I sit down with Darren that evening to let him know how I'm feeling.

"I have the power to create change in the world around me."
(YESmum card)

Friday 17th January 2020

Out with the girls to the cinema this evening. We buy our contraband sweets and drinks in the Tesco next door before heading in to watch *Little Women*. I love chatting to Mel, Becky and Nicola. Not sure then why we've chosen to sit in a dark room where we can't actually chat to each other! As I'm playing taxi tonight, I get to have my chats on the way home. Get to hear what's going on in their worlds.

Saturday 18th January 2020

Cancer Comms

Local Yocals:

"How are you doing, Em?"

"Morning ladies. I'm sorry I won't be able to make it, just got up! Bit of a funny old week this week. So tired and achy, so really needed a good sleep last night. Also had a bit of a wobbly day Wednesday when the fear came out of nowhere, but you know me, not down for long, spoke to my nurses and I've got my head back in the game. Sorry to miss you all but have a lovely catch up and see you soon. Xx"

"Oh, Emma, so sorry you're not feeling great. Can't imagine how

you're feeling but please know we are all here for you and wish we could surround you. Take it easy, love you loads. Xx"

Monday 20ᵗʰ January 2020

Couple of appointments today in preparation for 'The chop' tomorrow.

Firstly, it's another visit to the Nuclear Medicine department for a dye to be injected into me. Once I've taken on board enough water and kept exercising my right arm to move the dye around, it's off for another scan. The purpose of this is to take images of my lymph nodes so my consultant can whip out the sentinel lymph node (lymph node closest to where lumpy used to reside).

Tuesday 21ˢᵗ January 2020

"With each new day I let love lead me."
(YESmum card)

Getting 'the chop' today.

Wide Local Excision (lumpectomy) and Sentinel Node Biopsy

What the subtitle says, that's what I'm having.

There's no cancer left but the area it was in is being removed with a margin of clear tissue around that area to make sure the cancer has completely buggered off. This will reduce the risk of it coming back.

At the same time, they will also remove and do a biopsy on the sentinel lymph node. The sentinel node is the first node that drains away from the breast. If this node is clear of tumour the logic follows that all the ones further away will be too. If there was tumour in the sentinel node then I'd be looking at more surgery.

I have to be on the ward with my 'invitation to attend hospital' by 7.30am. Having not eaten since yesterday evening, and only allowed some water up until 6.30am, my stomach feels like my throat's been cut!

Now that 'D Day' has arrived, I'm not actually feeling nervous anymore. I'm feeling a sense of calm.

I get my designated bed and, as has become customary, a fetching gown to get changed into. I also get measured up for some very fetching Nora Batty stockings (compression stockings to decrease the risk of blood clots). With my pink sparkly fluffy slippers to complete the outfit, this is indeed a strong look.

I get visited by various people, a number of them asking if I know what I'm here for and where I think I'm having surgery. This is disconcerting, surely they know?! Of course they do, but they're just checking I know what's going on, what to expect and that I'm still consenting to this treatment. Hell yes, get the remains of this bugger out of me.

The anaesthetist arrives to explain his role. He does not look old enough to be in charge of putting me to sleep and being my snoozing guardian. He explains that he will inject a substance into my cannula and off I'll go, blissfully unaware of what is going on.

A researcher from the medical department at The University of Exeter turns up. I've consented to them having lumpy's remains, or probably, in my case, his former lodgings, so they can conduct studies on it. It won't help me, but it could help future patients with cancer. Yes, of course I still consent to this. It's not like I've got any use for it. Or maybe I should pickle it and lovingly display it somewhere? No, they can have it.

First bit of business is to have a thin piece of wire inserted into my right boob. This will be placed to assist the consultant with locating the marker. This can then be removed during surgery together with the surrounding area.

Now today is a special day for the team as they are trying a new piece of kit and guess who's their guinea pig? Me! They are testing out inserting this 'seed', which indeed looks just like a seed. I was rather underwhelmed at the sight of it, but apparently if you're medically qualified and are testing it out for the first time it rather floats your boat! It's been used elsewhere in the country before, so I'm not actually Guinea Pig #1, but they're making me feel a little like a Z-list celebrity here.

I'm asked whether a couple more colleagues can watch the insertion but to not feel pressured if I don't want a bigger audience. On the assurance that they're not taking pictures and eating popcorn, I guess the more the merrier. The wire is inserted first with a local anaesthetic and is relatively pain-free. With a small incision, 'the seed' is also inserted and that's that.

The benefit of the seed is that it can be inserted at any time to suit the patient in the lead up to surgery. With the wire sticking out of me, coiled around and stuck down, I can see why this needs to be done on the day.

Then I'm off to surgery, still feeling calm and actually quite excited to get this over and done with. The HCA who accompanies me is lovely. She chats away whilst I'm waiting to go in and answers any questions I have. To be honest, I'm all questioned out, so we mostly chat about the joys of small humans.

My consultant comes out with a colleague, all excited to talk about the seed. She runs a device over me that indicates when she has located the seed and its depth. I can only describe it as one of those treasure seeker devices (metal detector) you use with headphones when scanning the beach for bounty. Well, they've found their bounty and I happily let her colleague have a go.

I don't remember going to sleep. I remember it feeling a bit uncomfortable in my arm and then waking up in recovery and bloody crying! Apparently, it's quite common. At least I'm not mooing like my mate Jo!

Back to the ward and that tea and toast is so good. I fear I'm going to get lynched, though, as there are plenty of other ladies who are still waiting to go down to theatre.

My booby consultant comes to see me and tells me it all went well. She made two incisions, one under my nipple and the other in my arm pit. She took two lymph nodes, as in my case they were close together. She was also happy that she didn't need to reposition my nipple, but we could review how it all looks after radiotherapy.

Before I get dressed, a nurse checks my dressing and advises me to keep this dry. I'm reminded about breast lymphoedema (swelling) and to call in if I have any concerns. Lymphoedema is a long-term swelling of the breast. It is caused when the lymph channels in the breast and armpit become blocked due to scarring caused by radiotherapy and surgery. To help prevent this and promote movement in my arm, I'm encouraged to start the exercises I've been given in a couple of days and keep these up until I'm back in to see my consultant in a fortnight.

Job done. With a bit of help from Darren, I get dressed and check out early afternoon the same day with strict instructions to rest and not lift heavy objects. I've moved my mum in for a bit and between her and Darren they'll be doing the small human pick-ups and drop-offs. They're also sorting the running of the house. I feel like I should milk this situation for as long as possible!

Facebook:

Stage Two – The chop ✎
I give you the (slightly chubby) GI Jane look for 2020.

Modelling the **NHS'** preferred gown and **Nora Batty** stockings, I think you'll agree this is a strong look. My fluffy pink glittery slippers finished it off a treat.

So, I had the big chop. Slightly dramatised, as there was no chopping involved, just the removal of my evicted tenant's former lodgings and some lymph (ha, autocorrected to nymph!) nodes.

Of course, I always make things interesting and I was the breast team's first patient to test this new 'seed' thing. Basically, prior to surgery, I had to have a wire inserted to locate the marker that was inserted into the tumour at the start to make sure they take the right area. The wire then sticks out of you. This new seed is tiny and can be implanted whenever. During surgery, they use a scanner to locate the right area. Quite interesting really and gained me an audience. To be honest, I've got my baps out so many times the past six months that a few more faces won't hurt! The team were all quite excited. Whatever floats your boat, I suppose!

All went well and back on the ward I've never enjoyed tea and toast so much. The same welcome feast after having a baby!

Off home by 4pm, peeing turquoise superhero pee from the dye they injected.

No driving, heavy lifting or household chores for two weeks now. God, am I going to stick to doctor's orders on that one. The things you have to do for a rest! Over to Darren and my live-in nanny (Mum).

So that's it until 31ˢᵗ January when I'll find out the results from the bits and bobs they removed. Unlikely they'll find anything untoward, so will stick with that.

Poisoning 💀 ✅
The chop 🔪✅
The frying (radiotherapy) 🔥 to be arranged.

Thank you for all your messages. In terms of practical help, we're all sorted, thank you. I love the messages. They really do help. They make things seem normal and normal is what I like.

"Beautiful socks, did you sneak them out? **Ah, I didn't. They were mine for the keeping. Missed opportunity there."**

Cancer Comms

"All finished with the chop. Off home now. Another task ticked off the cancer list. Xx"

Circle of Trust:

"Well done, my beaut. Now rest up and take it easy. xx"

"Awesome. Another good job done. Enjoy two weeks of no driving and cleaning. Xx"

"Yay, just one hurdle left and you're running for the finish line! You've totally got this."

"Take it easy, my beaut! Hope it all went okay and you are not too sore."

"See, I would have told a little white lie and said three weeks' rest. Hope you're not too sore and let me know when you want to escape one night for a drive/change of scene. xx"

"Bugger, yes, I missed a trick there. Will do. I'm enjoying the idea of sweet F-all, but I know I'll be bored pretty soon, so a drive would be great!"

Massaging Mummies:

"Yay! Thank goodness for that! Glad you're home at a decent time. Rest up. Lots of love. x"

"Yay. Well done, Em. You're amazing. Rest well and be kind to

yourself. Here if you need anything. xx"

"So pleased for you, another task completed, well done. Rest lots and here if you need anything. Big hugs. Xx"

"So pleased it's done and you're home my lovely. Big hugs. Let me know if we can help at all. Working all week but around at the weekend if you need anything. xx"

"Amazing, my beaut. See ya, lumpy, and don't fucking come back. So proud of you. XX"

Strong Randy Ladies:

"Glad you're off home. Hopefully you can rest! x"

"Argh, glad you're all done with that one. Take care of yourself. See you on the 29th if you're up for a visit."

Local Yocals:

"Well done. Hope you're feeling okay."

"Aw, so pleased you are heading home, Emma. Thanks for taking the time to update us, bless you. Been thinking of you. Xx"

"That's wonderful to hear, Emma."

"Amazing, Emma. Well done. Been thinking of you lots today. Xx"

ED Fan Club:

"You'll be back with us soon then. x"

"Great news. Hope to see you soon. X"

"Stage two complete. Let's get stage three over with. Good work, Emma. Remember to milk this and rest up as much as you can while your mum is around. X"

Wednesday 22nd January 2020

Cancer Comms

Shits and Giggles:

> *"Morning lovelies. How's it going, Em? Still turquoise pee? xx"*
> **"Morning. No, disappointingly it's back to normal! I'm feeling considerably good considering the wonky bruised booby! How are you doing? xx"**
> *"Ha, I hadn't been on FB before I read this, so the turquoise pee had me baffled! Looking good, Em. You really are cracking on with this treatment journey, aren't you? No messing… bish, bash, bosh!"*

Friday 24th January 2020

Cancer Comms

Local Yocals:

> *"How's recovery from the op going so far, lovely? Xx"*
> **"All good, my friend. Bit achy/tired, but I'll take that. Xx"**

Monday 27th January 2020

Time is a funny old thing. This time last year, I'd just returned to work following maternity leave. I was quickly swept up in the Monday to Thursday four-day small human/work sandwich. The day started at 6.30am with a mad dash to get everybody where they needed to be, act at being a professional by doing a bit of lawyering, then reversing the day with collecting overexcited/tired small humans and dealing with the bedtime routine. The days were long but would flit past.

Now it feels like I have more time than ever. I still drop the small humans off to their respective destinations for the day, and pick them up (well, not at the moment while I rest), but the time in between is mine to do with what I want. Now I'm in the convalescence period of this situation and literally have to take it easy, I've got all the time in the world to have a think about how I might like to go forward from here.

Historically, I've always banged out a load of New Year resolutions, but I've always gone 'too hard, too soon' and they've fallen by the wayside in February along with motivation. This year I'm even more mindful that I'm more of the tortoise in the race, rather than the hare.

Last year I decided to do things a little differently. I had goals and dreams for 2019. I decided to break them down into much more manageable bitesize pieces and make small changes instead of big gestures. The standard goals involved my weight and health.

I had quite a bit of weight to lose, so I joined Slimming World last year. I set an end goal, an interim goal and a goal for when I turned forty in April. By the time the C-bomb was thrown at me in June, I had nearly lost three stone. As you know, I've whacked it all back on, and some more. But now I'm starting afresh. I know what to do and now I just need to do it. I have the support and advice of the NHS 'eating well, lose weight' group and the support of my personal chef (Darren!). Like last year, I have set mini targets, but most importantly I just want to put the good stuff back into my body.

Last year I committed to fifteen minutes of exercise every day. It was tricky with the children/work sandwich to actually find the time to fit exercise in, but I did. Gradually I built it up and started the *Couch to 5k*. This year I have more time on my own during the day and already I have started going out walking around where we live. The problem I'm finding is that I will feel fine, go out and about doing my walking, and then suffer for it the next day and feel completely knackered. That tells me that I need to be more tortoise in my approach and gradually build back up.

So now that I'm seeking a bit more structure to my days again, I'm going back to what worked well for me last year, just mindful about what's going on with me this year.

So, listening to last year's advice, I'm going to:

1. Set a goal(s) and write it down. I'm old school and like good old pen and paper but you could do this on your laptop or phone. Make it visual.

    Mine are to lose weight, exercise more and finish this book (if you're reading this, I've at least achieved one out of the three!).

2. Understand 'why' that goal is important to you. So, for me:

    Weight loss – I want to be healthier in general. To have more energy. To decrease the risk of cancer coming back by fuelling my body with the good stuff. My skin will be better. I want to practise what I preach to my children about healthy eating.

    Exercise more – All of the above really.

    Finish this book – It's always been a dream of mine to write a book. I love books and always have done since I can remember. It wasn't until adulthood that I started reading non-fiction and self-development books and saw the massive benefits in reading about other people's stories. I've mentioned that I've found writing cathartic, so firstly I want to finish this for me. To have my story committed to print so I can look back at this in years to come and think 'bloody hell you were awesome'. I also want to finish it for you, so you've got someone holding your hand as you continue through your journey.

3. Set a deadline then break your goal down into manageable bitesize pieces of action. Keep it realistic.

4. Set reminders. I have a memory like a sieve, so use my phone's reminders to kindly remind me to take action.

5. Start. Make one small change. That's all it takes to gather momentum. If not now, when?

Once I'd decided that I was going to collate my mini blogs and write a book, I immediately felt overwhelmed. It was too big. Too much to do. And who was I to write a book? I wasn't sure where to start but I just started typing. I'd ask myself to write an hour a week, split up if necessary. Once I got going, the momentum followed, and I just had to keep going. The same could be said with anything, really.

6. Manage your own expectations. I know I'm not going to be running any 5k races anytime soon, but by just moving a bit more each day, and slowly increasing the duration each week, I could be in a few months' time. 1lb a week is four stone over a whole year. A few paragraphs a day turns into chapters, turns into a book.

7. Tell people about your goal/dream. The more you talk about it, the more you start believing in yourself. You'll also really benefit from the support and encouragement from others, especially those trying to achieve similar goals. Find your tribe.

I read a load of self-development books in 2018 but by far my favourite is *The 5 Second Rule* by Mel Robbins. I'll leave you with a little something from her:

> *"There is no right time. There is only right now. You get one life. This is it. And it's not going to begin again. It's up to you to push*

yourself to make the most of it and the time to do it is right now."

I sign up to do the Race for Life 5k Pretty Muddy sponsored event in Exeter in July. Madness, I guess, given that I've just had surgery, but it feels good to have a goal to aim towards.

Cancer Comms and Facebook:

"Morning.

Hope everyone is well with this drizzly January Monday!

So, I've signed up to do the 5k Pretty Muddy on the 18th July at 11am Westpoint. I needed to set myself a goal to aim for and to kickstart getting my fitness back.

Now I could do it on my own, but where's the fun in that? I've not done any of this journey alone, so I'd love for anyone to join me. I've created a fundraising group so you can tag along with me.

When you sign up, pop a comment below."

Circle of Trust:

"Count me in."

"I'll hold your bags and greet you at the finish line with refreshments."

"I'll think of you while chilling at home. Nah, well done dude for signing up, but I've done one run and that was enough for me!"

"Running and mud, I'll pass! Happy to sponsor though."

Massaging Mummies:

"Yes, go Em. I'd love to join but will be away. I shall indeed sponsor you though."

"I'm doing the walk for life like I've done the last four years but I'd be up for a muddy one too. Count me in, bird. xx"

"Miss fitty Pattison, I trust I can count on you?"

"I'm in please. Send me the link."

"Well done, hun, I will definitely sponsor you and this is a great cause. I don't think I can cope with the amount of mud, though!"

"I'll do it, Em, if you come camping with me for a week? xx"

"A week? Are you trying to kill me?"

"Ems, you fought off cancer! A week camping will be a breeze. xx"

Local Yocals:

"Amazing, Emma, well done you. So strong, determined and focused. I'd love to be alongside you. Xx"

"You are a queen! Well done you. Fuck it, I'm going to do it with you. I've always told myself I'm not sporty or physically fit, but if you can go through treatment and sign up to do it then I can do it alongside you. Count me in. xx"

"Oh exciting. I want a pink army. Xx"

"Read that with disbelief that you could be even contemplating this, but Emma you are a legend, so I will be with you all the way (walking with a slight jog, yeah?) xx"

"Excellent. I'll only be quick shuffling. Xx"

"Oh, wow, I definitely don't want to do this but of course I'm gonna do it with you. You're amazing, Em (and all of you)."

Wednesday 29ᵗʰ January 2020

Cancer Comms

Strong Randy Ladies:

"Hey ladies, just to pre-warn you I've got a cold. I'm feeling better today but just wanted to check in case you'd rather I didn't come tonight in case you catch it. x"

"I'm constantly surrounded by one snotty child, so doesn't bother me

unless you decided you're going to sneeze and snot all over me, which I may object to. xx"

"If we abstain from tongue kissing, I'm still game. x"

"Oh, balls, I was looking forward to that .x"

Friday 31ˢᵗ January 2020

"I am open to positive changes in all areas of my life."
(YESmum card)

Post-op assessment today.

Seven months ago, I walked into the consultation with Darren to leave knowing I had breast cancer. Well, if my booby consultant's appalling poker face of grinning like a Cheshire cat is anything to go by, I'm guessing I'll be walking out of here knowing that I've seen it off. It's confirmed. NED. Who's he? 'No Evidence of Disease.' It also hadn't travelled to my lymph nodes, either. So that's it. Other than radiotherapy – just to cross all the T's and dot the I's – lumpy has well and truly been sent packing.

There's no uncontrollable shaking this time. No inhuman sounds escape from me. I'm just really bloody smiley and thank my booby consultant and her team so much.

I phone my mum straight away and draft my text to my captive audience.

Then I'm off to the pub with Darren, Russell, Charlene and Dad for a celebratory meal. My brother must be excited, as he dips into his pocket to buy us a bottle of bubbly to celebrate.

Cancer Comms and Facebook:

BreastIT.

My alternative to BREXIT.

Today will be full of mixed emotions up and down the country. No difference here. After the post-op appointment, I'm happily toasting to me being free of the booby bug (it hadn't even made it to the lymph nodes) and consoled Darren as he does not get to move in his young Swedish au pair!

Bring on the frying (radiotherapy), then we're done.

Circle of Trust:

"Fantastic news, Em. I'm so proud of how you've dealt with this whole charade! Love you lots. xx"

Massaging Mummies:

"Yes, Emma. Smashed it. Well done, hun. So happy for you. Can we drink champagne now? No radiotherapy?"

"Emma Davies, you superstar. Best news ever!!!!!!!!!!!"

"Thank you. Still some frying to do, but bloody hell it's such a relief."

"Okay, so we'll hold off on the champagne for now but celebrating inside anyhow. That is the best outcome possible. xx"

"Oh, hell no, crack on. I'm going out to celebrate for lunch. The things you need to do to get a new car!"

"Such wonderful news. Get on, my beaut."

"That's amazing news, hun. You are a superwoman and hope you celebrated at lunch. Roll on the radiotherapy and then the treatment completed. You're almost there. So pleased for you. xx"

"You absolute beaut, Emma! Always had full faith in your ability to kick lumpy's arse. He should have known he'd picked on the wrong woman to mess with. Good luck with the final stage but do celebrate this milestone. You're amazing. xx"

Shits and Giggles:

"Well, isn't that just the best news ever?"

"Hooooo zahhhh. That, my friend, is what they call closure."

"Thank you. Still some frying to do but bloody hell it's such a relief."

"What are you both up to right now?"

"I'm going out for lunch to celebrate with Darren, my brother and his wife and my healthy wonky tits!"

Strong Randy Ladies:

"Fucking amazing. Wooooo hoooooo so happy for you. xx"

"Bloody amazing news. So pleased for you. I've just had a celebration dance in the office for you. xx"

Local Yocals:

"That's bloody fantastic news, Emma! I'm so pleased for you. Happy bloody Friday. Xx"

"Oh, that is so brilliant, Emma. Huge hugs."

"Fuck yeah. Wonderful news."

"YASSSSS! Amazing news! When can we celebrate? So happy for you!"

"I need a PA again to organise my many responses for celebrations!"

"I feel like I could hug every single one of your other mates having walked with you through this. We all love you and want to celebrate."

"Yes, I think I'll have one date for a party, and everyone can come have a look at me and my wonky tits! x"

"Yes, joining the wonky tits gang. So happy for you, Emma."

"I've got wonky tits because Nell prefers one over the other. Can I join?"

Cake. Always Cake:

> *"Yesssss. Tell your friends booby bug. Time for cake. Xx"*
> *"Boom. Agree with cake statement – I'll bake brownies. Xx"*
> **"What is the answer? CAKE. Xx"**
> *"Woohoo, fuck you, cancer. I hope you are having celebratory drinkypoos tonight, Em. Also, there's a group of us from work doing the pretty muddy. I'm up for starting running again if you fancy it, Em. Me, you, Jo Whiley and the open road. Xx"*
> **"I can't start running just yet as my tit is a bit sore, but I'm up for walks. Xx"**
> *"Happy to start with walks and work up to it when you have happy titties. X"*

ED Fan Club:

> *"That's amazing news, Emma. I'm sure your attitude to the whole process has helped also, as you've been so incredibly positive in fighting it. Really happy for you."*
> *"Yay! That's absolutely amazing. I'm so happy for you. Incredible news. X"*
> *"Whoop whoop!"*
> *"Fantastic news – really thrilled to hear. And really happy for you and all your family. Xx"*
> *"So happy for you, Emma. That's amazing news."*
> *"Yay. Do they still want to fry you?"*
> **"Thank you. Still some frying to do but bloody hell it's such a relief."**
> *"Wahoo! That's awesome news, Emma. I'm super chuffed for you. X"*

The demise of the cumulative side effect nasties:

- Fatigue seems to come and go now.
- Spotty teenager skin.

- The hair is returning. Current trend – GI Jane.
- Taste continues to slowly come back.
- Zombie nails (turning black and yellow and raising off their nail bed – thank goodness for my lovely friend Paula who keeps them nicely painted).
- Hot sweats have put in a reappearance.

January – Looking Back

A month of mixed emotions again. I think I've experienced it all this month. Calm to start with. Happiness with positive results. Not knowing what to do with myself and feeling a bit 'flat'. Sheer fear again. Anxiety in the lead-up to surgery followed by calm on the actual day. Restfulness and contentment as I watched my loved ones deal expertly with the family logistics post-surgery, so I didn't need to bat an eyelid. Relief at the post-op consultation.

I'm not sure how I thought I would be feeling after such good news, but I'm a bit underwhelmed to be honest. I thought I might feel ecstatically happy but that isn't the feeling. Maybe after all the craziness of chemo, kids' birthdays and Christmas, it's just a feeling of relief that the cancer's gone and treatment is nearly over. For the time being, I'm just going to enjoy the peace as it's sure as hell not going to last for too much longer! People keep telling me to rest. Who am I to argue with them?!

February 2020

Tuesday 4th February 2020

I've signed up to a monthly membership (OTEUnlimited) with two amazing people called Kelly and Martin who run an online community called 'Over the Edge'. Their community is about *"Inspiring a collaborative community to develop extraordinary results."* Their membership group helps people reach their potential.

I've not joined this membership because I see myself as an entrepreneur or have a business to grow, but for more personal reasons. To join a positive space that will most importantly help me focus on my two personal goals – weight loss and exercise – but to also help me maintain momentum and get this book written!

Today is my first one to one coaching session with Kelly and it's amazing. I feel like I'm doing this for me. Investing in myself to work out what my 'new normal' is going to be going forward. I'm not going to get all deep and meaningful, but I've been left feeling a little lost these past few weeks (a bit like when I was a first-time mum, actually). A bit flat perhaps. Uncomfortable in this albeit fabulous body that has achieved amazing things but one that feels a bit old and achy and doesn't look how I remember myself.

Kelly is also writing her own story, so I've no doubt she's going to be a great help in that department.

If you'd like to check them out, here's their website www.weareovertheedge.com or you can find them on Facebook and Instagram.

Wednesday 5ᵗʰ February 2020

I don't want to jinx this, but I've had two full nights of sleep. No hot sweat wake ups. No small humans tag teaming for our attention. I feel like a new woman.

I feel ill prepared to write about the actual act of sleeping. I own a six and two-year-old, so in the words of Faithless: "I can't get no sleep". Before this little run of two nights, I think the last good sleep was 2013 pre-pregnancy insomnia.

I thought I'd been tired in the past, maybe after a heavy night on the tiles, but nothing prepares you for the lack of sleep or continued breaks in your sleep in the years that follow the small human's arrival. The sleep deprivation from two small humans, the cancer fatigue, the constant waking from hot sweats. I feel the small humans have equipped me well for this new sleep deprivation journey. I can see why it's used as a form of torture, as after a particularly bad spell I start losing the plot.

Pre-pregnancy I took for granted my eight-hour solid block of sleep. I remember thinking 7.20am was an early start for work, now anything past 6am is considered a bonus and I can function pretty well on a good block of four to five hours.

I am also very partial to a daytime nap now. I think I will have to discuss this with my boss when the time comes to return to work and we're discussing reasonable adjustments. Perhaps I can store some soft furnishings under my desk and take myself under there when I need to catch some zzz's.

Thursday 6ᵗʰ February 2020

A hat-trick on the sleep front. Three whole glorious nights.

I meet up with (Boss) Becky today at Starbucks. So many choices! My chemo brain would have short-circuited at the ridiculous number of options for a hot beverage, but 'back in the game' brain confidently selected a 'tall vanilla bean macchiato'.

It's so good to see Becky again. It's even more exciting to show her that I can string a sentence together as opposed to our last encounter, which we'll agree to never talk of again! She is fantastic at keeping me abreast (ha, I do still chuckle when I get to use booby-related words) of everything that is going on at work, but at the same time putting no pressure on me to return.

We deal with formalities, we catch up about my colleagues and we chat about nothing in particular.

Friday 7ᵗʰ February 2020

Lunch is on Mum today as we venture down to the beach. She's back to work on Monday with a phased return, so this is the last full day, in a while anyway, that we can hang out and be 'ladies wot lunch'.

All good things must come to an end and some sort of normality needs to resume at some point. In the absence of paid work, we would also require a lottery win to sustain our dining lifestyle.

As I've already written, I will look back at this precious extra time I have had with her these past five months as an unexpected gift. Yes, we have both struggled in our different ways, and would rather it hadn't happened at all, but it's also been absolutely amazing. The kids have seen so much of her, I think they'd prefer her to live here rather than me!

Monday 10ᵗʰ February 2020

I'm worried today. Whilst out on Friday, I popped to my friend Gabbi's 'Snack Shack' to check in on her and it was closed. I met Gabbi during chemotherapy when she was being treated for cervical cancer. Her and her sidekick Lynn were being treated together and were always laughing and joking.

Then today I've seen a post on Facebook announcing that the business will be closed due to serious illness. I don't like the sound of this. I'm not fishing for information, but I drop her a message saying I popped round, have seen her message, and I'm sending love if she's going through a difficult time.

I'm floored by her response telling me that the bastard thing has spread to her liver and more in her lung.

Like a slap in the face, she'd been given the all-clear on the cervical cancer to be told eight days later that the cancer on her lung was inoperable and had also spread to her liver. She has also chopped her long curly hair off in preparation and donated it to The Little Princess Trust. What an evil disease that I suppose I will never understand.

I hesitate over sending my response. Will she appreciate our usual comedic approach? Am I being insensitive? Suddenly I know how my friends and family must have felt. I don't know how she's feeling. Yes, I've had a cancer diagnosis and know only too well the feeling of extreme fear when you don't know what your prognosis is. But then I was so lucky. My plan worked and my cancer has buggered off. I cannot even begin to imagine what Gabbi must be feeling.

But I decide to go for it. From the little I know of Gabbi, she was always smiling and being silly. A bit like me. This feels right and so I go for it. It was the right choice as she enjoys my (awful) singing!

"Bastard stuff. Right then, keeping it at bay is the new game plan. Is there anything I can do to help? That isn't an offer to help at your shack, as I can't cook for shit! I'm still off work whilst I wait to start radiotherapy, so would be more than happy to come be a 'chemo sitter' on your watch. Look at the fun I used to have. I've also got some

scarfs and hats if you'd like them? I was going to give them to FORCE.

When I shaved my head I felt the need to do this... enjoy!"

I send her the video of me singing Sinead O'Conner.

Tuesday 11ᵗʰ February 2020

Another day, another lunch. I meet my mum for lunch today with her work colleague Julie. Julie has been a fantastic support to my mum and with all the updates she's been receiving would like to meet me! Mum tells me that she was inundated with colleagues wishing her well and asking after me. I feel like a 'Z-list celebrity' to her team and wonder if I ought to offer Julie my autograph.

Excitingly, today I got a call from The Willow Foundation to offer me a special day. I give her an update on where I am in my treatment. I tell her I now feel a bit of a fraud because I don't actually have cancer anymore and surely someone else more worthy could benefit from this. She reassures me that I am absolutely still entitled to my special day. Given what me and the family have gone through over the past months, it will be a special treat for us to have some family fun.

So, I asked to visit Legoland. I thought this would be a nice day trip. What they are offering is two days of entry to the park and putting us up in a hotel for three nights so we have enough energy to take on this adventure. They recommend we go in term time, so we can fully enjoy the experience without crowds of people, and will even write a letter to Toby's school. I'm blown away and start sobbing to this lady who has shown such compassion and kindness.

We agree that I will phone them back once I have dates for radiotherapy so we can book in the experience. I've got a year to take it and I've bagged it just in time before I turn forty-one!

Wednesday 12ᵗʰ February 2020

Goodness me, it takes a while to get the old bones moving when the alarm rudely wakes me at 6.20am. I feel like I'm in the body of somebody a lot older than my forty years and it's rather frustrating. But move I must, as the show goes on. I tell myself that in two hours I can be back home and, if necessary, back in bed.

But I always find that once I do get moving, and the small humans have been safely deposited to their requisite places, it is a rare occurrence that I do sneak back to bed.

I'm excited to be writing today. It really feels like the scrambled chemo brain of last year has buggered off and I'm feeling mentally sharp.

Today is session three of my NHS fat club. I wasn't overly optimistic about the 'sad step' indicating a weight loss, so am pleasantly surprised with -2lb. I thought Mr Ben & Jerry's and Mr McVities were going to cause me some ongoing problems in the weight department. Thankfully, my burst of increased exercising and sporadic days of healthy eating have made some difference.

Going forward, we're tasked with food diaries, exercise diaries and personally for me to record how energised I'm feeling. I'm struggling with fatigue again at the moment, so want to identify any trends.

I feel quite energised to get properly on my game after this session and also because of the good sleep I had last week when I wasn't inhaling chocolate, crisps and ice cream at an impressive rate.

Our OTEUnlimited challenge today is to do a 'live' post on our Facebook wall asking people to comment on our strengths and weaknesses. I'm not a big fan of doing Facebook 'lives' and not least now because I'm not a massive fan of the person staring back at me. In my head, that's not how I look, so it feels a bit intimidating to have to look at myself and start yabbering away. So why I chose to do it outside as I was walking to school carrying a scooter is beyond me. I can barely walk up the hill without getting out of breath.

Not surprisingly, there were a number of comments that my weakness could be cardio and my inability to walk and talk! The reason I write about this here is that I was bowled over by all the lovely comments:- kindness, humour, positivity, determination, turning a sad situation into something positive, strong, brave, amazing. To tell you the truth, I'm absolutely buzzing after this little mini challenge and it's really given me the extra drive I need to keep forging forward. So, if you're feeling a bit down in the dumps, I'd recommend you ask others what your strengths are. I think you'll be pleasantly surprised.

Thursday 13th February 2020

I'm catching up with Dawn (remember I met her on the chemo ward and married her off to her brother!) today for a cuppa. I tried to resist the cake, but she said she'd treat me. I thought it would be rude to refuse.

I love talking to Dawn. Although she reports that she's still tired, I think she looks amazing and better again from the last time I saw her. We spend a lovely couple of hours talking about everything, anything and of course cancer-related stuff. She enlightens me on what to expect in respect of radiotherapy and assures me I've done all the hard work.

Friday 14th February – Valentine's Day

Even though we're now on year fourteen together, I still make a big deal of this in our house (for personal reasons I won't embarrass Darren with here!). He's got pretty good over the years buying flowers and has even progressed to writing more than just 'Dear Emma, Love Darren' in his cards! This year I get a lovely card from him, with heartfelt words. Feeling a bit guilty about my plain black card that reads "There's no one I'd rather spend this annual obligation with than you".

Joking aside, though, I love him to bits, and he has been an absolute rock throughout this shit storm. I've already devoted a whole lot of love to him back in our anniversary diary entry in September, but I just wanted another nod to him here.

We enjoy our M&S meal for two, as has become our annual tradition, and an evening of maybe a few too many bubbles and lots of laughs.

Monday 17th – Friday 21st February 2020

Half Term!

I shan't bore you with all the ins and outs of our activities in the (vain) hope of keeping Toby entertained during a wet and windy week.

Needless to say, there were visits to soft play. Four of them, in fact. #livingthedream. Just to change it up a bit, I took Toby to the museum with Mum one day. We enjoyed ourselves but we might as well have substituted that for soft play number five, as far as Toby was concerned.

Thank God it's only a week. I'm knackered! Thank you to reinforcements who came with me to assist with the whirlwind child that is Toby Davies!

Saturday 22nd February 2020

It's my friend Jo's fortieth birthday, so we're heading 'out out'.

Darren is a party animal and could keep going until the sun comes up or he becomes comatose from too many sherbets. Whichever comes first. I know he's excited to go out, so I tentatively remind him to manage his expectations and let's just see how the evening goes. I'm really looking forward to this, but also at the same time I already feel tired at the thought of staying up past 9pm!

I get a little down-hearted when I realise I should have given a little thought to what I was going to wear more than thirty minutes before we need to leave. Nothing fits! I have one dress I kept from years ago when I hadn't shifted the baby timber, so that will have to do. This will also be the first time 'out out' without the head scarf and impish-looking hair. I'm a little self-conscious but remind myself that this is a private party for a good friend.

As it turns out, I have a fantastic night, mostly sitting chatting with Darren and my friends Pippa and Gareth. The time flies and, before we know it, the lights are coming on. Darren looks at me: "Clubbing?" I was thinking "taxi".

Part 3 – Radiotherapy 'The Frying'
Wednesday 26th February 2020

I was merrily going about my business at 9am, all ready for Fat Club, when I get a call from oncology inviting me in for an appointment at 11am with my consultant to discuss radiotherapy and to have a scan so they can prepare for it. The phone calls to the secretary over the past couple of days have paid off and we're now getting the finale of this show on the road.

Radiotherapy

This is the final piece of the puzzle in my treatment plan. Whereas chemo wanders around your whole body, radiotherapy treatment delivers powerful X-ray beams to a defined area. In my case, the right breast and – rather catching me unawares – a bit of my lung, as it's close to the area to be treated.

First, I talk to the registrar who explains that I'm having 'external beam' radiotherapy, which means it's delivered by a machine outside of my body. The radiation is only produced when the machine is turned on and I'm told that I will not become radioactive during or after treatment. Rather reassuring to hear!

With any treatment there are risks and side effects:

- Tiredness.
- The breast might become slightly swollen or I may experience pains.
- The skin might become sore or red, a bit like sunburn.
- Ribs might feel a bit sore.
- Lymphoedema.
- Secondary cancers (this is the one that shits me up the most. Any mention of secondary cancer and I then have to ask my follow-up questions. I'm told that there is more chance of my breast cancer returning, which is highly unlikely, and why this treatment is recommended, than developing a secondary cancer. I'm happy with that explanation).

I'm given a leaflet that explains various ways to look after my skin and who to call if I need help. Looks like I'll be slapping on that cream again.

Before you start treatment, the team need to plan. Again, I'm given a fetching garment to 'maintain my dignity', which gives the radiographers easy access. I'm asked the usual questions to correctly identify it's me and this time they take a snapshot, which I'm told is used each day during treatment to identify me.

I'm then positioned on a 'Breast Board' ready for the CT scan. The radiographers take out their pens to start their measuring and marking and tape a small piece of metal around the area to be treated. I'm then fed into the polo mint (CT scanner). After they've got what they need, they remove the metal markers and tattoo three small permanent dots onto my skin. These will be used to accurately position me for treatment each time.

The CT scan allows the planning team to create a highly focused treatment plan based on my individual anatomy. This plan will then be used during each day of treatment to accurately target the defined area. The course of treatment runs for fifteen days, Monday to Friday, and will last about ten to fifteen minutes. On each day of treatment, I'll be taken into the treatment room and set up in the same position as I was during the planning scan.

When the treatment is being given, I'll be on my own, but it only lasts a few minutes and the radiographers will be able to see and hear me at all times. I won't see or feel anything, just the machine making a buzzing noise and a bleeping noise indicating it is switched on.

Once the course of radiotherapy has finished, any side effects can continue to worsen for up to fourteen days.

Cancer Comms

"Stage three – The Frying.

Player one please proceed to level three.

Right then, peeps. Settle back because the finale is about to begin. Thank God for that I hear you sigh, so you won't be subjected to these updates for much longer!

I got a cancellation appointment to discuss radiotherapy and got scanned so they can make their frying plan.

As I'm lying on the CT scanner bed, norks out (again), chatting to the radiographer (who looks so young I consider asking him for proof of his qualifications) whilst he attaches wire with tape, my immediate concern at the last minute appointment is, "Shit, what state are my armpits in?" and "Bugger, I deffo know there's three hairs on my chest I should have plucked out!" He didn't mention it!

I also get three new tattoos. Wasn't expecting to add to my collection. Although, to be fair, they are literally dots to assist with measurements, so I won't be needing to go on Tattoo Fixers when this is all done.

And that was that. Got to model a new fetching **NHS** garment with easy access poppers, my favourite to date, and now I wait whilst they work out my plan. Likely starting in four to five weeks (to coincide beautifully with the Easter hols – arghhhhh!). I'll be fried for three weeks, every day, Monday to Friday. I'm told that in comparison to chemo, this is a walk in the park, so let's get the walking started.

Hope you all have a great day. I'll leave you with a pic so you can enjoy the latest fetching garment and my *Sonic the Hedgehog* hair. **Xx"**

Circle of Trust:

"I love hearing your updates. Three weeks every day?! Blimey! I know you'll cope with it just fine, as you have done with all the other nasty stuff. You're almost at the end and then we can focus on the finish line of this muddy run thing we've set ourselves up for! Got my number the other day and then realised quickly how unfit I am right now. So please let me know when you're ready to prepare. x"

"Wow, where has all that hair come from? Good thing with radiotherapy it's a lot quicker process than chemo. It can burn your skin, though, so worth asking what you can put on it to help soothe it. xx"

"Ha, tell me about it. Don't know what to do with it. Yes, I've heard that. I hear that moisturising is the way to go, so I will be creaming my tits up."

Massaging Mummies:

"What an inspirational hedgehog you are, my beaut. xx"

"That new style of garment is so much better than the flaps. One gust and you've flashed everyone your behind. I think you're rocking the look, hair and all, and am in awe of you. Love you so much. xx"

"Gorgeous and strong as ever. xx"

(Sonic the hedgehog GIF) "They got the colour right and everything. You walking through radio! I'm picturing Sonic foot tapping whilst he's waiting for the plan. Can you tell I had a Megadrive?"

"Rocking it, bird. If only you had all those gold rings too, Em. We'd be in the Bahamas."

Shits and Giggles:

"Your hair looks bloody fab! Short really suits you. How's it gone?"

"You think?! I'm not convinced, but not much say in the matter."

"I think it's awesome, genuinely. You've got such a fantastic face, it suits you. Shows it off. xx"

"My favourite comment on this was the 'frying plan'. Very fetching easy access onesie – do you get to take it home?"

Local Yocals:

"That blue suits you!"

"Ahh, that is great that you've got in quickly. I totally feel you on the armpit situation. I'd be the same. I'm sure they get all sorts in! Awesome, glad it will be easier going than chemo, hope it all goes smoothly. Love the pic. Nearly there, lovely. Xx"

"Definitely should have ID'd the boy. Thanks for the update, hun, and as always keep us informed of how we can be of use please. Anything!"

"Emma, if you ever fancy a change in career that 'NHS Blue' looks good on you. As always, it's lovely that you keep us up to speed with what's going on. Let us know when you get a 'frying' start date and don't hesitate to reach out if you need any extra support during that time. Xx"

"Loving the dark blue. Great things are on the move, although not *great for Easter hols, so if you need a hand with childcare give us a shout. Lots of love. Xx"*

Cake. Always Cake:

> *"Oh, blue is definitely your colour. Maybe get some blue tips put on the hair to match? Hairy armpits!"*
>
> *"Oooooh, it's the final countdown. Did anyone read that without music in your head? Maybe you can add NHS outfit modelling as photo pages in your memoirs? Tell yourself enough times that your armpit hair maintenance was up to date and you'll be able to rewrite that memory. Xx"*

ED Fan Club:

> *"I love your updates. X"*
>
> *"Your hair is awesome, Emma. Fab update. Great to hear from you. X"*

The demise of the cumulative side effect nasties:

- I think I'll downgrade the fatigue to tiredness because rest and sleep does seem to do the trick.
- Spotty teenager skin – although I am noticing a difference. I don't know if this is because the chemo drugs haven't been in the system for a while, the fact I'm eating better and drinking more water, I'm trying to be a bit better with my lovely Tropic skincare products that were collecting dust or a combination of all four.
- The hair continues its strong return. Current trend – goodness knows what you'd call it. It's coming back thick and fast, though. The greys are also returning in the same place, so if left undyed I will resemble a badger towards the end of the

year. So, this is what my natural colour is. A darkish brown that isn't at all bad.

- Taste – I can taste stuff. Not as vividly as before but it's not something I notice I miss anymore. I only remembered to mention it now because I looked back at previous months.
- Zombie nails – have stopped turning yellow and black. Where they've raised off the nail beds and broken off, I've got short stubby nails. Nothing painful and looks a damn sight better than they did.
- Hot sweats are pretty intermittent. Not bothering me too much at the moment.

February – Looking Back

If January was the month of mixed emotions, this month feels a lot calmer and more positive. Maybe it's because I've done the bulk of the work and I've been told I don't have cancer. Let's just pause and digest that a moment. I. DON'T. HAVE. CANCER.

Looking back to January I can see why I felt the way I did. I'm not very good with January/February in general. They can always seem quite bleak months and you're coming down from the over-indulgence of Christmas and excitable small humans. This year I'd also come down from a chemo high. One minute I'm being repeatedly pumped up with drugs, attending various medical appointments, scans and waiting for results. The next that drops off and I'm at home with some phone numbers for back up.

I've continued to have time to look back and think, 'Wow that was big'. However, I've spent my February trying to just embrace the good news and be a 'human being' rather than a 'human doing'. I felt pretty good, so wanted to make the most of that before starting radiotherapy.

March 2020

Monday 2ⁿᵈ March 2020

One of my revamped 'forty things at forty' was to make more use of my National Trust membership.

I'd arranged a play date today with Charlotte and her three-year-old, Violet. I thought it might be nice to visit A La Ronde in Exmouth and then maybe stroll on the beach. A La Ronde is a quirky little house documenting two sisters' travels. As soon as we got inside and Chloe screamed, "No, outside!" repeatedly, I knew this was not going to go well. A whistle stop tour and ten minutes later we were outside to complaints of, "Cold, Mummy." Sometimes you just need to concede that there are days when you'll feel that everything is an uphill struggle.

Tuesday 3ʳᵈ March 2020

Today I am the chemo sitter to Gabbi.

I'm really looking forward to catching up with her, albeit I would have preferred it wasn't in these circumstances. Conscious of the effort my 'chemo sitters' went to, I've stocked my bag up with snacks and entertainment to the brim.

It feels really strange returning to the ward as a visitor rather than a patient. But once I'm in, I forget all about that because today is not about me. It's about catching up, chatting, laughing and hopefully helping Gabbi pass the time with humour and positivity.

She's busy talking to the nurses, so I catch up with her partner Tal first. He gives me all the updates on what happened. The joy at being given the all-clear that only lasted eight days. The news that they couldn't operate on her lung, as it had grown and also spread to her liver. The pain she's been experiencing and the hope that they can sort her out with some drugs. The new diet they were trying. The practical arrangements they were making. I also check in with him to see how he's doing because I remember all too clearly the worry and fear Darren had to shoulder.

Then she's done and she shoots me a massive smile. I let her do all the talking. Let her get it all out. We're soon laughing and joking. I start going through my bag of tricks and apologise that my crisps and Mr Kipling French Fancies are no longer suitable snacking items seeing as she's eating a plant-based diet. No red meat. No sugar. Lots of leafy greens. Lots of juicing. The last-minute grape purchase was a good shout, so we get those out.

I give her my hats/scarfs and a few other practical bits that might be useful. We also get involved in the 'stack the emoji poo' and 'top plops' games I've brought. But mostly we talk. Before I know it, over three hours has zoomed past and we have a huge hug and 'see you later'.

That night I get a message from Gabbi:

"Just got home now. Thank you so much for all the lovely goodies, much appreciated, love it all. Great to see you; had a lovely day, despite where we were. You're looking fantastic, your positive vibes have done me the world of good and I thank you for that. See you soon. x"

"Blimey, what a long day. Way past your bedtime then! Take it easy today. I loved meeting you guys yesterday, albeit I would have preferred better circumstances, getting sloshed sipping some cocktails perhaps! Always here if you need a chat. I won't intrude on your family time but just know I'm always thinking of you and here if you need an injection of ridiculousness! xx"

Spending time with Gabbi today has really made me stop and think again. Am I doing everything I possibly can to live a fulfilling and healthy life? My own cancer diagnosis kickstarted a more spontaneous approach to life but I realise I'm still not fuelling my body properly. Why am I still eating crap?

Something clicks inside my head tonight and I promise myself that I'm going to sort my weight out once and for all.

"Stop wishing, start doing".

Saturday 7ᵗʰ March 2020

I've escaped! I'm off to my friend Michelle's house this arvo in Torquay for girly chats, dinner, theatre and a lie in! I hope the excitement in these words is being accurately portrayed.

I make reasonably healthy choices at Las Iguanas when it comes to the food, but I am indulging in their 241 cocktails. (That looks like I had 241 cocktails, I did not. I had two for the price of one). Not so sure if this was a good idea pre-theatre, as I'm a bit giggly and don't really have a clue what's going on to start with.

Such a good evening and now for a whole night of uninterrupted sleep. Zzzzzzzzzz

Monday 9ᵗʰ March 2020

Cancer Comms

Circle of Trust:

"Ever since it was brought to my attention that you can say 'Covid-19' to the tune of 'Come on Eileen', I've been unable to read it any other way."

"If I get it, it had better not finish me off from an 'underlying health condition'."

"I reckon it would take a lot to finish you off."

Tuesday 10ᵗʰ March 2020

One of our OTE challenges today was to look in the mirror. Look at the person looking back and have a think about who we see. Look at the frown lines. Look at the laughter lines. Think about everything we have achieved. Think about everything that has happened to us. Think about the person we are.

This couldn't come at a better time. At a time when I'm really struggling with the physical appearance of the person I see looking back at themselves in the mirror every time I brush my teeth. I see a person that looks a lot older and doesn't look like me at all. I try not to look too much. When I took pictures of myself to document my weight loss, I didn't look at them for very long either. I gasped and thought I looked horrendous.

But I've now done this exercise. Looking at my face in the mirror and the full body pictures.

I look at my face. Yes, my hair is short and spikey and not the long thick brown locks it once was, but it's growing back. A sign of life and bloody hell am I glad to be alive. Yes, the bags under my eyes are darker than ever but I remind myself of the amount of poison that my body has processed. The sleepless nights from the side effects and anxiety. The extreme stress it has endured. Yes, my skin isn't the best, but if I fuel my body with healthier food and water that will sort itself out.

I smile. That's the same me. Nothing has changed there. I look at my eyes and see that there is a sparkle in there. I remember everything I've been through over the past months. I remember the kind words spoken by so many people and, in that moment, I realise that I need to use those kind words myself when I look in the mirror. This is the face of a bloody strong woman who got through something she never saw coming, never wanted, yet faced head on and showed cancer who was boss.

My body is amazing. It may not currently look how it used to. It may not currently work how it used to, but it's coming back. It has served me well and I should be very proud of it.

I shed a little tear. Not because I'm sad anymore about the way I look but because I'm bloody proud of myself. No more unkind thoughts about myself. Drops the mic and walks away… Enough now.

Monday 16th March 2020

Move over cancer, there's a new C in town – Coronavirus. Well, actually, it's been in town (not ours yet thankfully) for a while but when it isn't on your doorstep it's easy to fall into a false sense of security and go about your business as usual.

Well, that business stops today, as following the government's announcements, I fall into the 'vulnerable category' and will have to 'shield' myself away for twelve weeks. I have two children still going to school and nursery and a husband who works in an industry classified as an 'essential worker'. I can personally limit my exposure, hell I've been practising for nine months now and have got pretty frigging good at it, but how do I deal with our family logistics?

If one of us shows symptoms, we're also now required to quarantine ourselves for fourteen days. All cooped up, the four of us, for fourteen days! Bloody hell, if the cancer didn't and the coronavirus doesn't kill me, this might well do.

I jest, of course, because joking is what I do to defuse situations where I can feel the fear trying to rear its ugly head. I will keep heeding the professionals' advice, keep talking to Darren about our family dynamic, keep calm and carry on.

Tonight, I still go to Pippa's house for our 'Local Yocals' meal as planned. There's only four of us and we adopt my new elbow bump and toe tap as a greeting. This could be the last group interaction for some time. I feel it's worth the risk to get some in-person lols before I cocoon myself away for who knows how long.

The days of meeting up with friends and family are now temporarily put on hold.

Tuesday 17th March 2020

St Paddy's Day. Darren and I have been together for fourteen years today! At year thirteen, cancer put in an appearance, but thirteen is my lucky number. On your bike, cancer. And now we face another big 'C'.

The cancer was all about me, but this new 'C' is about everyone. It's about everyone coming together (not literally!) to get each other through this.

I wrote a blog today sharing my experience of how I kept my shit together through the most trying time in my life and how love plays a massive part. It's written in respect of the coronavirus, but it could easily apply to a cancer diagnosis or any big testing event/time in our lives. I share this again now as a reminder of just how strong we all are.

My favourite saying is:
"If you don't like it, change it;
If you can't change it, change the way you feel about it."
Feel the fear. A cancer diagnosis hit me like a ton of bricks. I did not see it coming. I did not want it. Overnight, everything I had planned was put on hold, and for how long? Was I going to survive it? The treatment available is amazing but there were no certainties. We know this is coming. We can prepare to minimise the risk and if we're lucky we won't get it or suffer too badly.

In times when you're tested, look for love to push aside the fear. In a unique situation, open your mind up to the positives. Look for alternative and innovative solutions. Who knows, this could radically change how we work and function for the better once it's gone. If you get your mind in the right place, you can find a place of calm in the madness.

Positivity and humour in abundance. I communicated to my friends and family early on that I was going to be approaching cancer with the same humour and positivity that had got me through life so far. That got me through cancer, and it will get me and my family through the next big 'C' that has come knocking at our door.

Don't google the shit out of this. Dr Google will scare the shit out of you. When I googled 'ringing in ears' a few years back, I'd diagnosed myself with a brain tumour when in fact it was tinnitus! Listen to the experts and follow their guidance. After all, they get paid a shit ton of money to get this right.

I've turned my radio station to 'chill out' music. I'll listen to the news once a day to make sure I'm fully informed, but I don't need to hear it multiple times a day.

Embrace the kindness that will flow from this, whether it be practical support or supportive words in a WhatsApp group.

Distance yourself from negativity, it will only cause you worry. Find those people that lift you up. Keep talking about the usual stuff. The stuff you find funny. If you like toilet humour, keep talking to me, I've got enough material to take it on tour! Facetime with people so you still get to see them.

If you're allowed out, get out in nature. Exercise. Look up. I live in a beautiful neck of the woods but didn't really appreciate it enough until I was forced to stop.

Take one day at a time. If you're still breathing today, you're winning.

At the end of the day, think of three things that went well. You'll always find something.

If you're stuck indoors, now's the time for all those little jobs you never find the time to do. Pick up old hobbies. Try something new. I might try cooking!

Music. I used to jump in the car and whack up the happy hardcore. Sing like nobody is listening. Play a musical instrument. I've seen Italy with their tambourines. I don't own a tambourine, but I have a clarinet, saxophone and piano. Not so good on the latter but I could fill my street with a rendition of 'Puff the Magic Dragon'.

I turned to my children. They can bring perspective in the madness. Don't get me wrong, I don't particularly relish the thought of us all being cooped up, but they can find joy and amusement in the silliest of things. One of my friends has created a Facebook group where people are already growing an online community, sharing ideas to keep us sane and the small humans occupied. I'll share my tactics on here. Please share away.

My one plea for help. If anyone could let me know how to get a thumb sucker to quit, I'd be forever grateful. I hear cutting the end off dummies helps with that but not sure I can enforce the same tactic here!

Okay, two pleas. I fall into the vulnerable category now, so have to stay away from every man and his dog. Actually, dogs are probably okay. So, if you see me out and about trying to keep my distance, I'm not being rude. In the words of Dionne Warwick, "Walk on by."

To bring my ramblings to an end, we might not have a choice about some of the things that we have to do in the coming months, but we do have a choice as to how we react to it all.

Massive non-contact virtual hugs to everyone. Xxxx

Today was also a day of some more practicalities. I emailed both the nursery and school with suggestions as to how I could avoid being in close proximity to lots of other people. Both were fantastic. With nursery, I don't have to step foot on the premises. I buzz and someone will collect Chloe and bring her to the gate. With school, I've arranged an earlier pick up time to avoid the crowds. Another fantastic show of how people come together in times of need and help each other out.

Toby, of course, is ecstatic at the news that he will be finishing school twenty minutes earlier than all his mates. He hugged me and said it meant he could spend more time having fun with me. Chloe is, as always, rather indifferent to the goings on.

Wednesday 18th March 2020

All change on the radiotherapy front. My oncology consultant phones today to advise that due to the coronavirus, and wanting to limit people's risk coming into hospital or risking treatment stopping early, they will be reducing my radiotherapy to one week. My immediate concern is how effective this is when, originally, I needed fifteen sessions and this has been reduced by two thirds. She explains that there have been trials that were shortly due to report, but because of the current times, this new process is being rolled out nationally. I'll also be getting the same dose, just a bigger dose each time. This will then be followed up with a telephone consultation.

I'm game to be honest. Only five fryings instead of fifteen. Not having to deal with childcare logistics all over the Easter hols and the icing on the cake is that I will now no longer be frying on my birthday.

I ask whether I fall into the vulnerable person category and her thoughts on my children both currently being in nursery and school. She sounds positive that I'm only at a slightly increased risk. I've had chemotherapy within the past six months but my chemo finished three months ago, I've always responded well and been fairly well throughout, I'm young and the radiotherapy isn't being used to treat cancer as there is no cancer. This is so reassuring to hear.

I thank her for her time and all that her colleagues are doing in this difficult time.

Friday 20ᵗʰ March 2020

Cancer Comms

Massaging Mummies:

"Hey lovely ladies. Well, what a shit show. How is everyone holding up? xx"

"I'm enjoying being in our self-isolating bubble but then it's only day two! Life is so much calmer. How's everyone else? Occurred to me how lucky I am to be on sick leave and how stressful this must be for all of you guys. xx"

"Work is a stress, but tonight's announcement will help. Hats off to Boris! Kids finished today, so day one starts tomorrow, I guess… dum dum dum… Glad you're okay. Are they still doing your radiotherapy?"

"We are all okay, thanks. Very stressful at work and shit. Going to get worse, I'm afraid. Just trying to juggle work and kids. Keep safe and stay strong everyone. Glad you're both okay and keep isolating wherever possible. x"

"Yes, they're condensing it down to one week with bigger zaps, but it's delayed a week because we're having to isolate. Chloe came home with a temperature on Wednesday but she's just full of snot now. Better safe than sorry. We'll all get through this together. Just keep talking. xx

I've been practising for nine months. I'm ahead of the game!"

Saturday 21st March 2020

Cancer Comms

Massaging Mummies:

"Massive virtual non-contact hugs to everyone. It's an unprecedented time and I think now more than ever we've got to be kind to ourselves. We can only do so much in any given day, let alone this. Emotions are going to be massive. Stress is going to be massive. But if we just keep talking we'll share the fear and we'll get through this together. xx"
"Keep talking, deep breaths, we will get through this and all have a new outlook on the important things in life."

Thursday 26th March 2020

Well, hard to believe that your world can change beyond recognition within such a short space of time. It would appear that last year was not extreme enough and things are about to change again.

Last Wednesday, Chloe was sent home from nursery with a slightly high temperature. After her developing a new cough, we took the decision to self-isolate for fourteen days, as per government guidance. All four of us cocooned away in our family home for fourteen days.

I had to inform my consultant that we were self-isolating, so that has put my radiotherapy back until the 6th April. Still only one week and still fully fried before my birthday, thank goodness. I hear that hospital parking is looking quite good given the current state of affairs – every silver lining and all that.

So back to the cocooned situation and I spent two days trying to do some 'school stuff' with Toby. After the initial excitement on day one, that quickly waned on day two. For both of us to be fair. I don't know shit about how to teach the curriculum to a six-year-old. Hell, I'm not even sure what the curriculum is, if I'm honest. I'm in the dark ages with technology and I'm damned if I can get Microsoft Teams and One Note to work properly. I'm of the era of blackboard and chalk. Not even whiteboards!

After Friday, all the schools shut. Toby's school has created an awesome virtual school with registration, assemblies and lessons throughout the day where you can submit work.

Day one and I was stressed to the max trying to get all the damn technology to work. Trying to get Toby to engage. Trying to do an online shop, as per guidance, yet there being no slots with anyone, ever!

Safe to say, it all got a bit too much and Monday 23rd March was a bit of a dark day. I felt that same fear come flooding back that I experienced following my cancer diagnosis. Back then it was just me and my battle to keep my body alive. Now this is everybody's fight.

My experience helped me to gain perspective again pretty quickly. Yes, it was scary last year, but once I knew there was a good plan I cracked on with it and tried not to think too far ahead. The same can be applied again. All we've got to really do this time is just stay in to greatly reduce the risk of contracting the virus. I just have to keep our family of four inside our little bubble and ride it out until it's safe to come back out.

With that in mind, I went into day two feeling more relaxed and confident. We started with thirty minutes of Joe Wick's PE, which was being streamed live on YouTube. All four of us laughing and far from stressed. We managed thirty minutes of phonics and thirty minutes of maths. We also made half a cake out of a packet mix (I'm still shit at baking and only manage to produce half cakes that we sandwich together) and a bug hotel for some spiders called Rosie, Rowan and Tom. Whilst I worked on my blog, I left the children 'unsupervised' in the garden. I could see that all the patio furniture and cushions had been piled sky high, but I could hear singing and laughing.

Within their little lives, my children have experienced a mum fighting off breast cancer and a world pandemic. When they look back at this time as adults, I want them to think, 'Wow that was big, that was really scary, but all I remember is spending time with Mum and Dad and lots of fun.' It will only be then that they appreciate how we kept the worry from them and kept them safe.

Small humans are a law unto their own. There's nothing you can do about that and it's just easier to go with the flow. If you have a pants day, know it will end, they will lose consciousness at some point and tomorrow is a new day.

Similarly, with this new scenario, I'm reverting back to my chemo days of taking one day at a time. Who knows how long this will last and when you're in it (like sleep deprivation) you think it will go on forever, but we all know it comes to an end eventually.

I'd been striving for perfection this last week. Trying to keep everything as normal for the children but I was stressed right out. I need to remember to be kind to myself. The small humans weren't bothered with perfection, they just wanted me there engaging with them.

I asked Toby what his best bit was about today: "Playing with you, Mummy."

I asked Chloe the same thing whilst she was failing miserably at social distancing and stroking the emerging furry caterpillar on my upper lip: "Mummy and eating beans."

My work here today is done.

Cancer Comms

Massaging Mummies:

"Well, ladies… this is a lonely and shit way to live… how is everyone holding up? xx"

"Morning. What day is it? I've got no clue. Ah, yes, Thursday. No Joe Wicks PE for me today as, after two days, I'm walking like I've shit myself. Tena Lady does not hold up for those bunny jumps, either! Not too bad here. All still breathing! #winning Bloody lovely weather, though. I shall be partaking in The Davies Beer Garden later. A cheeky G&T at lunchtime, why not? Anyone else going anywhere nice today? We're staying in. x"

"For someone who often has always struggled to want to get up and carry on each day. Who some days prefers isolation and finds it easier than facing the world. Who finds panicking and overthinking a part of every hour of every day. This has really shown me how much there is to do and worrying really can't fix much.

For someone who loves to be busy, to crack on each day, to go out, to always be on the go (the latter of you all).

Take this time to rest, breathe, no pressure, when life is full of it daily. Accept it happened. Do the things you always say 'I wish I had the time to do that'.

I'm no counsellor and I'm struggling today to want to get on with it, but I've done a list on the fridge and I'm following the instructions.

It would be easy to stay in bed all day and watch films.

I'm using my counselling techniques of just half an hour by half an hour.

I love you all millions and we have to do this so we can all be together again. It's life-changing but for the good in some ways. Keep talking. xx"

Monday 30ᵗʰ March 2020

Today is Blursday the fortyteenth of Maprilay!

I've completely lost track of what day it is. I know it's 2020 and I'm pretty sure we're still in March.

We go out for our prescribed daily allowance of exercise to the field. Keeping a safe distance from neighbours at the top of the hill, we engage in some friendly conversation. To my horror, one of their children keeps kicking their ball in our general direction and keeps running to get it. I recoil in horror and want to screech at them like some mad woman to stay back.

On the one hand, I want to stay cocooned in the house, safe in our family of four bubble. But on the other hand, I know that unless we get out at least once a day, we're likely to go bat shit crazy. It's just a case of controlling the bloody anxiety and keeping my wits about me when we're out.

But in a relaxed moment later in the day, Toby is stroking my hair that's getting very sticky-uppy and gives me this gem:

"Mummy, your hair is growing really good. You don't look like Uncle Russell anymore."

Excellent. I no longer look like a bald bloke. Things must be on the up!

Tuesday 31st March 2020
March – Looking Back

You're getting more for your money with my monthly look back today!

Well, hasn't this month been one for the records, trumping all that have gone before! We certainly saw 'something coming', so it wasn't a curveball out of the blue, but bloody hell what a difference a month can make. At the start of the month I was having discussions about a return to work in May, talking about holidays and days out. Now, as a family, we're confined to our own four walls, only allowed out once a day to exercise and for other essential business.

Listening to friends and family talking, the fear is palpable. But ever the optimist, I believe that if we club together, we can get through this. Shit, I didn't have the NHS spend a shit ton of money on me last year to beat cancer only to be taken out by the new 'C' word on the street.

So, it got me thinking about what has made me happy and what happiness really is:

On Saturday it meant going 'out out in' with my crazy mate Sarah. Three and a half hours we sat and laughed on Messenger with me being a foot for the majority of the time thanks to crazy filters. I went to the bar (the fridge) repeatedly to replenish my G&Ts. I don't remember getting home from the kitchen, but it was a bloody good night. Cheap too.

Today it meant getting out for a stomp around the top field for our daily exercise. Toby was happy bashing his monster truck to shit in the stream, whilst I sat with Chloe on a nearby log singing 'Old MacDonald' twenty million times. Apparently, he had a dinosaur on his farm. Not sure how accurate that is, but who am I to question how long ago Old MacDonald actually lived?

Today it meant jumping on the bike in the garage that sits on a bike stand and journeys along the road to nowhere. I might have got a bit overexcited with my happy hardcore and found myself in my own little spin class conducting my invisible orchestra to the tunes. I was spinning like nobody was watching and it felt bloody awesome. What might not feel so awesome tomorrow is my twernt (you know the bit in-between your front and back bits, which if it 'twernt there' your innards would fall out) as it felt like it was on fire when I finally got down off my happy hardcore spinning high.

Limited dramas and meltdowns today. It seems we might have found a pocket of calm in this madness as we woke up to day thirteen cocooning away. Many years ago, pre-children, we decided that fourteen-day holidays were slightly too long, and we found ourselves in Zante trying to meet people in bars. Not for some 'swinging' fun, you understand, just as some extra company. Seven days were too short. Ten days was the happy medium. We're now in unchartered territory again and maybe day thirteen is the calm before the storm and from tomorrow it's every man and woman for themselves (in this house at least).

I'm going to the theatre on Thursday and a Zumba class on Friday. So much virtual stuff out there to keep us entertained whilst we ride this storm. Darren takes himself off to his mancave where he loses himself for hours doing God knows what.

A couple of years ago, I wrote a blog about happiness. Back then, I said that happiness wasn't about 'stuff' anymore, but spending time with my friends and family, seeing smiles and hearing laughter. What an opportunity I had last year to slow down and appreciate what really matters. Now I get to continue to experience this and so does everybody else, regardless of who you are and how much 'stuff' you've got. It's about the little pockets of happiness that can be found every day and, even on the most challenging days, there's always something.

This is one of my favourite sayings doing the rounds on Facebook at the moment:

"In the rush to return to normal, use this time to consider which parts of normal are worth rushing back to."

I think this is very apt, as I continue to find my way after getting cancer to bugger off. I've never considered me 'normal' anyway, so I'm not entirely sure what that would entail.

The demise of the cumulative side effect nasties:

I'm pleased to report I can't really produce a list anymore, so this will be the last one.

Physically I take longer to uncurl first thing in the morning. My joints (mostly my knees) are a bit achy and I do a ridiculous show of heaving myself up off the floor after changing Chloe's nappy. I definitely think continuous gentle exercise and losing some more weight will help with that. I still feel tired and old before my time, but then sometimes I seem to have loads of energy.

The nails are pretty much back to normal as the manky bits

have grown up and off. Hair still continues on its marvellous comeback. It's growing thick and straight up, so I think I'll need to get some kind of scarf to tame it back. All other hair-removing paraphernalia is in full use.

April 2020

Thursday 2nd April 2020

Cancer Comms

"Hi, ladies. I'm just sitting here continuing to pen my bestseller! I'm including all the comments from my wonderful friends and going back through them all is making me smile so much. So, I just wanted to say thank you. Thank you for being so awesome then and continuing to be so awesome now. It's such friendship that got me through my darkest times and what will get us all through this now. Big love to you all. xx"

Massaging Mummies:

"Well, start giving back now, as these are some dark times we're having now. You were and are the awesome one, my beaut. Did they go ahead with radiotherapy btw? Loves ya. xx"

"I'm a hugger and I want to hug. You lovely lot are amazing and more than I bargained for when I went to that baby massage course. Love you all so very much. How is everyone holding up? xx"

"That's fun looking back now you're out of the woods. You've been incredible and it was inspirational to go on that journey with you. x"

Strong Randy Ladies:

"Right back at you. It's times like this you realise what is important and great friendship is priceless. X"

Local Yocals:

"*Right back at you, amazing woman.*"
"*Aw, lush, Em. Can't wait to read it. You are incredible and we love you to bits. Xx*"
"*Aw, absolutely. Very much look forward to reading it too!*"
"*Same back to you and look forward to it. Xx*"

Monday 6ᵗʰ April 2020

The things you have to do these days to get some time outside the house!

So, with 'The Poisoning' and 'The Chop' successfully completed, it's time for 'The Frying'.

With the other new 'C' kid on the block, I'd not really thought too much about the final piece of the cancer treatment puzzle.

I was actually quite excited about the prospect of driving around in the car for five days on my own listening to some tunes. But then on Frying Eve, I got a bit anxious at the thought of venturing out. I haven't ventured outside the boundaries of my estate for eighteen days, so although I was intrigued to see what civilisation looked like, I was also quite anxious about leaving the safety of my Davies family cocoon.

I was also a bit worried about my driving abilities and whether it would look like I'd got my licence off the side of a cereal packet. But the journey was uneventful and parking at the hospital, as always, a challenge! It was free, though, so that's a Brucey bonus.

And then the fun begins. I was supposed to be having fifteen treatments every day, Monday to Friday, for three weeks. This has now been condensed down into five treatments. Same dose.

I was more anxious about going to the hospital itself rather than the treatment. But, as to be expected, there's stripy tape marking out where people can stand, and chairs spaced apart. They were also conducting temperature checks and all staff are masked up. I'd worn my own sexy blue latex gloves, so looked more like I should be entering Willy Wonka's Chocolate Factory. I probably looked a bit of a nob to be honest, but it made me feel better.

I got to wear, and keep for the week, the fetching NHS garment with easy access poppers in a popping shade of blue.

Now, I've had my experiences of a fair few different machines throughout this process, but they've clearly kept the big guns for the finale. The machine was a beast. Good thing about it, though, is that it doesn't really come anywhere near you and you're not fed into it like the giant polo (CT) one.

It didn't hurt, you don't feel a thing, and didn't make much of a noise. To be honest, it was really rather pleasant for the ten minutes I was lying there in a dimly-lit room with my norks out. And side effects aren't likely to show themselves for a couple of weeks, so when people tell you that radiotherapy is a 'walk in the park' (wouldn't a walk in the park be nice right now?) compared to chemotherapy, it would appear that it is indeed the case.

Although I was really quite anxious yesterday, I'd built it all up in my own head and the reality was quite uneventful. I like uneventful. I just need to keep hydrated and creamed up. I will make the most of my extra opportunities to escape this week and then I really hope I never have to utilise the amazing oncology services at the RD&E other than for review appointments.

So there we have it. Cancer has completely buggered off and the treatment is nearly done with.

"What doesn't kill you makes you stronger."

Cancer Comms

Shits and Giggles:

"Morning, chaps. Hope today goes well, Em. Enjoy the solo drive!"

"**Thank you. I feel fine about the radiotherapy, just shitting myself at the thought of going past my estate boundary! Eighteen days I've been safely cocooned away! It'll be fine once I've done it, though. xx**"

"You will be, and the hospital are going to be dead careful anyway, and you'll only be in the car and hospital, won't you?"

"**All went well, and it was great to escape! x**"

Local Yocals:

"Is radio still going ahead tomorrow? If so, good luck. Let's hope the good looking young one is not around tomorrow. xx"

"**It is indeed. I'm excited to be getting out! Not worried about treatment but shitting myself about picking up the bug in hospital. Hats off to all the bloody excellent NHS workers going in every day. Xx**"

"Yes, make sure you wash your hands before and after. Good luck. Xx"

"Oh, bless you, Emma. Good luck, will be thinking of you, hun. And don't touch your face!"

"**Worst part has been making a conscious effort not to pick my nose! Been doing that for forty years!**"

Tuesday 7ᵗʰ April 2020

Cancer Comms

Local Yocals:

"How are you feeling about going back to work, Emma?"

"**Mixed, I guess. When I haven't been feeling shit, I've actually enjoyed being off. The slower pace of life. When do you ever get that opportunity? I know we're all off now but** that's cocooned away with children. I had time for me, and it was bloody amazing. I've done so many amazing things and I've now written over 70,000 words of my book! But equally, I've been on full pay, so there's been no financial impact. Unless I learn to magic money out of my arse, I need to go back. My job can be done from home and I will be on a phased return too."

"Damn our arses not magicking out money."

Friday 10th April 2020

So, radiotherapy has been rather uneventful. Nice. I felt exhausted Wednesday afternoon. Went for a nap and woke up three hours later! Thursday and Friday, I enjoyed an hour's nap. Darren asked me if it was an excuse to get some peace. I hadn't actually thought of that, but I was genuinely quite tired. Not like fatigue, though, because once I'd had a nap, I felt good to go again.

Cancer Comms

"**Player One: Congratulations, you have successfully defeated the baddy booby bug. GAME OVER.**

Today was the last frying and I hope I never have to utilise oncology again.

I'm feeling quite emotional as I look back at what has gone.

How amazing my body is to have got through that.

How bloody amazing our **NHS** is and the shit ton of money they spent fixing me.

For being forced to slow down and actually finding out how wonderful it is to do that.

But what I will remember the most is the unconditional

love and kindness. From family, old friends, new friends, **NHS** staff, **FORCE** Cancer Charity. I was never alone on this journey. When I asked for help, I had an army of people just waiting to do something.

So, I know we're all stuck inside this bank holiday weekend but look who we're with. The people that matter the most and only a phone call or social media post away from anyone. We're all in this together and we can all get through it with love and kindness, just taking one day at a time.

Simply, I wanted to say to you **THANK YOU.** You may not think you did anything much but to me your company and kindness was **EVERYTHING.**

Right, that's enough of my emotional outpouring. I'm off to get a cider. xx"

Circle of Trust:

"Woohoo, you fucking did it! We knew you could, and we knew you would. You are a legend! Now you've overcome that unexpected hurdle, you can get back on track to 'normal' everyday life, knowing that inside you are a superhero. We need to celebrate when we're allowed out again. Well done, my lovely, you rock! Love you xx"

"I cannot wait to celebrate. We are all legends. I think it takes great strength to be the cheerleaders. I reckon we should have some kick ass party when we're allowed out."

"Okay, so you just made me cry! But happy tears. I really am so very proud of how you have dealt with this. I don't think I would have been as strong as you. You inspire me! It never really stood a chance with you, did it, to be fair. If you look back on everything you've done in your whole life, it's full of successful moments and this is just one of them. Okay, enough of that now. I know we can't be with you right now, but I will celebrate with a beverage and will be thinking of you and your triumph! Love you lots. xx"

"*Well done, Em. Enjoy your cider. Look forward to celebrating the end of a long journey! xx*"

"**I am so grateful to you guys as a collective and individually. You are all awesome, amazing ladies who always took the time to check in with me despite your own busy lives. xx**"

"*Congratulations and well done, Em. So happy about this. xx*"

"*Amazing text, Em. I will be having a cider for you and ditto to what all the ladies have said. You've been so brave and so positive through this.*"

Massaging Mummies:

"*Massive congratulations, Emma. You are a superwoman and I am so happy for you. We all need a bit of good news right now and this is just the best. As I said in my message to you when you first broke the news, lumpy chose the wrong girl to mess with! Love you. xx*"

"*Emma, this is the best news EVER! I wish I could hug you right now. Prepare yourself as you may have to detach me when I finally get to you! Take your time, enjoy your family and a large cider. You always had this in the bag. I'm so proud of you and to be able to call you my friend. xx*"

"*Woohooo. CONGRATULATIONS. What a day! Sun is shining for your cider in the garden/pub garden too! I shall raise a glass to you and your amazing body and amazing mind, which has dealt with this like it was just any other challenge! Lots of love to you and your lovely family who I am also super happy for. xx*"

"*You WON, my beaut, and lumpy lost, what more could anyone want to hear? Your positive mental attitude also played a huge part in this, so when you look in that mirror later (if you can after a few ciders, you might have to shut one eye), the person looking back is the one who fought the hardest. Enough soppy shit. When is taking the piss out of you appropriate again? xx*"

"*That's amazing news, the best news ever. You have and are an inspiration and a superwoman. The perfect day to celebrate the news and the end of this long journey. Can't wait to give you a hug and celebrate with you when we can. xx*"

Shits and Giggles:

"What wonderful news! You bloody star. I'm so proud of you but not surprised how well you've done. You've just bossed it! Enjoy the cider."

"Absolutely chuffed and emosh."

Strong Randy Ladies:

"Amazing. Brought a few tears to my eyes. Well done you for being so strong. We bloody love you and I feel lucky to have you and Emily as my friend. Enjoy the bank holiday weekend with your cider, you bloody deserve it. I certainly will be enjoying the weekend with this lovely weather and the fact you have finished your treatment and beat the booby bug. xx"

"Argh, so happy to read this one. The end of an era (is that the right thing to write?)! It does feel like a real journey going through and waiting anxiously for your weekly updates. I'm so glad we were able to do a little to help and no matter what happens for any of us in the next chapter we all know that friendship is all we need to get through it (and loved ones, although they are driving me slightly mad right now). I'm currently hiding in my bedroom. Argh, big breath. THE END. I love it. You rocked it, Em, and kicked the f**k out of cancer, which was never in doubt for a minute. Much love. x"

Local Yocals:

"FAN-BLOODY-TASTIC, Emma! Beyond thrilled that you beat it and with incredible strength and humour. I for one am so thankful to have you in my life and happy beyond words that it's over. Love you!"

"Well done and very proud of you. Lots of love. Xx"

"Ah, this is so brilliant. You were amazing yourself and so so glad you're out the other side. Loads of love."

"This is flipping awesome news. So happy for you. Xx"

ED Fan Club:

"Well done, love. X"

"Cheers to that."

"Great news. Your own version of Easter. Also inspiring! Bless you and yours and enjoy your Easter celebrations. X"

"Well done, ED, you did it. Sending loads of love. X"

Wednesday 15ᵗʰ April 2020

LOCKDOWN BIRTHDAY!

This was not quite the celebrations I'd envisaged for this birthday!

Forty-one was going to be the new forty. I spent our anniversary on a chemo ward, so this birthday was going to be a celebration for seeing another birthday (dramatic, I know), the end of treatment and the end of cancer. So, I find myself in lockdown! I couldn't make this shit up!

But, true to form, I was going to make the most of the card I had been dealt and we all had a pretty awesome day. I even put make up on for the first time in four weeks!

As a child, my birthday always fell during the Easter holidays. For the first time, I find myself in a classroom set up with me as the makeshift teacher. We sacked that off at lunchtime for a game of pass the parcel. Then, adhering to government guidance, I stayed at home drinking fruity cider in the sun whilst the children turned feral from the pass the parcel sugar inhalation.

Throughout the day, little random gifts and cards kept turning up at the door with the giftee miraculously vanished!

The annual text from Mum telling me how the bells were ringing on a sunny Easter Sunday all those years ago. What a bonus getting choccy for breakfast on your birthday.

Tea was in the form of a BBQ *al fresco*, suspended in my garden 'egg' chair. This was my attempt at 'dining in the air', seeing as I'm not going to be ticking that off my bucket list anytime soon.

With the gift of Facetiming, my mum got to join in singing Happy Birthday as Colin the Caterpillar cake put in an appearance. That's a birthday made right there when Colin shows up.

We finished the night off with a street pub quiz consisting of six teams. We failed miserably but I was delighted to present the winning prize, a loo roll, to our neighbours.

All in all, it actually ranked up there as a blimmin' awesome day. Never in a million years would I have foreseen closing my birthday sitting in a fold up chair out on the street playing a quiz with my neighbours. The community spirit was amazing, and I think we all enjoyed the company of different adults (from a very safe distance of course.) I believe bingo is being organised for next week.

And to finish, I raised just over £600 on my Facebook JustGiving page for FORCE. I didn't need any more 'stuff' and this, I have no doubt, will greatly help a very worthwhile cause. A massive thank you to everyone who was so generous, especially in these difficult times.

Add that to my MacMillan Coffee morning and that's £850. Not too shoddy a job, if I do say so myself.

Friday 17ᵗʰ April 2020

I get the wonderful news from my friend Gabbi that her tumours have shrunk by two thirds. The pain she was experiencing was an infection and strong antibiotics are sorting those bad boys out. Her chemo is carrying on. The relief and tears come flooding in for my beautiful strong friend. So, although her cancer is not curable, this is a much better outlook than when I met up with her a couple of months back.

Monday 20th April 2020

I get a call from the radiotherapy team today to check in with me. The tiredness seemed pretty short-lived and touch wood there's nothing funky going on with my skin. The hot sweats seem to have ramped up again but other than that this really is nothing in comparison. It's short and sweet and I'm invited to ring in if I have any concerns.

That's it. My next appointment is for a check in with my oncology consultant on the 19th June.

Sunday 26th April 2020

This seems to be the month when I'm getting my head together and looking forward.

I have a call with my friend Michelle G today to chat about surgically induced menopause and healthy eating. I've been considering joining her Facebook group for a while given that I've been thrown into the world of menopause, albeit medically induced. I first had a chat with her back in February when she offered up her advice on nutrition-rich foods, topping up on my vitamins B, C and D and getting in the green stuff.

Within her group, she provides loads of research-based supportive advice and motivates/supports you to achieve realistic and sustainable health goals. I've been digesting all her information this past week.

Monday 27th April 2020

I check in with (Boss) Becky today to discuss logistics of returning to work. We're still working towards the 26th May so I can virtually attend the introduction day of the Management Development Program. After that, I'll immediately be taking some annual leave!

I'll have accrued a load from last year and of course I've got all of this year. Rather lucky given the current 'stay in your house' circumstances.

I'll have another referral to OH, we'll look at any reasonable adjustments required, and further down the line will decide what a phased return will look like. The person currently doing my job will stay on to do a full handover and my workload will be monitored.

Now is a good point to say a massive thank you to Becky. Yes, she's my line manager, but she's also a good friend. We're the same age, we have two children, we work hard, we get our heads down, but we also look for humour and fun where we can. She's hit the right balance of giving me space to concentrate on treatment when I was in the throes of it but also making sure I wasn't forgotten. She's sought out information from HR, and signposted me to information and services she thought I would find helpful. More lately, she's been guided by me and has forwarded me internal information so I can start easing myself back in gradually.

I'm looking forward to putting the brain matter back to work and being an effective member of the team again. Given current events, it feels even more poignant as I'm sure the nurses we represent need us more than ever.

The End but also the beginning!

These 'cancer stories' need to come to an end at some point and here seems as good a place as any.

You might think I've run out of steam with my diary entries of late, but the reality is that cancer, and the treatment that comes with it, no longer dominates my days. So, it's in fact a good thing that I have less to share on the subject.

The cancer has gone. I've finished all active treatment. I have no more words of wisdom to dispense in that regard.

Next month, I'll be returning to work on a phased return and hopefully be able to resume some form of professionalism. I'm looking forward to it. I've changed again and think I'll bring a more empathetic approach to the people who need me in their time of crisis.

Am I glad I had cancer?

Hell no. I wouldn't wish it on myself or anyone. But what it did do was force me to slow down, and not only slow down but STOP. I didn't have a choice in the matter.

It taught me to be kinder to myself, to acknowledge my new limitations, to ask for help, to accept help, to not be afraid to talk about difficult things.

It taught me to let go of any negativity. To look up more and notice the beauty around me and the little wonderful things that were right there under my nose for the taking.

It taught me to spend more time properly noticing what the children were doing and trying to tell me rather than saying 'in a minute' or 'I've just got to do this first'. To say 'yes' more and be led more by what they want to do rather than what I thought they wanted to do.

It taught me to spend more time on myself doing the things that make me happy. Complementary therapies, reading, going for walks, time out with friends and family, listening to music. Just sitting and being a 'human being' rather than a 'human doing'.

It taught me that I'm a lot stronger than I thought I was. A lot of people along the way said they didn't think they'd be able to deal with it the way I had. I don't think you'll ever know how you'll deal with such a situation until it's sprung on you, but everyone would find their way. It's not a race, it's not trying to get to a destination. Who knows how long you'll be in it for but just taking one day at a time I was one day closer to the end and here I am.

People have asked whether it is one of those life-defining moments.

Yes. I'm going to get divorced, change jobs and start running Ultra Marathons! (Said with the biggest amount of sarcasm!)

Although I'm sure some people do make massive changes, I was pretty happy with my lot before. I'm endeavouring to be more spontaneous going forward. Doing more as a family and not overly worrying about the logistics.

I'm looking forward to our special day at Legoland and completing the 5k Pretty Muddy challenge.

I also have two long-term dreams I want to fulfil. Visit Venice and write a book.

Another thing I've pondered is: did having children prepare me better for cancer?

Before you think I've lost the plot with that comment, hear me out!

I've grown and nurtured two small humans. As I've gone through this cancer ride, I can't help but notice some similarities.

It took me nine months to fondly (well not fondly on the days I felt pants and the ten days they were overdue) grow something inside of me. It's taken nine months to kill something that was illegally squatting inside me.

When you're pregnant, everyone wants to touch your tummy. When you get a bald swede or fluffy hair growing back, everyone wants to touch your head!

I craved salt and vinegar crisps and rice cakes with Chloe. When I lost my taste, due to chemo, I would also chow down on salt and vinegar crisps, as that was one of the few things I could actually taste.

The small humans were not great sleepers. I was not a fan of night after night of broken sleep when I would prefer a solid eight hours. But I survived. The medically induced menopause and constant waking due to hot sweats were not the best of times. But I survived. Cancer fatigue is a different kettle of fish to sleep deprivation, but I worked on the same principal that I just needed to go slower and rest as often as I could.

The kids kept me going. I had to get up every day. I didn't have a choice. Apart from the days that I felt proper shit and then I didn't have to get up as reinforcements swooped in. But generally, throughout this process, I've been up at 6.20am Monday to Friday doing the school and nursery runs. Some mornings I was a sorry state dragging my arse out of bed but, to be honest, I'm not really a morning person anyway. It was, of course, safe in the knowledge that once I got home I could rest all day if need be. I really didn't have too much time to dwell on things as they kept me busy. Kept me smiling.

I was surrounded by family and friends, old and new, following the births of the small humans. Those same amazing people were right here again so selflessly when I needed them most.

What I do know is that I could not have done this without the amazing support of so many different people, family and friends, from so many different areas of my life. If you're going through this, surround yourself with your people. If you've got a friend or family member going through it, just being there for them, on whatever terms they need, will mean the world.

So as much as this was a book written for me, about me, it's also about all my amazing friends and family and the story of when I needed them the most. To just keep things normal. They entertained my desire and did just that.

I also wrote it for Toby and Chloe. I always tell them they can achieve anything if they really want it and I really wanted to write a book.

As I was finishing off this final bit, Toby crept in and we had a little conversation. I thought I'd use it as a little interview, and I leave you with his words:

"Mummy, what are you doing? Are you writing your cancer story?"

"Yes, I am. Would you like me to write some of your words?"

"Yes."

"What do you think this book is all about?"

"Mummy had to have an injection in her booby."

"What did you think cancer was?"

"Just a nasty bug."

"How do you think you get rid of the nasty bug?"

"By going to hospital and the doctors."

"How did you feel when Mummy told you I had the nasty bug?"

"A bit sad. We didn't get to do much fun stuff."

"Are you kidding me? We did loads of fun stuff over the summer holidays!"

"Yes. I got to come to the doctors with you. [PICC line care]*."*

"What did you think of Mummy's hair when I lost it?"

"You looked very funny, Mum. You looked like Uncle Russell."

"Are you glad it's all over now?"

"Yes."

Gives me a big hug then runs off.

Later (when he's supposed to be in bed!), he comes back with some writing.

"Mummy, this is for your book."

It simply reads:

"You had lots of cuddles."

Yes, I did, and it was those cuddles and love that got me through this.

Gifts

People feel helpless and compelled to do something. They will ask, "If there's anything I can do to help, please let me know." They don't really know what they can do to help and when I was first diagnosed, I didn't know what would help me and us as a family.

I quickly realised the biggest gift anyone could give me was that of their time in the form of companionship or well wishes. This could be in the form of text messages, phone calls, cards through the post. And my amazing chemo sitters who gave up their time to come and sit with me.

My friends and family who would arrange a catch up at my house and then swoop in cooking for me and bringing the lols. The cooked meals in the early days that we popped in the freezer made life just that little bit easier when we'd had a busy day or were feeling a bit emotionally battered.

I've had an amazing cleaner for a couple of years, and she is worth her weight in gold. Actually, that's doing her a disservice as she's tiny! Friends and family could help out with practical chores around the house, so you can fully rest.

Friends and family were so generous buying me lovely gifts. Amongst the most helpful, and which I didn't fully appreciate just how helpful they would be from the outset, were:

- Mints (for when I lost my taste).
- A headscarf (self-explanatory!).
- Moisturising cream (for when the chemo started drying me up).

- Lip balm (same as for skin).
- Biscuits (I had so many visitors it was good to have something to offer them. Also great for chemo days).
- Anti-sickness sweets, Werther's Originals (again great for something to taste and to calm any queasy feelings).
- Books – I have got through so many books it's been amazing. Lots of waiting around for appointments, scans, treatment, etc.
- A book about cancer – perhaps a bit personal but judge your audience. Will they like a factually serious one probably written by professional medical people or one written by someone with a stupid sense of humour who just so happened to get cancer and thought she could write a book about it? If the latter, buy them this one!
- iTunes vouchers to download some of my favourite tunes. I love music and this was another way to escape and/or pass the time.
- Fruity teabags.
- Chocolate. There was a point that I actually went off chocolate. Shocking, I know. No one was more shocked than me. When you need to get some extra calories in as your body is working hard to sort itself out in between treatment, small bitesize bars popped in the fridge are great.
- Positive affirmation cards. I appreciate this isn't everyone's cup of tea but actually reading something positive that reaffirms that 'you have got this' can be a real pick me up.
- Flowers are always gratefully received. They are beautiful, but what I find more beautiful is the thought that came with them. My kitchen looked like a florist shop for a good six months. There even came a point when I considered a change in vocation!

Cards – and a Load of Them at That

I've been really fortunate to receive loads of lovely cards.

As the months continued to pass, each time I received a funny text or a card through the post I felt touched that someone had taken the time out of their busy lives to think of me and take the time to do something.

A couple of my favourites:

Boobs, tits, melons, jugs, norks, bangers, knockers, bazookas, baps, funbags… Whatever you call them, I'm sorry yours are giving you shit!

Cancer picked the wrong bitch to mess with. When it rains, look for rainbows. When it's dark, look for stars.

And some of the lovely messages:

"Dear Emma. Just wanted to drop you a card to say your sense of humour and positivity are inspiring! When faced with such scary news it would be so easy to hide away, but you continue to be so strong, it blows me away. Cancer messed with the wrong bird! I'm 100% here for anything you need. Don't forget to keep pulling the cancer card. Love you lots. Jo, Gary, Olivia and Sylvie. Xx"

"Dear Emma and Darren. Just a note to say that we are thinking of you during this challenge that has come your way. We are so sorry that you are going through this but know that you are strong and will get through it together. If we can do anything, please let us know. Helen and Paul. xx"

"*Dear Emma. As much as flowers are lovely, I wanted to get something that might be a bit more helpful than a bunch! Good luck with the start of treatment, lumpy isn't going to know what's hit him. Be strong, be brave, be fearless and give that lumpy a bitch slap. Always in my thoughts, my beaut. Please remember, I'm here for anything. Love Kelly and Nick. Xx*"

"*Dear Emma, beautiful lady, fantastic friend and awesomest work buddy. Just a few things that I thought might help you over the next few weeks and might cheer you up. You are the strongest and bravest lady I know, and I have no doubt that your positivity will get you through. You are in my thoughts and if there is anything that you need, or I can do to help you in any way, I am always only at the end of the phone. All my love to you and your family. Kate. xx*"

"*Dear Emma. I was so very sorry to hear you are undergoing that ghastly treatment for breast cancer. You are too young, Emma, and have a precious young family. I know you'll have support from everyone, and you'll try to keep that Emma spirit up! Abi and I have walked The Moon Walk – a marathon (26+ miles) around London overnight. She's done it three times and I have walked it seven times. We shall be registering soon to do it again in 2020. This time we shall walk for you, Emma. Breast Cancer Research has had much success in finding cures for some of the cancers and it's a wonderful cause. I hope your treatment is working. Remember, I am a survivor of it – twenty-six years now, so be encouraged. With love, Mollie. Xx*"

"*Dear Emma. I have been meaning to send you this hug in an envelope for a while. Please keep it near you and have a virtual hug whenever required. Know that you are loved and special and cared for. The journey may not be easy, but hopefully each day you will find some good or something to cheer you up/make you smile. We are already missing your smile and laughter in the office! I've sent this hymn as it has been a comfort for me, especially verse four. I have been speaking to the Big G for you and will continue to do so. Sorry, I am not good on Facebook. However, I have got WhatsApp on my phone. No pressure, though, as you'll have lots to do and I can keep up with Ruth and hear how you are. My love and very best wishes for you, Darren, Toby and Chloe for the next months. Margie. Xx"*

"To Emma. Happy final chemo day! I feel lucky to count you as a work colleague, desk buddy and most importantly a friend. Your bravery and courage in facing this chapter of your life has been inspiring. Here's to many more years of inappropriate office banter, play dates and alcohol-fueled nights out! Do one, lumpy! Lots of love, Charlotte."

And saving the best until last, loads of cards and drawings from Toby, including hearts and smiley faces telling me to *Get Better Soon*.

The Thank Yous

If Carlsberg made chemo sitters, they'd pick these guys

Darren
Jo Selley
Michelle Garret
Nicola Dumenill
Anna Dickenson
Kelly Yeo
Pippa Bateman
Paula Pattison
Mum
Emily Strong
Jo Steer
Becky Wheeler
Helen Matthews
Charlotte Freeman

The amazing professionals

Cherrybrook Unit for pumping me full of the wonderful poison
Yeo Ward for when I was poorly and admitted
My amazing booby and oncology consultants
My amazing booby nurse in the breast care team
FORCE
The District Nurses at Budlake Unit, Whipton Hospital for
    keeping my plumbing working
Suzanne, my nurse at Reframe, my extra support via work

My tribe

Friends and family. Any of you who texted me, phoned me, sent me a card or a prezzie. You might think you didn't do much but just your acts of kindness meant more than I guess you'll ever know.

Dad

Thank you for showing up every 'Happy Chemo Tuesday' to drive me in style for my poisonings and occasionally popping into the pub after! We had some laughs, didn't we, and it was lovely to get to spend some time with you. xx

Mum

I know I've said it before, Mum, but thank you. You are everything to me and everyone who meets you. You give unconditionally, sometimes to your own detriment. When people say they want to give their children more than they had, I'd be happy if my children feel exactly how I did throughout all my life. Not just as a child but right into adulthood. So, I'm sorry that my bloody illness broke you a bit but look at all that amazing quality time we had. As my number one fan and supporter, always, I know you'll be reading this. Given the emotional bugger you are, I hope you're close to a box of tissues! I love you. Xx

Darren

I know you don't like PDAs but I'm going to have to say something here, not least else I'll look like a right unappreciative cow! You really have been my rock. I think we make a pretty awesome team, and we've shouldered a few tricky bits over the years, but look how we got through this. I'm not sure people knew how to take our dark sense of humour but hey, it works for us, so why change it. I secretly know you didn't mind cancelling the blonde Swedish au pair when we realised the drugs were working. Right? Don't think I didn't see the fear in your eyes, which was why I kept asking people to check in on you. So, thank you. Thank you for being there for me, for us and keeping this ship sailing. I love you. Xx

Toby and Chloe

And finally, my beautiful 'lively' children. I am so proud of you both and how you just kept being you throughout all this. Chloe, I know you are too young to really know what's going on, but your gorgeous little smile and energy kept me smiling. Toby, you did know something was up. Thank you so much for all the little cards and gifts you kept giving me. For the tender little cuddles and hugs when you could see that Mummy wasn't feeling very well. When people wondered how I'd get through this with children, I actually think you both were my reason for getting through it. And thank you for helping me write this book. It's always been my dream to write a book and with your encouragement I've done it! I love you both very much. xx

References

Charlie Mackesy (2019) *The Boy, the Mole, the Fox and the Horse*, Ebury Press

Mel Robbins (2017) *The 5 Second Rule: The surprisingly simple way to live, love and speak with courage: Transform you life, work and confidence with everyday courage*, Post Hill Press

YESmum Rebel Cards. Available to purchase from http://www.londonhypnobirthing.co.uk/product/yesmum-original-cards/

Dr Peter Harvey, Consultant Clinical Psychologist *After the Treatment Finishes – Then What?*

Useful information

If you're local to Exeter, you can contact FORCE cancer charity on 01392 406151

Macmillan Cancer Support: www.macmillan.org.uk

Breast Cancer Now. The research and care charity: www.breastcancernow.org 0808 800 6000

Surburban Turban www.suburbanturban.com

Willow Foundation www.willowfoundation.org.uk info@willowfoundation.org.uk

Look Good Feel Better: Facing cancer with confidence www.lookgoodfeelbetter.co.uk

My own website (parenting and cancer blog) www.lightboxblogger.co.uk